Advances in

OPTICAL *and* ELECTRON
MICROSCOPY

Volume 3

Advances in

OPTICAL *and* ELECTRON
MICROSCOPY

Volume 3

Edited by

R. BARER

Department of Human Biology and Anatomy,
University of Sheffield, England

AND

V. E. COSSLETT

Department of Physics,
Cavendish Laboratory, University of Cambridge,
England

ACADEMIC PRESS · 1969
LONDON AND NEW YORK

ACADEMIC PRESS INC. (LONDON) LTD
BERKELEY SQUARE HOUSE
BERKELEY SQUARE
LONDON, W.1

U.S. Edition published by
ACADEMIC PRESS INC.
111 Fifth Avenue
NEW YORK, NEW YORK 10003

Library of Congress Catalog Card Number: 65–25134
Standard Book Number: 12–029903–8

PRINTED IN GREAT BRITAIN AT
The Whitefriars Press Ltd., London and Tonbridge
England

Contributors

J. R. BENFORD, *Scientific Instruments Division, Bausch and Lomb, Inc., Rochester, New York, U.S.A.* (p. 1).

R. P. FERRIER, *Cavendish Laboratory, University of Cambridge, Cambridge, England* (p. 155).

D. W. HUMPHRIES, *Department of Geology, The University, Sheffield, England* (p. 33).

H. E. ROSENBERGER, *Scientific Instruments Division, Bausch and Lomb, Inc., Rochester, New York, U.S.A.* (p. 1).

R. S. THOMAS, *Western Regional Research Laboratory, Agricultural Research Service, United States Department of Agriculture, Albany, U.S.A.* (p. 99).

M. A. WILLIAMS, *Department of Human Biology and Anatomy, The University, Sheffield, England* (p. 219).

Preface

The reception accorded the first two volumes of this series has encouraged us to continue on the same lines, with articles on both optical and electron microscopy in each volume. Tempting though it is to try to assemble a more homogeneous set of contributions, to do so would be bound to delay unduly some topical treatment in one or other of the two disciplines. In the present volume the two articles on optical microscopy reflect the growing interest in variable magnification and in quantitative measurement, respectively. That by Benford and Rosenberger presents a comprehensive account of the design and operation of various types of zoom systems, many of them hitherto only described in the patent literature, whilst Humphries describes in similar detail some techniques of stereology, particle size measurement and related topics.

In electron microscopy the article by Thomas is a timely review of the promising techniques for localisation of the mineral content of tissues by microincineration. That by Ferrier describes the potentialities of the very new procedures for carrying out small angle electron diffraction in the electron microscope, equally applicable to the study of magnetic domains and of long spacings in macromolecules. In the final article Williams discusses the adaptation of autoradiographic procedures to the special conditions of electron microscopy, emphasising the precautions necessary if meaningful results are to be obtained.

The preface to our first volume ended with the hope that its appearance might stimulate offers of articles. We are happy to find that this is now happening, though we would still welcome suggestions and offers. The list of topics on which articles have been promised now stands as follows:

Optical transfer theory and the electron microscope.
Quantitative metallurgical microscopy.
Use of lasers in microscopy.
High resolution electron microscopy.
Photomicrography and its automation.
Energy loss analysis in the electron microscope.
Three-dimensional reconstruction from electron micrographs.
Electron mirror microscopy.
Negative staining for electron microscopy.
Remote control microscopy.

Display of microprobe analysis results.
Optical processing of electron micrographs.
Lorentz microscopy of magnetic films.
Localisation of enzymes by electron microscopy.
Superconducting electron lenses.
Phase contrast electron microscopy.
New techniques in optical lens design.
Fluorescence microspectrometry.

June 1969   R. BARER
                                                         V. E. COSSLETT

Contents

Zoom Systems in Microscopy

JAMES R. BENFORD AND HAROLD E. ROSENBERGER

Mensuration Methods in Optical Microscopy

D. W. HUMPHRIES

Microincineration Techniques for Electron-microscopic Localization of Biological Minerals

RICHARD S. THOMAS, Ph.D.

Small Angle Electron Diffraction in the Electron Microscope

R. P. FERRIER

The Assessment of Electron Microscopic Autoradiographs

M. A. WILLIAMS

Zoom Systems in Microscopy

JAMES R. BENFORD AND HAROLD E. ROSENBERGER

Scientific Instruments Division, Bausch & Lomb Inc., Rochester, New York

I. HISTORICAL BACKGROUND

A. *Prior Art*

MAGNIFICATION changing in microscopes was for many years restricted to objective-changing devices such as revolving nosepieces, loose eyepiece interchange, or to built-in interchangeable relay lenses in the microscope body. The magnification changes, with any of these systems, were abrupt and quite large. The advantages of a continuously variable magnification, or "zoom" system, where the image stays always in view and controllable to exactly the desired size, were long obvious but the technical problems of achieving such a system were formidable, and it was not until high-speed electronic computers became available to the lens designer that the solution to these problems became feasible. Indeed, many design problems remain today, particularly in regard to extending the zoom range to approach the 40 : 1 magnification range which has long been possible by simple objective interchange on the laboratory microscope.

a. *Nosepiece devices.* The desire for more magnifications in the laboratory microscope was made evident by the progression from double nosepieces to triple to quadruple and eventually to sextuple nosepieces. In the stereomicroscope a similar evolution took place, but after the triple nosepiece the next step was to an internal lens system equivalent to two pairs of Galilean telescopes which could be used forward, backward, or rotated out of the light path altogether. These could, for example, be 3X and 2X Galilean systems which when used backward would give 1/3X and 1/2X factors, and when removed would produce a 1X factor, so that we had the equivalent of five different objective magnifications.

b. *Focusing condenser systems.* Probably the first application of zoom lenses in a microscope was in the substage condenser system. During the 1930's the firm of Zeiss marketed a "Pancratic Condenser", which was a complete microscope illuminating system, in which a relayed aperture diaphragm image was zoomed to control its size in the substage condenser. Later the firm of Bausch & Lomb made a different type called a "Panfocal Condenser" in which the field diaphragm image was zoomed in synchronism with the mechanical motion of the aperture iris so that both field and aperture sizes conformed to the requirements of the various low and high power objectives. These condenser systems were of course not very demanding in their requirements on image quality, but did represent a first primitive step toward introducing continuously variable lens power as contrasted with the traditional abrupt power change occasioned by swing-out or interchangeable condenser lenses. A good many years passed before this same advance was found possible in the microscope proper.

c. *Body tube magnification changers.* To get around the nuisance of loose eyepieces, relay lenses within the body tube were sometimes used to effect step changes in magnification. These relay lenses were separated positive and negative lenses similar to little Galilean telescopes and were generally built into the body so that various powers could be conveniently interchanged. The firm of Zeiss marketed these under the trade name "Optovars". N.A. did not change with power, hence, these were optically the equivalent of eyepiece change rather than objective change.

d. *Stereomicroscopes with Galilean systems.* This same principle of magnification changing was extended to stereomicroscopes by Zeiss and later by American Optical Co. and Wild Heerbrugg Ltd. Here the

Galilean systems were used either forward or backward, so that a 2X Galilean served also as a 1/2X Galilean, etc., as previously described. Stops within the Galilean systems served to control the N.A. appropriately.

B. *Zooming Eyepieces*

It is possible to design eyepieces such that they can be zoomed within a modest power range. To date they have not been commercially successful due in part to the tendency of the designs to cause a field lens to move through the image plane. Very tiny surface blemishes, as well as dust and dirt, on the lens cause this construction to be objectionable.

C. *Zooming Objectives*

A more practical approach to zooming was found in modification of the objective rather than the eyepiece. Here the N.A. varied with zoom, so that a real change in resolution was achieved as the power was changed. This subject will be discussed at some length in the succeeding sections of this article.

In 1959 the firm of Bausch & Lomb introduced zoom in a microscope for the first time in the form of a continuously variable objective lens system in a stereomicroscope with a 4 : 1 zoom ratio, and with N.A. changing to correspond to the magnification. The microscope, shown in Fig. 1, will be described in more detail in Section III B.

Bausch & Lomb followed up this development with two zooming student microscopes having systems of intermediate N.A., introduced in 1964. These two systems zoomed from 25X to 100X and 50X to 200X respectively. The former has a maximum N.A. of 0·12 and the latter 0·25. The lenses in the 25X to 100X system are shown in Fig. 9D.

Subsequently, in 1967 Bausch & Lomb introduced a zooming student microscope with still higher N.A. for the region 100X to 500X. This system has a maximum N.A. of 0·55 and its lens system is shown in Fig. 9E. All of these student microscopes will be discussed in Section III D.

D. *Zooming Body Tube Lenses*

In 1960 the firm of Bausch & Lomb introduced a 2 : 1 zoom system within the body tube of the conventional laboratory microscope. This system did not change N.A. as it zoomed, hence was more equivalent to an eyepiece change than to an objective change. It will be described more completely in Section III C. The lens system is shown to scale in Fig. 9C.

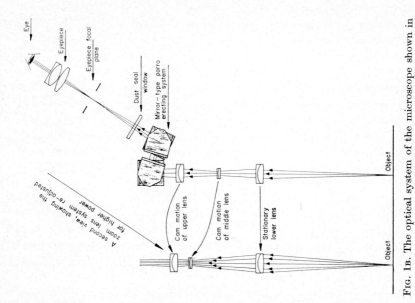

FIG. 1B. The optical system of the microscope shown in Fig. 1A.

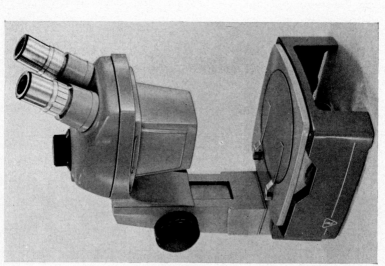

FIG. 1A. The first zooming microscope. Photo courtesy Bausch & Lomb, Inc.

II. THE DESIGN OF ZOOM SYSTEMS

A. *Introduction*

Experience in lens design has shown that an optical system designed for one set of operating conditions rarely gives optimum performance when used under some other set of conditions. In a sense, zoom systems must be designed in defiance of this experience since the conditions under which they operate are constantly changing throughout their zoom range. To overcome this problem, the optical designer must tailor each zoom system to its particular application so that the conditions under which it works are as favorable as possible throughout the zoom range. As a consequence of this fitting of each zoom system to a special set of conditions, the patent literature discloses a seemingly endless array of what appear to be different zoom system concepts.

While each of these concepts differs in one way or another from all others, all zoom systems have certain common characteristics and depend for their performance upon the behavior of dynamic combinations of individual lens groups. The following characteristics are foremost among those common to all zoom systems and merit particular attention:

1. A zoom system makes possible a continuous change in magnification over some designated magnification range.
2. The change in magnification is achieved by means of a continuous motion of one or more (usually at least two) groups of optical components.
3. The image formed by the zoom system, real or virtual, remains stationary at least within the depth of focus of the observer throughout the designated magnification range.

The significance of these three characteristics will be considered in some detail.

Referring to Fig. 2 which illustrates schematically the simplest of optical systems, L and L' represent the object and image distances respectively for a single lens having a focal length designated F'. The quantity K represents the sum of L and L', the object to image distance.

The sign convention for all subsequent mathematical relationships will follow the rule that all distances measured to the right of a reference plane are positive and all distances to the left are negative. The lens will always be the reference plane for L and L', so L is negative in Fig. 2. The object plane will always be the reference plane for K, so K is positive in Fig. 2.

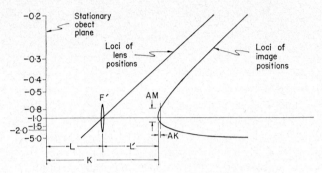

FIG. 2. A simple variable magnification system.

From the well known thin lens equation

$$L' = \frac{F'L}{F' + L},\tag{1}$$

and magnification equation

$$M = \frac{L'}{L},\tag{2}$$

we may derive an expression for K as a function of F' and M. Thus,

$$\begin{aligned} K &= -L + L' \\ &= \frac{-F'(1 - M)^2}{M} \end{aligned}\tag{3}$$

Zoom systems are designed to keep both the object plane and image plane in fixed positions throughout the zoom range and therefore the object to image distance represented by K in Fig. 2 must remain constant. But an analysis of equation (3) shows that except for one special case, and then only for a very limited magnification range, K can be held constant as the magnification is changed only by a continuous change in the lens focal length F'.

Concerning this one special case, differentiating (3) with respect to M gives

$$\frac{dK}{dM} = \frac{F'(1 - M^2)}{M^2}\tag{4}$$

Now if K is to be held constant as the magnification is changed, $\dfrac{dK}{dM}$ must be zero. From (4),

$$\frac{dK}{dM} = 0 \text{ when } M = \pm 1\tag{5}$$

The case for which $M = +1$ turns out to be trivial since in this case the object, the image, and the lens all lie in the same plane.

The case for which $M = -1$ turns out to be of some significance. Differentiating (4) with respect to M,

$$\frac{d^2K}{dM^2} = \frac{-2F'}{M^3}, \tag{6}$$

from which it will be found that at $M = -1$, $|K|$ is a minimum. Thus for a given focal length lens, the object to image distance remains constant only at $M = -1$ and only over an infinitesimal range $\pm dM$.

In practice we may permit the infinitesimal dM to take on a finite value ΔM which reaches its limit when any further increase results in a ΔK which exceeds the depth of focus of the observer. This is illustrated in Fig. 2 where K is plotted as a function of M for a lens of unit focal length. Even when advantage is taken of the observer's depth of focus, ΔM is rarely sufficiently large for this type of system to be of practical value as a zoom system. Hence as stated above, the object to image distance K can be held constant as the magnification is changed over a useful range only by a continuous change in the lens focal length F'.

To date, no practical method has been found which permits the focal length of a single lens to be varied. However, when two (or more) lenses are used in combination, the equivalent focal length of the combination depends not only on the focal lengths of the individual lenses but also upon the spaces separating the lenses.

For example, recalling the well known formula for the equivalent focal length of a two-lens combination

$$\frac{1}{F'} = \frac{1}{F'_1} + \frac{1}{F'_2} - \frac{T}{F'_1 F'_2} \tag{7}$$

where F' = focal length of the combination,
$\quad\quad F'_1$ = focal length of the first individual lens,
$\quad\quad F'_2$ = focal length of the second individual lens, and
$\quad\quad T$ = separation between the first and second lenses,
it is evident that the equivalent focal length of the combination can be varied within limits by changing T.

This scheme of producing a continuously variable focal length lens by altering the separation between two or more individual component lenses turns out to be quite practical and in fact is basic to all zoom systems. Furthermore, since any number of individual lens components may be used to make up the equivalent lens and since the focal lengths of these individual components may be chosen individually, an infinite variety of zoom systems, each with characteristics different from all others, is possible. Practical considerations make the seemingly impossible problem of selecting the number of lenses and their focal lengths reasonably manageable as will be seen later.

To date, two broad classifications of zoom systems have evolved, viz. the Mechanically Compensated and the Optically Compensated systems. These two classifications differ from each other sufficiently to warrant separate descriptions.

B. *Mechanically Compensated Zoom Systems*

The Mechanically Compensated Zoom System may use any number of moving lens groups but most often only two groups are used. Fig. 3A illustrates one of the infinitely many variations. Each of the two lens groups is represented schematically by a single simple lens although in practice each group is composed of at least two and often three or more individual elements.

In this particular design configuration the image plane lies to the right of the object plane and both lenses remain within the space between the object and image planes throughout the zoom range.

Some applications in which zoom systems are used require that the image plane must fall to the left of the object plane as illustrated in Fig. 3B in which case K is negative. Other applications require that both the object plane and image plane lie to the right (or left) of both zoom lenses. The former case is illustrated in Fig. 3C.

Usually the relative positions of the object and image planes, i.e. K, and the space relative to these planes which may be occupied by the zoom lenses are imposed as predetermined design restrictions. Accordingly, the first task of the designer of a zoom system is to select values for F'_1 and F'_2 for the given K and then determine the exact lens positions for all magnifications throughout the designated magnification range. The task of selecting focal lengths involves a certain amount of trial and error which can be reduced to a minimum through the use of the Zoom Systems Catalog described more fully in a later section of this chapter. Finding the exact locations of the lenses is accomplished through the application of equations (8), (9), (10) and (11) below.

$$T = 1/2\,[K \pm \sqrt{K^2 - 4aF'_1F'_2 - 4K(F'_1 + F'_2)}] \tag{8}$$

where

$$a = \frac{(1 - M)^2}{M} \tag{9}$$

$$L_1 = \frac{-F'_1[K - T(1 - M)]}{F'_1(1 - M) + MT} \tag{10}$$

$$L'_2 = K + L_1 - T \tag{11}$$

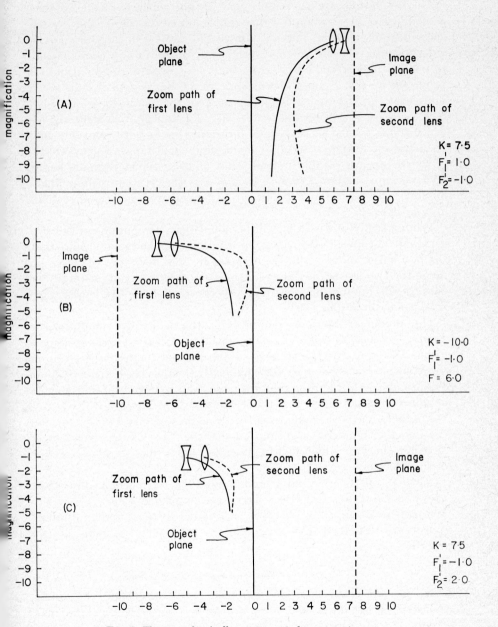

FIG. 3. Three mechanically compensated zoom systems.

These equations are completely general. The object to image distance K may take on any finite value (plus, minus, or zero), the desired magnification may be plus or minus and the focal lengths may be independently chosen and may be plus or minus in any combination. It will be understood, of course, that only certain combinations of values for K, F'_1, F'_2 and M will work for a zoom system of some given configuration. Also, it will be apparent from the quadratic relationship that for a given set of values of K, F'_1, F'_2 and M, two solutions for L_1, L'_2 and T exist at each magnification. One or both solutions may be imaginary over part or all of the desired zoom range. Such systems, of course, are useless and indicate that a change must be made in the relative values assigned to F'_1, F'_2 and K. Other systems will be found in which the value for T turns out to be negative and these systems also must be discarded.

From a study of Fig. 3, it will be noted that the motions of the two lenses are not linear with change in magnification and furthermore that the two lenses move at different rates. In fact, over part of the zoom range the two lenses may move in the same direction and over another part the direction of one lens may reverse so that the two lenses move in opposite directions.

The nonlinear motions required by the lenses to maintain the constant object to image distance must be imparted by mechanical means and it is this requirement which has led to the designation of this type of zoom system as a Mechanically Compensated Zoom System. Traditionally, the required motions have been achieved through the use of cam systems, examples of which are shown in Fig. 6.

Another, and relatively recently developed device (1967), for imparting the required lens motions is the Crank-Link Non-Linear Motion Generator which will be described more fully in a later section of this chapter.

Because of the flexibility and versatility of Mechanically Compensated Zoom Systems, they have been employed widely in modern microscopes of virtually all types. A number of these zooming microscopes are described in some detail in subsequent sections of this chapter.

C. Optically Compensated Zoom Systems

In the very early days of zoom systems development, the optical industry regarded the potential problems associated with the mass production of cams with a great deal of respect and concern. The industry has long since solved the problem of precision cam production, but the early concern of some optical designers led them to develop a type of zoom system which required only linear lens motions and thus obviated the need for cams.

Zoom systems of this type have come to be designated as Optically Compensated Zoom Systems because they depend entirely upon the optical behavior of linearly moving lens groups to achieve a nearly constant object to image distance.

The manner in which the object to image distance changes when a single positive focal length lens is moved linearly in the region of -1 magnification was illustrated in Fig. 2. A negative focal length

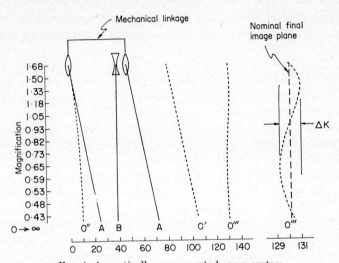

Fig. 4. An optically compensated zoom system:

A   Zoom paths of first and third lenses.
B   Stationary second lens.
O   Object for first lens at infinity.
O′ Image locus for first lens and object locus for second lens.

O″ Image locus for second lens and object locus for third lens.
O‴ Image locus for third lens.
$F'_1 = 80 \cdot 000$.
$F'_2 = -20 \cdot 000$.
$F'_3 = 30 \cdot 000$.

lens moved linearly in the region of -1 magnification will give the same kind of change in object to image distance except that the locus of the image positions will be a curve concave to the left instead of to the right.

Thus the changes in object to image distances are in opposite directions for positive and negative lenses and the net change in object to image distance for well chosen combinations can be reduced almost to zero.

One of the most frequently used lens configurations for an Optically Compensated Zoom System is illustrated in Fig. 4. In this configuration, the two positive focal length lenses are mechanically linked and constitute the moving components of the system. The negative focal length lens remains stationary. The object O for the system is at infinity. The image O' formed by the first moving lens becomes a moving object for the fixed negative focal length lens, and so on.

The loci of the intermediate and final image positions throughout the zoom range are plotted to scale in Fig. 4. The final image position curve is also redrawn to a 10-time longitudinal scale to the right in Fig. 4 in order to show more clearly the manner in which the curve is made to cross and recross the nominal final image plane. For magnifications above and below those plotted, the curve of the image positions would rapidly move away from the nominal final image plane and would not return.

If the value of ΔK for the system in Fig. 4 exceeds the depth of focus of the observer, it can be reduced by a small change in the focal length of the second moving lens; however, the zoom range will also be reduced, i.e. the two outer points where the curve crosses the reference plane will each be shifted toward the center. The zoom range can be increased with a simultaneous reduction in ΔK by the addition of a second fixed lens and a third moving lens. The curve of image positions for the five lens group combination crosses the reference plane at five points. Similarly a seven lens group combination crosses the reference plane at seven points.

Referring again to the three lens group combination illustrated in Fig. 4, the equivalent focal length of the complete system is directly proportional to the focal length of the first lens, but the magnification values contributed by the second and third lens, and recorded along the ordinate, are independent of the focal length of the first lens. The equivalent focal length of the complete system in Fig. 4 varies from $80 \times 1.68 = 134.4$ to $80 \times 0.43 = 34.4$. Since the primary function of the first lens is to form an image which moves along O', a lens of some other focal length may be substituted provided it is positioned by means of the mechanical linkage so that its back focal plane falls at O' and its back focal length is long enough to permit the full lens excursion without interference between moving and stationary lenses.

When the object to image distance is finite as in microscopy, a stationary lens must be added in front of the first moving lens. In microscopy, this lens takes the form of an infinity corrected objective. If the focal length of the objective and first moving lens are designated F'_0 and F'_1 respectively and the magnification values appearing along the ordinate in Fig. 4 are designated M_z, then the overall magnification

M of the system is given by:

$$M = \frac{F'_1}{F'_0} \times M_z \qquad (12)$$

For the complete microscope, the eyepiece magnification also must be included.

While there are many successful Mechanically Compensated Zoom Microscopes being marketed today, no Optically Compensated Microscope known to the authors has been introduced. The explanation for this exclusion is that the one advantage of requiring no cam is more than offset by three serious disadvantages, viz.,

1. The Optically Compensated System requires more lens elements.
2. The Optically Compensated System is less flexible in conforming to the space limitations imposed by modern microscope construction.
3. The lens arrangement necessary to achieve optical compensation is frequently not optimum for correcting lens aberrations.

Although the possibility of developing an Optically Compensated Zoom Microscope will always exist, the demonstrated superiority of the Mechanically Compensated concept makes such a development improbable.

D. *The Zoom Systems Catalog*

In the discussion of Mechanically Compensated Zoom Systems it was stated that the designer must select by trial and error certain of the parameters appearing in the zoom equations on p. 8. Upon his choice of these parameters depends the success of the design in meeting certain predetermined first order characteristics and achieving the required level of image quality over the entire zoom range.

Examples of the kinds of first order characteristics often demanded of zoom systems are:

1. Exceptionally long front or back focus.
2. Systems which control the entering numerical aperture in such a way that the numerical aperture varies linearly or nearly so with change in magnification.
3. Systems which maintain a constant entering numerical aperture throughout the zoom range.
4. Systems in which the two zoom lenses must lie between the object and image plane or in which both lenses must lie outside the object to image space—either to the right or to the left.
5. Systems which have a zero Petzval sum or a Petzval sum of magnitude and sign which compensates for that of other optical subassemblies of the overall optical system.

Other factors which frequently must be considered in the selection of first order parameters are:

1. Finding a system which requires the minimum number of lens elements for reasons of cost.
2. Finding a system which requires the minimum lens excursions so that cam slopes do not become excessively steep.
3. Finding a system for which the allowable tolerance on lens focal lengths and cam dimensions are within manufacturing capabilities.
4. Finding a system which does not require that either zoom lens moves through or near a real image plane.

Even if a zoom system conforms to all of the requirements above, the system still may be unacceptable because it does not permit the degree of aberration correction necessary to achieve the required image quality throughout the zoom range. Clearly, with so many factors involved, a procedure which permits a systematic search for likely solutions is highly desirable.

A study of the problems associated with the selection of parameters for Mechanically Compensated Zoom Systems has shown that while there are infinitely many potential combinations of parameters and hence infinitely many potential zoom systems, in practice the useful solutions can be grouped into a manageable number of families and each family can be represented by a relatively small number of cases.

About 650 cases are sufficient to represent all of the potential two-lens Mechanically Compensated Zoom Systems and a catalog of these 650 cases has been compiled. For cataloging purposes the 650 cases are divided into two groups, one representing positive magnification systems and the other representing negative magnification systems.

Each case is displayed in graphical form similar to that used in Fig. 3. The data in Fig. 3 are plots of L_1, T, and L'_2 from equations (8), (9), (10) and (11) for given sets of values assigned to K, F'_1 and F'_2 over a range of values for M.

For convenience, the value assigned to F'_1 is always either plus or minus unity and values assigned to K and F'_2 are chosen relative to that of F'_1. This permits the easy ratioing of any given system to the final desired dimensions.

A suggested range of values for K is from -25 to $+25$ and for F'_2 from -6 to $+6$. A suggested range of values for M is 0 to ±16. When there are two real roots for a given set of parameters, both solutions are plotted on the same graph. This practice is of particular importance since the combined plots will reveal the possibility of zoom systems having special features which can be obtained by switching roots at some point in the magnification range. The 7 : 1 range StereoZoom microscope described in a subsequent section of this chapter utilizes this kind of zoom system. The lens system of this microscope is depicted in Fig. 9B.

E. *Objective Zoom* vs. *Eyepiece Zoom*

The preceding sections have dealt with the general principles of zoom systems. In this section the actual integration of zoom into the compound microscope will be considered.

Although the zoom system of a microscope may appear to perform as a separate and distinct optical subassembly, in reality either the zoom system and eyepiece work together as a zooming eyepiece or the zoom system and objective work together as a zooming objective. The distinction between the two concepts will be illustrated by examples.

Figure 5A illustrates schematically the optical components of a zoom Laboratory Microscope. The objectives for this microscope may be any of the standard achromats, fluorites, or apochromats or may be any of the newer flat field objectives. The only requirements of the objectives are that they match the tube length and objective shoulder position for which the zoom system is designed. Frequently standard eyepieces may be used. The actual lens system is drawn to scale in Fig. 9C in which a 10X objective and 10X eyepiece are included to depict the complete lens system of this microscope.

The free apertures of the zoom lenses are made large enough to transmit the full apertures of the objectives so that the objectives work at their full numerical apertures throughout the zoom range. Since the objective numerical apertures remain fixed, the upper limit of useful magnification introduced by the zoom system is reached when a further increase results in empty magnification. The usual upper limit is 2X although where photomicrography is an important consideration, magnifications as high as 3X may be used.

Since real field coverage varies inversely with magnification, the usual lower limit of magnification for zoom systems represented by Fig. 5A is about 1X. The reason for this limit is that if lower magnifications were permitted, both the objectives and the condenser-illumination system would be forced to cover larger field sizes than those for which they are designed.

It will be apparent that a change in the zoom setting of the system illustrated in Fig. 5A, with the resulting change in magnification and field coverage but with no change in objective numerical aperture, is equivalent to varying the eyepiece power. Hence, the zoom system represented in Fig. 5A may be considered as part of a zooming eyepiece.

The zooming microscope illustrated in Fig. 5B is representative of

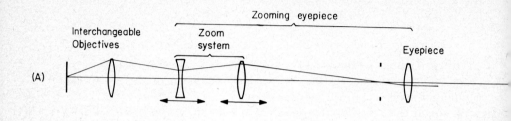

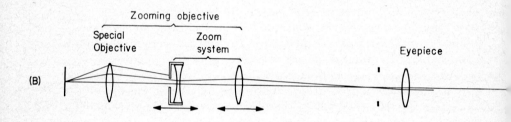

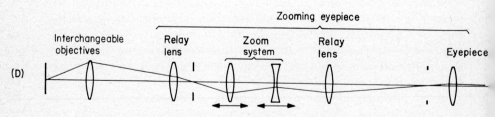

FIG. 5. Microscope zoom systems (schematic).

the type of system used in Teaching Microscopes for high school and junior college levels and used almost exclusively in zooming stereo-microscopes. In this system the effective objective numerical aperture is made to change almost linearly with change in magnification. This is accomplished most economically by choosing zoom systems for which one or the other of the zoom lenses follows a zoom path which can be utilized to control the numerical aperture. For example, the first zoom lens in Fig. 5B moves toward the objective for low magnification and away from the objective for high magnification. If the aperture of the stop which is attached to this lens is made just large enough to pass the full objective aperture at high magnification, then it will pass a smaller and smaller percentage of this aperture as the lens moves to the left for the lower magnification. Thus, the aperture varies with zoom magnification, permitting zoom ranges of up to seven times in Stereomicroscopes and up to five times in Teaching Microscopes. This system is representative of the zooming objective type microscope. In addition to the variable numerical aperture feature, it differs from the previous system in the design characteristics of the objective. The zooming eyepiece system is designed to work with standard inter-changeable objectives. The zooming objective system requires a special objective which, for aberration control, must be designed as an integral part of the zoom system.

The microscope illustrated in Fig. 5C is another but simplified version of the zooming objective system. Here, the first lens serves both as the objective and as the first zoom lens. This lens also carries the aperture stop which controls the effective numerical aperture.

The relative simplicity of this last system and the excellent aberration correction which can be achieved make it ideal for use in Teaching Microscopes intended for use in elementary and junior high school levels as proven by the many thousands which are in daily use in these applications.

While the three microscopes just described differ from each other in many features, they are alike in two respects, viz. they are amenable to short compact microscope design configurations and they form inverted images in the same sense that the images of non-zooming microscopes are inverted. Where erect images are required as in Stereomicroscopes, a porro prism or mirror erecting system must be added.

The microscope illustrated in Fig. 5D, which must be classified as a zooming eyepiece system, utilizes a zoom-relay which greatly extends the distance between the objective and eyepiece (Fig. 5 is not drawn to scale). This is the type of zoom system used in large console Research Microscopes and Metallographs where the added length is needed for operator comfort and where provisions must be made for such built-in accessories as phase contrast, high power stereo, interchangeable reticles, and a variety of photomicrographic facilities. Since there is an intermediate image plane between the objective and the eyepiece focal plane, the observer sees an erect image of the specimen. The actual lens system is drawn to scale in Fig. 9F, and is incomplete in that the viewing is achieved through an additional telescope, not shown.

F. *Cams and the Crank-Link Non-Linear Motion Generator*

Mechanically Compensated Zoom Systems must employ some kind of mechanical drive to impart the required nonlinear lens motions. The first mechanical drives to be employed were cam arrangements, two types of which are illustrated in Fig. 6.

The concentric arrangement shown at the left in Fig. 6 consists of an outer tube into which the cam slots are machined, an intermediate tube which acts as the main support for the entire zoom system, and a pair of short inner tubes or cells into which the lenses are mounted. Very close fits must be maintained between the inner and outer diameters of these tubes.

Two longitudinal slots are machined through the wall of the intermediate tube. Cam pins which are screwed into the lens cells protrude through both the longitudinal slots in the intermediate tube and the cam slots in the outer tube. As the outer cam tube is rotated about the intermediate tube, the forward or backward forces determined by the slopes of the cam slot at the point of contact with the pin are transmitted by the pin to the lens cells. The longitudinal slots in the intermediate tube prevent the lens cells from rotating in the intermediate tube but permit the longitudinal travel of the cells along the tube axis.

The basic shapes of the cam slots are calculated directly using the zoom equations on p. 8. If the cam tube were opened up and flattened out into sheet form, the cam slots would look like the zoom path curves in Fig. 3. The rate of change of magnification with cam rotation is constant when the cam is made in this form.

At the discretion of the mechanical designer, the rate of lens motions with cam rotation may be speeded up or slowed down over any part of the zoom range, resulting in a rate of change of magnification which will not be linear with rotation. In some zoom systems, the zoom path of one of the lenses may turn out to be almost linear in which case the path may be made linear arbitrarily and compensating corrections made in the shape of the second cam slot. Figure 7 shows how this is accomplished and also how the change affects the rate of change of magnification with cam rotation. In other zoom systems, the slope of

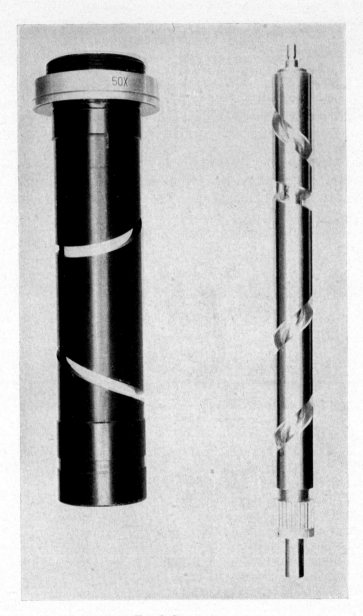

FIG. 6. Cam systems.

one of the cam slots may turn out to be excessively steep over some region of its length. Here again the mechanical designer may choose to arbitrarily reduce the slope of the cam slot and introduce the necessary compensation in the second cam slot. The graphical method illustrated in Fig. 7 for altering cam slot shapes demonstrates the concept but is not recommended as the best procedure. A better procedure is to determine roughly the desired arbitrary cam shape and then write an expression for the shape as a function of magnification. Four or five

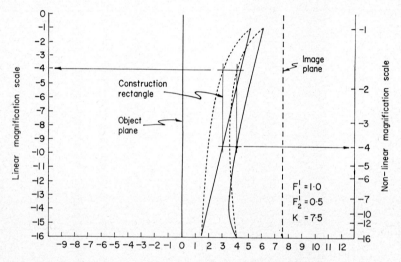

Fig. 7. Variations in relative cam shapes; – – – – original zoom path;
——————— modified zoom path.

terms in a power series are usually sufficient. The cam shown to the left in Fig. 6 is an example of a cam made according to the procedure just described.

The cam shown to the right in Fig. 6 is an example of a second type used in microscopes, viz. the off-center type. Here, the lens cells are secured to and driven along two guide rods. The two cam slots are machined into the cam rod. Cam pins which are screwed into the lens cells protrude into the cam slots and transmit the longitudinal force which drives the cells along the guide rods.

There is no fundamental difference between the two cam types, hence the remarks made concerning the shape generation of the cam slots and the arbitrary alteration of one of the shapes applies to both types. The off-center type is the more costly of the two but offers the advantage of better stray light control.

Although the techniques of cam design and production have been adequately mastered, the manufacture of cams involves rather large tooling costs. This problem tends to restrict the application of zoom to those instruments which are marketed in relatively large volume. The Crank-Link Non-Linear Motion Generator* (hereafter abbreviated to "Crank-Link") developed by the firm of Bausch & Lomb substantially reduces the initial tooling costs and in many applications also lowers production costs.

The concept of the Crank-Link is illustrated in Fig. 8. The two zoom lenses are mounted in individual cells which are attached to guide rods or mounted in an outer tube as shown in Fig. 8. Both methods restrict the motion of the lenses to a longitudinal motion along the optical axis. A crank R and linkage S is attached to each lens cell. Rotational motion about the point O is converted into longitudinal lens motion by means of the crank and linkage.

Since the Crank-Link is simply a substitute for the cam, it follows that it must impart the same motions to the lenses that a cam would impart. The device can be made to achieve the required motions as closely as desired through the proper selection of values for the linkage parameters. The relevant parameters are: (1) the crank lengths R_1 and R_2, (2) the linkage lengths S_1 and S_2, (3) the vertical distances Y_1 and Y_2 between the point O and the points P_1 and P_2, respectively, (4) the constant Q for one of the lenses, and (5) the starting values for θ_1 and θ_2. It should be noted that the two cranks are rotated together at the same rate, i.e. $\theta_2 - \theta_1 = $ constant. It should also be noted that if the point O were moved to the right by a distance equal to the constant Q, then Q becomes a factor associated with the first lens rather than the second.

The exceedingly small tolerances which can be permitted between the resultant motions produced by the Crank-Link and the theoretical motions called for by the equations on p. 8 make impractical the manual determination of optimum values for the large number of Crank-Link parameters. The obvious solution to this problem is an optimization program written for a high-speed computer. The optimization program may be written to accept as starting data a representative set of values for X_1 and X_2. The computer is instructed to vary one or more of the parameters and select values which result in the best fit between the resultant device and the theoretical motions. Experience has shown that the fidelity of the Crank-Link motions to the theoretical motions is at least as good as can be achieved with conventional cams.

* Patent applied for.

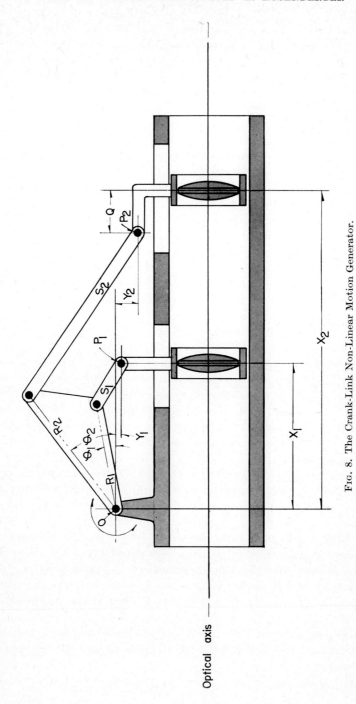

FIG. 8. The Crank-Link Non-Linear Motion Generator.

G. *Why Zoom?*

In preceding sections the principles of zoom and the application of these principles to microscopy have been discussed without reference to the question of whether any real advantages are gained from the addition of the zoom feature.

A good starting point from which to look for answers to this question is a review of the conditions which exist when standard objectives on a Laboratory Microscope are used in conjunction with the usual 10X eyepiece. The first column in Table I gives the magnifications and numerical apertures of the most commonly used microscope objectives. The second column gives the total microscope magnifications. The third column gives the maximum useful total microscope magnification for each objective before the point of useful magnification is exceeded, i.e. before the total microscope magnification exceeds 1000 times the objective numerical aperture. The last column shows the useful magnification which may be introduced by the zoom system.

TABLE I

Objective magnification and N.A.	Microscope magnification	Maximum useful magnification	Maximum useful zoom magnification
4X, 0·09N.A.	40X	90X	2·3X
10X, 0·25N.A.	100X	250X	2·5X
40X, 0·65N.A.	400X	650X	1·6X
100X, 1·25N.A.	1000X	1250X	1·3X

Thus, when the zoom system is used with discretion, it can serve a very useful purpose. For example, if 200X is required for the proper examination of a specimen, the microscopist will have to go all the way to 400X using the 40X objective if his microscope is non-zooming. With the zooming microscope, however, the specimen can be examined at the desired 200X using the 10X objective without introducing empty magnification. With the 10X objective, (1) the working distance is about 6·5 mm as compared to about 0·5 mm for the 40X, (2) the real field is doubled, and (3) the depth of focus is about seven times that of the 40X.

The example cited above illustrates how the zoom system permits selecting the best compromise between magnification and such other factors as working distance, field of view, and depth of focus. In other applications such as dark field and fluorescence microscopy, image brightness often becomes the factor of primary importance in which case the zoom system again can be used to great advantage. For these applications there is a definite advantage to be gained in replacing the usual 10X eyepiece with a 5X eyepiece which, in combination with the zoom system, permits the use of relatively high N.A. objectives at relatively low total microscope magnification. The advantage to be gained from this practice will be apparent when one remembers that for a given total microscope magnification the image brightness is proportional to the square of the objective N.A.

As an aid in doing measurement work with the microscope, the zoom system provides a convenience not available by other means. With the zooming microscope, a single eyepiece equipped with a single reticle can be used interchangeably with any of the microscope objectives. Using a stage micrometer, each increment in the eyepiece reticle can be calibrated to equal some specified increment of length in the specimen plane by simply adjusting the zoom magnification to the required value.

In photomicrography a kind of zoom system in the form of an adjustable bellows has long been regarded as a necessity. The advantages of replacing the unwieldy bellows with a compact zoom system are self evident. For microscopes equipped with one of the smaller accessory cameras, the zoom system is practically a necessity. Frequently these smaller cameras are designed with a built-in noninterchangeable camera lens, hence, the microscope zoom system provides the only means of composing the picture so that the image area of interest exactly fits the film frame.

Perhaps the most significant contribution zoom has made to microscopy has been in its revolutionary impact on the concept of the Teaching Microscope.

When the student changes the power of the non-zooming microscope, the large discrete steps between objective magnifications and the temporary complete loss of any image as objectives are being changed make difficult his recognizing the small specimen area which he sees at high magnification as being a part of the larger specimen area he had seen at some lower magnification. The continuous and uninterrupted change in magnification achieved with the zooming microscope eliminates this problem.

In industrial applications where stereomicroscopes are used in such production line operations as engraving, drilling, soldering, welding, and in the assembly and inspection of miniature parts, the operator must select the best compromise among magnification, field size, resolution and depth of focus. The continuously variable stereozoom microscope is uniquely adaptable to providing the operator with rapid and convenient means of obtaining this best compromise by direct observation during zoom.

III. Some Actual Zoom Microscopes

A. *Introduction*

In this section we shall describe some actual microscopes embodying the principles of the previous section. Fig. 9 shows scale drawings of several lens systems from such zooming microscopes.

In Fig. 9 the terms "Object Plane" and "Image Plane" refer to those of the movable lenses of the zoom system proper, not of the complete system. In accordance with the terminology of the preceeding section, the terms F_1' and F_2' are the relative focal lengths of the movable zoom lenses, F_1' always being unity and K is the object to image distance for the zoom system proper, again expressed relative to $F_1' = \pm 1$.

All of the systems in Fig. 9 are two-lens mechanically-compensated zoom systems, and in each case one zoom lens is positive and one is negative. Systems 9A, B, and E employ a special objective which is a basic part of the microscope design. In these systems N.A. varies with zoom setting so they are equivalent to zooming objective systems. Systems 9C and F are designed for use with interchangeable objectives, and here the N.A. does not change with zoom setting, hence, they are classified as eyepiece zoom systems. In system 9D the objective itself is the zoom system, and its N.A. changes with zoom.

Relay lenses and field lenses used in some of the systems of Fig. 9 serve to control the field and pupil positions and also the magnification levels. Prisms and mirrors used in most of the systems for inclined binocular observation are omitted from the drawing for space reasons. For the same reason, the final telescope actually used in the Fig. 9F system is omitted.

B. *Stereoscopic Microscopes*

The first application of zoom in a microscope was in the stereoscopic microscope shown in Fig. 1. Each half of the microscope comprises a fixed doublet followed by a negative zoom doublet and a positive zoom doublet. The negative doublet does most of the power changing while the positive zoom doublet follows focus to maintain a constant image position. The negative lens also acts as a moving aperture stop, causing the N.A. of the system to increase at high power and decrease at low

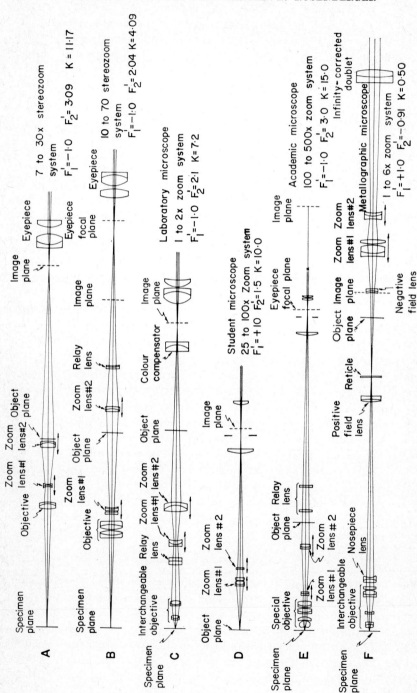

FIG. 9. Microscope zoom systems (actual designs).

power, as may be envisaged from the high and low power lens positions shown in Fig. 1B. This system zooms through a 4 : 1 range of power and has a maximum N.A. of 0·06 at the high power setting.

The lens system of this original stereozoom microscope is drawn to scale in Fig. 9A, shown here in the low power setting, and with a 10X widefield eyepiece in place. The object distance of this microscope is 108 mm at all magnifications, and the specimen plane to eyepiece focal plane is 329 mm, again a constant value at all magnifications. Table II gives depth of focus, N.A., and real field size for this system at various magnifications.

TABLE II

Mag.	Depth of focus	N.A.	Real field
	mm		mm
7X	0·88	0·025	28·6
8X	0·70	0·028	25·0
9X	0·45	0·035	22·2
10X	0·38	0·038	20·0
15X	0·24	0·048	13·3
20X	0·19	0·054	10·0
25X	0·17	0·057	8·0
30X	0·15	0·060	6·7

Depth of focus in Table II is based on the approximation $\lambda/\text{N.A.}^2$ and does not include eye-accomodation which will generally materially increase the depths in actual usage.

The usefulness of zoom in a stereomicroscope is attested to by the fact that practically all of the major microscope makers have now swung over to making zoom models in place of fixed-power models. Changing power by zooming creates the strong impression of moving the object toward and away from the observer, without ever losing sight of the object, and hence is a much more natural visual experience than the abrupt power changes of the older objective-changing models. Microscopes similar to the original design shown in Fig. 1 are now made by practically all of the major microscope manufacturers, some of whom have extended the zoom range and the maximum N.A. beyond the original 1959 design.

Thus, in 1962, Nikon introduced a stereomicroscope with 5 : 1 zoom range and maximum N.A. of 0·07. In this same year Olympus introduced a 4 : 1 zoom range and maximum N.A. of 0·06, which values duplicated the original Bausch & Lomb values. Watson, in 1964, introduced a 5 : 1 system with maximum N.A. of 0·085. Zeiss, in 1965, introduced a 4 : 1 system of 0·06 maximum N.A., again a duplication of the original B. & L. system values. American Optical Co., in 1967, also introduced a 4 : 1 system of maximum N.A. 0·06 and at the same time a 6 : 1 system of maximum N.A. 0·07. Bausch & Lomb in 1968 introduced a new design having a 7 : 1 zoom range and maximum N.A. of 0·10. This system is shown in Fig. 9B.

In 1968 Vickers and Beck together introduced a somewhat different zoom stereo wherein the lenses zoom from 1/3X to 1X, and then flip over and zoom from 1X to 3X. Its maximum N.A. is 0·055 (0·11 with 2X attachment lens in position). In the same year Zeiss introduced a 5 : 1 zoom stereo called their Model IV. Its N.A. is not known at the time of writing.

The above cited N.A.'s are those for the basic microscope. Attachment lenses are also generally available which increase the power and N.A., but with attendant shortening of the working distance, and increase of the convergence angle between the left and right optical axes in the object space. These lenses are large achromatic doublets or triplets which are large enough to cover both objective lenses of the microscope. Similarly, reducing lenses are also generally available. These are negative achromats which increase the working distance and decrease both power and N.A. These lenses decrease the angle between the two optical axes in the object space.

Wherever attachment lenses are used they modify the angle between the optical axes, with attendant change in the stereo effect. When a positive attachment lens is used, it exaggerates the stereo effect, and causes a flat specimen to appear convex. When a negative attachment lens is used it reduces the stereo effect, and causes a flat specimen to appear dished or concave.

C. Laboratory Microscopes

The optical system used in the Laboratory Microscope is shown in Fig. 9C and has been previously described as equivalent to a zooming eyepiece, since N.A. does not change with zoom. The relay lens shortens the object distance for the negative zoom lens to effect a substantial power change for a moderate lens motion. The zoom system is shown in its low power position (1X). The image distance of the second zoom lens is sufficiently long to work with a binocular or triocular body. This microscope is more fully described in Kingslake's "Applied Optics and Optical Engineering", Vol. IV, Ch. 2, pp. 36–7.

A variation of this system is also used in an inverted Bench Metallograph. In this microscope a relay lens system is utilized between the objective and the zoom system. This serves the function of extending the eyepoint to a convenient location, and at the same time forming a relayed real field image and a real pupil image, which are useful for reticle insertion and pupil-controlling devices.

A different approach has been taken by the firm of Leitz, in which an optional zoom accessory, fitting between the objective and the binocular head is employed. This system is shown in Fig. 10, which is a plan view of the accessory. The optical axis is perpendicular to the drawing at the point "X". The square surrounding "X" is a right-angled prism aluminized on its hypotenuse and reflecting the light to start it around the rectangular path as shown. After traversing this path the light is reflected upward by the same aluminized face, i.e. along the original optical axis. The movable lenses, indicated by arrows in Fig. 10 are cam driven via a rack and pinion motion. The zoom range is 3·2X to 1X. The dashed line indicates an intermediate real image plane. This system differs from those of Fig. 9 in that both zoom lenses are positive, whereas all of the systems in Fig. 9 are positive–negative combinations.

D. *Student Microscopes*

The first zooming student microscope is shown in Fig. 9D. This zooms through a 25X to 100X range, and its maximum N.A. at 100X is 0·12. The N.A. is controlled by the moving aperture of the positive zoom lens so that the image brightness and image resolution remain substantially constant. At 25X the N.A. is 0·03.

In addition to the above microscope, Bausch & Lomb also makes a 50X to 200X zooming student microscope, whose N.A. varies from 0·06 at 50X to 0·25 at 200X. The zoom system embodies 7 lens elements as contrasted with only 4 in the 25 to 100X microscope. Both of these systems are described in Kingslake's "Applied Optics and Optical Engineering", Vol. III, Ch. 4, p. 180.

A still higher power and higher N.A. zooming student microscope is shown in Fig. 9E. This system differs from the above two microscopes in that the objective lens does not move, the zoom being accomplished by the two movable doublets shown in Fig. 9E. This system ranges in power from 100X to 500X and its maximum N.A. is 0·55. It is designed for use at the high school and college level of biology teaching. The N.A. change with zoom is accomplished by the aperture motion of the negative zoom doublet.

E. *Metallographic Microscopes*

In 1967 Bausch & Lomb introduced a zooming metallographic microscope which utilized a somewhat different type of zoom system,

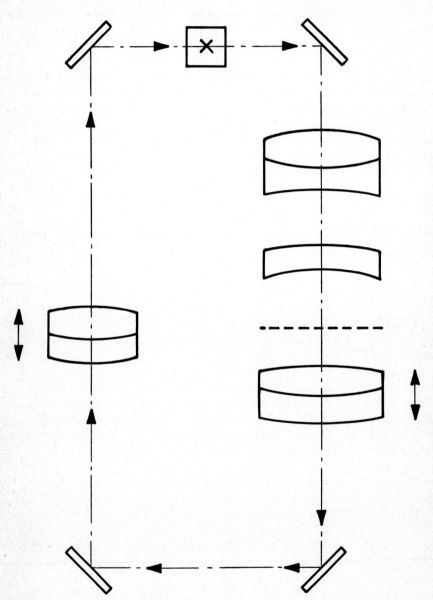

FIG. 10. An accessory zoom system. Drawing courtesy E. Leitz, Inc.

capable of quite extended zoom range. This system was designed originally as a 12 : 1 zoom system in a telescope, but was later modified to a 6 : 1 system for use in the metallograph. The system has a real object plane, but a virtual image plane, hence must be followed by a relay system to form a final real image in the eyepiece focal plane. It is shown drawn to scale in Fig. 9F. The system shown in Fig. 9F is incomplete to the extent that the viewing telescope which follows the large doublet at the right is not shown.

This system is a body tube zoom system basically similar to Fig. 5D, which does not change the N.A. of the objective during zoom. It is thus equivalent to a zooming eyepiece rather than a zooming objective. It was cut back from its original 12 : 1 range to avoid excessive empty magnification, i.e. magnification not justified by the N.A.'s of the objectives. The total magnification is so chosen as to be equivalent to a 5X to 30X zooming eyepiece.

IV. Trends and Limitations

In considering future development trends for microscope zoom systems, a division must be drawn between the zooming eyepiece concept and the zooming objective concept.

The zooming eyepiece has already been developed to a state where its zoom range is as large as can be utilized. The reasons for this were discussed in a previous section. Since the useful zoom range is limited, and since the aberration correction of current systems leaves little to be desired, the incentives for further development are small indeed.

In contrast, the need for further development of the zooming objective concept, particularly for Teaching and Laboratory Microscopes, is very evident.

A single zooming objective would have to have a zoom range of about *40-times* before it would replace the battery of objectives currently available for Laboratory Microscopes. At the time of writing (1967) only a 5-times zoom range has been attained. Clearly the need for further development exists.

The major problem to be solved in extending the zoom range is that of aberration control. This problem arises not so much in the design of the zoom lenses as in the design of the objective portion of the system.

The objective must be designed to cover a large field at low magnification and a high numerical aperture at high magnification and it turns out that the shapes of the objective lenses need to be convex toward the specimen plane at low magnification and concave toward the specimen at high magnification.

A possible approach to this problem is that of compromising the objective design and designing a zoom system capable of introducing compensating aberrations throughout the zoom range. This will entail the development of far more sophisticated zoom systems than have been produced hitherto and it is in this area where development effort is likely to be concentrated.

An "automatic" lens design program has been evolved for Zoom systems which gives promise of speeding up future designs. In this program the focal lengths are pre-selected from the Zoom Systems Catalog and the lens positions are controlled to keep their principal plane separations correct at various zoom settings. Like most automatic programs, it works on the figure of merit concept, and requires considerable intelligent guidance from the designer. It is nonetheless a powerful tool, and one which can speed up the evolution of new zooming microscopes.

Mensuration Methods in Optical Microscopy

D. W. HUMPHRIES

Department of Geology, The University, Sheffield, England

I. INTRODUCTION

THE measurement of microscopic objects is an important aspect of the analysis of a variety of natural and manufactured products. Such substances include, for example, sand grains, soil particles, plant seeds, fertilizers, pigments, fillers, liquid droplets, abrasives, fibres and many foodstuffs. The purpose of such measurements may be the control of a manufacturing process, the determination of the physical and mechanical properties of particulate materials or it may be the identification and distinguishing of particles, especially micro-

33

organisms. Measurement of particle size is also important in those substances in which individual particles are bonded together as in rocks, refractories, metals and slags, as well as in tissues in which individual cells are joined together to form a continuous network.

Many methods of size analysis have been, and are, employed, and each has its own particular virtues and limitations. The microscope as a measuring tool has found increasing favour in recent years and it is certainly no longer true to say, as did Rose (1953) that it should be looked upon as a last resource as a means of powder size analysis.

Amongst the virtues of the use of the microscope for mensuration is the possibility of examining very small samples of material. It also permits selection of the dimension to be measured. This is especially important where the shape of the particle is irregular (and this is usually the case) and overcomes the tendency associated with other methods of tacitly assuming that particles are spherical or are behaving as though they were spherical. The problem of shape will be discussed later, but it should be noted here that the irregularity of a particle has been used as a basis for suggesting that the microscope should *not* be used for size determination. Since shape may have almost as much bearing on the physical properties or behaviour of a particle as its size, such a view would seem to be unsupportable. Where materials are indurated or bonded, or consist of continuous networks of cells, the microscope is almost the only method of size determination, though the action of shearing or cutting the material for examination introduces certain problems of interpretation of the numerical data.

Perhaps the principal limitation of the microscope method of size determination is the low rate at which data can be collected. Another objection commonly raised is that the accuracy of the observations is influenced by operator fatigue. While this is as true of microscope observations as of any other type of observation, the recognition of its occurrence can lead to an estimation of its effects.

Despite these limitations, direct observation of particles using the microscope must be regarded as the only method by which the true size, rather than the apparent and behavioural size of microscopic particles can be determined.

Mensuration by the optical microscope is not limited to the measurement of the size of particles. It can also be used to determine the mass of small particles, the proportions of constituents of mixtures, the ratio of surface area to volume of particles and cells and the angles between the boundaries of cells and grains.

The techniques employed and some of the associated theoretical aspects are described in the following pages.

II. The Size of Irregular Particles

A. *Grain Shape*

If all particles were perfect spheres no problems of the definition of size would arise. The statement of a single dimension, for example, the diameter, would unequivocally specify the size and would incidentally define the shape of the particle. Very few materials even vaguely approach this ideal state, nor do they approximate to simple geometrical forms.

Wadell (1932) in a most thorough investigation of the size of irregular particles, maintained that "size" is best expressed by the volume of a particle since this is independent of its shape. He then defined the size of an irregular particle in terms of the *diameter* of a sphere equal in volume to the volume of the particle. Such a definition, however, would bring together such particles as a very thin disc, a long slender rod and a small sphere whose "size" by Wadell's definitions would be the same, but whose shape, hydraulic behaviour and the space occupied by the particle in the context of packing would be very different. Furthermore, this definition is almost impossible to apply to small particles viewed under the microscope. It is usual, therefore, to represent the size of the particle by the diameter of a circle having the same area as the projected image of the particle when viewed in a direction perpendicular to the plane of greatest stability. This diameter is referred to as the mean projected diameter. To determine the size in terms of Wadell's "diameter of a sphere", it is necessary to view the particle in more than one direction and to apply a "shape factor".

Numerous authors have attempted to derive coefficients relating the mean projected diameter of the particle to its volume or surface area. Heywood, in particular, has discussed the problem at length (for references, see p. 96) and contributions have been made by Beirne and Hutcheon (1954), Robins (1954) and Davies (1964) among others. In general, these authors have calculated shape coefficients for simple geometrical shapes, namely, rectangular prisms, tetrahedra and ellipsoids. Heywood (1954) has determined shape coefficients for irregularly shaped particles resembling these simple forms, while Hausner (1967) has attempted the characterization of a variety of "complicated shapes". Aschenbrenner (1956) has measured shape in relation to a rather less simple geometrical form, the tetrakaidecahedron, which he considered approximated more closely to the shape of sand grains than either the triaxial ellipsoid or simple plane-sided geometrical forms.

Although for the purposes of size determination it is desirable that the shape of a particle should be expressed by means of a single co-efficient, it should be borne in mind that the shape of a particle is, in fact, the result of the operation of two independent factors, the *sphericity* and the *roundness*. This was first realized by Wadell (1933) in relation to rock fragments and later extended to mineral grains. Sphericity is a measure of the form of a grain independently of the sharpness of the edges, whereas roundness is a matter of the sharpness of the corners and edges of a grain. Thus, the simple geometrical solids, cube, tetrahedron, prism, etc., have different sphericities but their edges and corners are equally sharp and they have the same (zero) roundness. A sphere and a cube have the same sphericity, but different roundness, whereas a sphere and an ellipsoid have different sphericities but the same roundness. Wadell defined sphericity and roundness initially in terms of a solid body with the sphere as the standard of reference and later, in terms of a plane figure (i.e. the projection area or cross-section) with the circle as the standard of reference.

Thus, sphericity is defined as the ratio of the nominal diameter to the maximum intercept through the particle. Roundness is the ratio of the average radius of the corners and edges to the radius of the maximum inscribed circle. Both coefficients have a minimum value of zero and a maximum value of one. The methods of calculation are tedious but the coefficients can readily be estimated by comparison with standard charts (e.g. Krumbein, 1941; Powers, 1953) (Fig. 1). Though these coefficients are readily determined, no attempt appears to have been made to utilize them in relation to particle size deter-mination.

Despite the numerous attempts to characterize the shape of particles, the true size expressed in terms of the equivalent sphere is rarely determined. For this, there seem to be two reasons. Firstly, the particles in a sample commonly show a very wide range of shapes which demand the determination and application of a number of shape factors. Secondly, the determination of these factors on real grains necessitates altering the orientation of the grain under the microscope. Heywood (1954) suggested mounting the grains in a viscous liquid with a cover glass on the slide. Lifting the edge of the cover glass and lowering it would cause the grains to roll over, thus permitting the thickness of the grains to be measured. Hulbe (1955) has described a technique for mounting grains in plastic rods to enable them to be examined in three dimensions. Humphries (1966b) has described an improved technique for mounting the grains, polishing the plastic rods and a jig for mounting the rods on the microscope stage which enables the rods

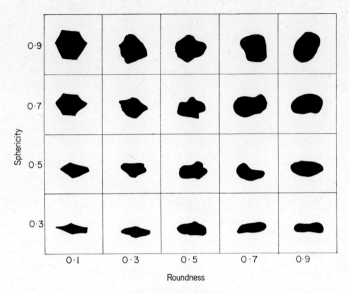

FIG. 1. Comparison chart for estimation of sphericity and roundness of sand grains (after Krumbein, 1941).

to be turned over through 90° (Fig. 2). These mounting methods have been used for particles as small as 100 μ. Many powders are, however, finer than this and the difficulties of handling individual grains are very considerable.

In view of the difficulties of defining and determining the "true" size of particles in terms of the three-dimensional form of the particle, it is common practice to report particle sizes either as linear dimensions or as areas. The size is then dependent upon the orientation of the particle with respect to the direction of measurement. Particles mounted in air (i.e. dry) or in liquids of low viscosity probably settle into a position of maximum stability. Thus the dimensions measured will tend to be maximum. If, on the other hand, the grains are mounted in a viscous medium, there is no certainty that any grains will have their maximum dimensions perpendicular to the direction of viewing. It is sometimes suggested that the cover glass should be pressed down in order to orient the grains and with grains that are uniform in size or shape this may be effective. Where, however, there is a considerable range of grain size present, the larger grains may be orientated under the pressure of the cover slip, whereas smaller grains will be unaffected by the pressure and may even be turned on edge as the mounting fluid is expelled. Grain mounts may therefore be regarded as consisting

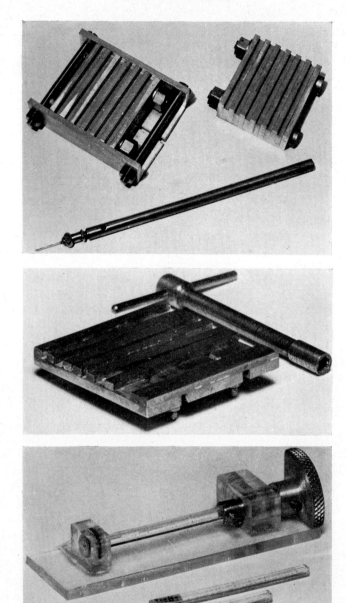

Fig. 2. Mounting grains in plastic rods for three-dimensional size and shape analysis (Humphries, 1966b). Top, moulds and grain lifter; middle, polishing jig for plastic rods; bottom, microscope stage jig for turning rods through 90° and plastic rods.

of orientated grains or completely random grains or an undetermined mixture. Hence, in reporting grain sizes, consideration should be given to the randomness or otherwise of the orientation of the particles. Failure to do so may lead to anomalous size frequency distributions.

B. *Grain Size Parameters*

Despite the inherent assumptions concerning the shape and orientation of the particle, the determination of particle size is commonly based on the measurement of the projection area of the grain or on linear measures of this projection area. In the case of loose grains

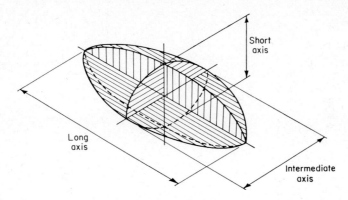

FIG. 3. Direct linear measures for the description of particles.

resting on their surface of maximum stability the long and intermediate axes are normally horizontal and the short axis vertical. Thus the long or the intermediate axis may be measured or the area of the grain projection measured or estimated. However, when grains are randomly orientated as in the mounts in a viscous liquid, it is unlikely that these mechanical axes or the maximum projection area can be measured. In this case statistical measures have to be adopted.

A further restriction on grain size measurement is introduced if the particles cannot be separated from each other as in indurated rocks, biological materials and metals. In these cases it is necessary to cut thin sections or to prepare polished surfaces. This introduces the added problem that the measured size depends not only on the orientation of the particle (generally unknown) but also on the position of the section or surface intersecting the particle (Fig. 28). The interpretation of size measurements of thin sections is discussed later.

The grain size measures most commonly adopted are summarized below:

1. *Direct linear measures* (Fig. 3)

    a. *Long axis*. The maximum overall length of a grain.

    b. *Intermediate axis*. The maximum dimension of a grain in a direction perpendicular to the long axis.

    c. *Short axis*. The maximum dimension in a direction perpendicular to the plane containing the long and intermediate axes.

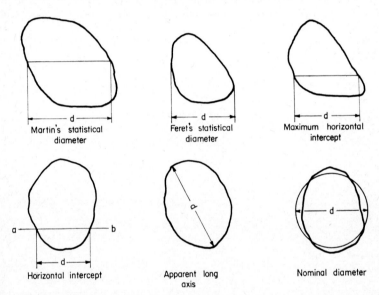

Fig. 4. Statistical measures for grain size description. d = grain diameter; ab is the reference line on which the horizontal intercept is measured (for details, see text).

2. *Statistical linear measures* (Fig. 4)

    a. *Martin's statistical diameter*. The length of the line which divides the projected area of the grain into two equal halves. The line is parallel to a fixed direction, e.g. the direction of traverse of the microscope stage and the division into two parts is made by eye (Martin *et al.*, 1923).

    b. *Feret's statistical diameter*. The maximum projected length of the grain on to a fixed line (Feret, 1931).

    c. *Maximum horizontal intercept*. The maximum length of a line parallel to a fixed dimension limited by the contour of the grain (Krumbein, 1935). The fixed line is usually parallel to the direction of traverse of the stage.

d. *Horizontal intercept.* The intercept that the grain makes with a fixed line parallel to the direction of traverse of the stage.

e. *Apparent long axis.* The maximum length of the grain in thin section (e.g. Rosenfeld *et al.*, 1953).

3. *Measures based on the projected area of the grain*

a. *Nominal diameter.* The diameter of a circle of the same area as the grain projection. Equalization of the areas may be by measurement of the projected area using for example, a planimeter or fitting by eye a circle of appropriate size (Wadell, 1935).

The relationship between certain of these measures has been discussed by Heywood (1946) who concluded that the mean values obtained with Martin's statistical diameter and with the nominal sectional diameter agreed closely with the values obtained by exact area measurements with a planimeter for mineral particles of normal shape. As particles become more elongated the size determined by Martin's diameter becomes progressively smaller than that given by the mean projected diameter. Feret's diameter on the other hand, gives progressively greater sizes. It is of interest to note that Heywood (1947) considered that Martin's diameter was a sufficiently accurate method of determining grain size, whereas in 1963 he expressed the opinion (Heywood, 1963, 67) that statistical methods by which an intercept of the particle image was measured were obsolete. He favoured instead the use of graticules comprising a series of circles which could be superimposed on the grain image.

Although the graticule method is that recommended in British Standard 3406 (1963) it is a method which lends itself least readily to automation and furthermore demands a high degree of skill in use.

Numerous authors have discussed the relationship between the size measures noted above and sizes determined by other methods, in particular by sieving. In all instances the comparison has been complicated by the problems of particle shape outlined earlier. In general it can be observed that for particles which can be said to be spherical, agreement is reasonably good, whereas for elongated, ellipsoidal or disc-shaped particles the agreement is poor. The point to stress is that whatever method of size analysis is adopted, the precise method should be explicitly stated in reporting analytical results. Heywood (1967, p. 357) has called for a standardized notation, but even without this much confusion could be avoided by a brief description of the precise technique and parameter employed.

A further aspect of reporting sizes in terms of grain diameters is the inherent risk of inducing in the reader's mind the impression that the particles described are spherical, since the only solid object uniquely defined by a single dimension is a sphere. To quote three dimensions for a particle implies that the particle is ellipsoidal or a prism. Thus, it is highly desirable that a description of the particle shape (or an illustration) should be given when sizes are quoted. The use of shape coefficients is not excluded, but as yet no such coefficient can be said to be fully descriptive of a particle. A brief example may emphasize the point. The fine particles of clay carried by rivers have a diameter of only a few microns and apparently are generally thought of as tiny spheres, whereas they are commonly very thin flakes. The difference in mechanical behaviour between spheres and flakes is, as might be expected, considerable.

C. *Limits of Size Analysis by Microscopic Methods*

The lower limit of particle size that can be resolved by visual light is about 0·2 microns, but the lower limit of practical particle size measurement is probably about 0·8 microns. Even at sizes up to 2 or 3 microns, the errors involved are likely to be appreciable unless the observer is especially experienced.

The upper limit of size depends to a very large extent on the method of measurement employed. The British Standard Specification 3406 suggests an upper limit of 150 microns, provided such particles do not exceed 10% of the total sample. Individual particles up to 2 mm or more can, however, be measured with the microscope.

III. TECHNIQUES OF SIZE ANALYSIS

A. *Measurement of Linear Dimensions by Graticules*

Basically there are two methods of obtaining linear dimensions of particles. One is by direct measurement against a linear scale, the other is by comparison with geometrical shapes, usually circles or discs, of known size. In the latter case, the linear dimension is actually based on the square root of the area. Either method can be applied by means of simple graticules or by more complex devices adapted for semi-automatic recording.

1. *Linear scales*

The simplest form of graticule comprises a glass disc—the standard size is 21 mm diameter—on which is engraved a fine line divided into a hundred equal parts. This disc is fitted onto the field stop of the ocular where it is in focus to the eye of the observer. Although the length of the scale is commonly 1 cm the scale divisions are arbitrary until related to a known objective magnification or calibrated against a stage micrometer scale for each objective.

Although objectives are commonly identified by their magnification, few lenses have precisely their nominal magnification. For example, a $10\times$ objective may be $\times 9$ or it may be $\times 11$ or some intermediate value. High power lenses may be even more in error. Thus reliance upon the nominal magnification can only lead to relatively inaccurate size measurements. For precise work the eyepiece scale must be calibrated by means of a stage micrometer under the exact conditions in which measurements will be made. The stage micrometers are usually glass or may be metal, slides on which an exact scale is engraved. This scale may be 10 mm or 1 mm long divided into 0·1 and 0·01 mm divisions. Stage micrometers with inch markings are also obtainable. It is not unusual to find that the rulings on the two scales when viewed through the microscope do not correspond exactly. Slight alteration of the microscope tube length may be sufficient to achieve exact co-incidence making the ratio of the number of divisions compared, a simple one. Many microscopes, however, lack means whereby the tube length can be altered and fixed in the extended position. It is therefore necessary to calculate the ratio of eyepiece micrometer divisions to stage micrometer divisions and to use this as a measure of the microscopic magnification. For particle size measurement the reciprocal of the magnification multiplied by the number of eyepiece scale divisions covering a given particle will give the size of the particle. It is easier to calibrate the eyepiece scale in terms of "magnified" units of length without determining the true magnification.

Many types of linear scale have been devised and many are currently available. Stage micrometers generally have a series of parallel lines at the appropriate spacing. Eyepiece micrometers may be similarly ruled or they may have a single horizontal line with short division lines at right angles. Alternatively they may have rulings of crosslines at right angles or they may be ruled in squares.

2. *Comparison methods*

Instead of measuring particles in terms of the number of divisions of a linear scale many microscopists prefer to compare particles with discs or circles of various sizes engraved on the eyepiece scale. Thus, instead of measuring an intercept on the grain it is possible to compare the nominal projected area with a circle of known area (diameter). The particle is actually classified and not measured.

The numerous variants of this type of graticule, commonly known as the "globe and circle" type differ essentially in the size ratio and positioning of the discs and graticule.

An early form of this graticule was that devised by Patterson and Cawood (1936) (Fig. 5a). The open circles and opaque discs each cover a 25 : 1 range of particle sizes in nine steps. The intervals between the steps is neither arithmetically nor geometrically constant. This was modified by Fairs (1943) to cover a much greater range of sizes (128 : 1) on three separate graticules (Fig. 5b, c, d). The sizes were arranged in a geometrical scale with an interval of $\sqrt{2}$ except for the two lowest sizes. On the basis of a statement attributed to C. H. Bosanquet, Fairs believes that a smaller size interval gives little improvement in accuracy. Fairs' graticules were designed specifically for sizing small particles. A graticule also utilizing the $\sqrt{2}$ progression was devised by May (1945) for obtaining the distribution of liquid droplets and has become widely known as the Porton graticule (Fig. 5e). A special feature was a system of vertical lines in a $\sqrt{2}$ spacing in addition to the globes and circles. This graticule was subsequently modified by May (1965) to increase the range of sizes. In the latter version (Fig. 5f) the range is 128 : 1 on a single graticule using the system of parallel lines and 32 : 1 using the globes and circles. In this graticule the diameter of the globes is made the same as the internal diameter of the circles thus obviating problems due to line thickness especially in the smaller particles. For certain purposes, the large number of size divisions of these graticules was considered excessive and Watson (1952) devised a graticule with only three globes and circles with their diameters in the proportions 5: 2: 0·5 (Fig. 6a). A rectangle engraved between the rows of circles and globes had the proportions 40 units by 20 units. This graticule was used essentially for counting particles in air-borne coal-mine dusts and using a 2 mm objective, the circles corresponded to 5 μ, 2 μ and 0·5 μ while the graticule was 40 μ long and 20 μ wide. This graticule was further modified by Hamilton et al. (1954). The three circles and globes were replaced by four with the same overall range but closer spacing (5: 2·5: 1: 0·5) (Fig. 6b). They also introduced a graticule with a series of vertical lines with spacings of 10, 5, 1 and 0·5 units (Fig. 6c). Using a 2 mm objective these units are approximately equivalent to microns, but for general use, these graticules have a much too limited range of sizes.

Fairs (1951) described a graticule for use with the projection microscope which was incorporated in the projection screen instead of being placed in the eyepiece (Fig. 6d). This graticule had nine circles in a $\sqrt{2}$ progression. The method of use was subsequently adopted as the basis for the British Standard Specification 3406: Part 4: 1963, for the

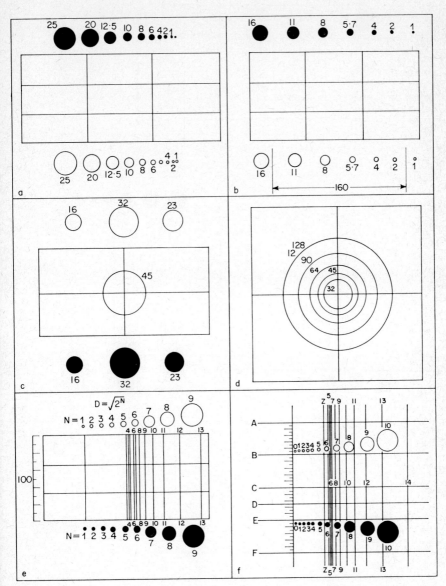

FIG. 5. Eyepiece graticules for particle sizing by comparison. a, Patterson and Cawood (1936); b, c, d, Fairs (1943); e, Porton graticule, May (1945); f, May (1965).

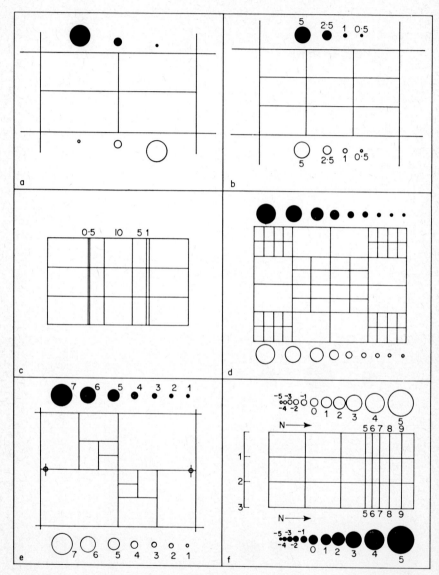

Fig. 6. Eyepiece graticules for particle sizing by comparison (cont.). a, Watson (1952); b, c, Hamilton, Holdsworth and Walton (1954); d, Fairs (1951); e, British Standard 3625 : 1963; f, Guruswamy (1967). Fig. 6e is taken from British Standard 3625 : 1963 and is reproduced by permission of the British Standards Institution, Park Street, London.

microscope method of size determination in powders. The standard graticule (B.S. 3625: 1963) for the method is somewhat simpler than that described by Fairs, though it retains the $\sqrt{2}$ progression (Fig. 6e).

In none of the graticules described above was consideration given to the subsequent arithmetic involved in calculating size and number distributions. With this in mind, Guruswamy (1967) has devised a graticule (Fig. 6f) in which the ratio between the diameter of the circles is 1·2589. The system of marking the circles and the fact that $\log_{10} 1·2589 = 0·1$ are claimed to facilitate the rapid calculation of results.

One other graticule may be mentioned here, though it was designed for determining the roundness of grains and not for size measurement (Robson, 1958). The graticule consists of a narrow strip of glass on which two rows of circles are inscribed (Fig. 7). The strip can be pushed back and forth in the slot which is normally present in the eyepiece of petrological microscopes. The circles are thus brought closer to the centre of the field of view than is possible with the other graticules described.

3. *Method of use of comparison graticules*

In most graticules of the "globe and circle" type the centre of the field of view is occupied by a grid of lines, the purpose of which is to delineate an area within which the particles present are measured. It normally plays no part in the measurement of individual particles, though in some cases some dimension of the grid bears a direct relation to the size of the globes and circles. The purpose of this is to facilitate calibration of the graticule.

In the case of linear scales, the scale is applied directly to the image of the particle to be measured. However, in the case of the comparison graticules the image of the particle and the appropriate circle or globe are not brought together. The observer has therefore to match the particle image against a circle outside the sizing area. Furthermore, the observer has eventually either to match an irregular particle against a distant circle by "squeezing" the particle into circular shape or by balancing the area of that part of the particle which falls outside a particular circle against the area by which part of the particle falls short of the circle (Fig. 8). The method is thus truly a comparative matter and not a method of direct measurement. Nevertheless, skilled observers can match particles against circles with considerable accuracy and consistency. In using this type of graticule it is essential that the magnification used gives adequately large images because the judgment of comparative sizes is more certain with larger images. This implies

Fig. 7. Robson (1958) graticule for roundness determination.

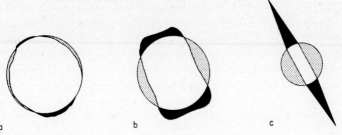

Fɪɢ. 8. Matching irregular grains to circles. The total black area in each grain (outside the circle) equals the total stippled area (inside the circle). The difficulty of accurate estimation increases as the grain becomes more elongated (left to right).

that the optical equipment should be of the highest quality and properly adjusted. As with all detailed observation, fatigue has a marked effect on the accuracy of the measurements and should therefore be minimized as far as possible.

Since size measurement by comparison graticules is largely a subjective process, it is highly desirable that adequate control by reference to standard powders should be maintained. Although it is preferable that the size distributions of these standards should be known, it is not essential provided that size determinations by different workers and by the same worker at different times are consistent with each other. In place of powders, Watson and Mulford (1954) have recommended the use of a particle-profile test strip for standardization of technique and for training microscopists.

B. *Semi-automatic Size Measurement*

Some of the problems of size measurement have been touched upon, but it has so far not been stressed that sizing and recording the analysis is a time-consuming and tedious procedure very liable to errors resulting from fatigue.

A number of devices have been described which greatly increase the rate of particle sizing, and most of them have means whereby the particles are counted automatically thereby reducing very considerably operator fatigue. Since these instruments require that an observer actually looks at the grain image but utilizes counting devices for recording the data, they are termed semi-automatic. This is in contrast to the fully-automatic devices, such as the Coulter counter or flying-spot microscope, in which the size of the particle is determined by the change in some physical parameter.

The semi-automatic devices fall into two groups according to the manner in which the particle size is determined. In the first group—the main group—are those which measure size in terms of intercepts. The second group is that in which the nominal projection area (diameter) is measured. Although the number of devices involved is small there is clear evidence that the measurement of linear intercepts whatever its statistical significance offers greater scope for automation than the measurement of nominal projection area. Some of the devices are quite complex in design while others are relatively simple, but demand a high degree of precision in construction.

1. Semi-automatic intercept measuring devices

The first two instruments under this heading are not strictly semi-automatic devices since operation and recording are both manual. They are, however, included since it seems likely that both could be adapted to automatic recording.

a. *Filar micrometer or screw-micrometer eye-piece.* This device is said to have been invented by William Gascoigne in 1639 for measuring the image of stars in telescopes, but the person responsible for its application to the microscope seems to be unknown. The instrument consists basically of a scale or crosshair which is made to traverse the field of view by means of a micrometer thread, the amount of the movement being indicated by the revolution of a graduated drum attached to the screwhead.

In most instruments the position of the zero line against which measurements are made is fixed. Consequently, a very small particle would be measured near the edge of the field of view instead of in the centre. To overcome this, it is necessary to provide some method of moving both hairlines into the centre of the field of view. An instrument incorporating this movement has recently been designed and manufactured by Malies Instruments Limited, Southwick, Brighton, for incorporation in the Firth "Hardometer" (Fig. 9) manufactured by Messrs. Firth-Brown Tools Limited, Sheffield, to whom the writer is indebted for permission to include this brief account.

In this particular design, the hairlines are replaced by metal jaws. The spindle controlling the width of the jaws and that for positioning the jaws in the centre of the field are made concentric with each other. The device can, therefore, be operated by one hand while the other is free for focussing the microscope, etc. This is an advance on some earlier designs in which both hands were required to operate the micrometer. A further modification, though this is not novel, is that the spacing of the jaws is read from a mechanical drum counter or "cyclometer" instead of from an engraved thimble. This counter can be read directly to 1 micron.

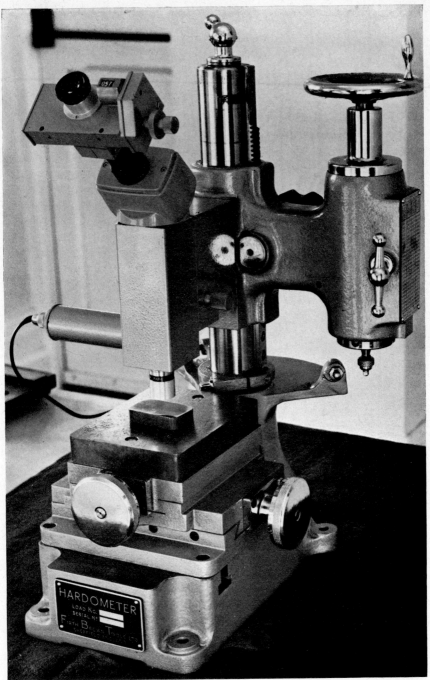

FIG. 9. Firth-Brown–Malies screw micrometer eyepiece fitted to Firth "Hardometer" (by permission of Firth-Brown Tools, Ltd., Sheffield).

An important application of the screw micrometer is the measurement of the indentation made for the determination of the hardness of metals. An investigation of the accuracy of measurement, with special reference to the Vickers hardness test, has been made by Wood and Marriner (1966). They emphasize that the nature of the illuminating beam of light can radically alter the apparent size of the indentation and they claim that for maximum precision, the greatest possible contrast between the indentation and the surround is required. They achieve this by ensuring that the incident and reflected light beams from the surrounds are coaxial and that the light reflected from the indentation does not enter the objective. It must be pointed out, however, that in size measurement by transmitted light such high contrast can lead to appreciable errors due to the Mach effect (p. 89). Wood and Marriner have devised a measuring system based on a divided glass disc attached to the micrometer screw and a graticule with a doublet setting line and horizontal scale. The instrument can be read to 0·1 micron but the overall accuracy is limited by calibration errors, focussing errors and observer errors in assessing the precise position of the corners of the indentation. Nevertheless, the accuracy of measurement by a single observer over a period of time is $\pm 0·2$ micron and better than ± 1 micron for a series of observers.

b. *Image-shearing devices.* The principle of this device is also reported to have originated in the field of astronomy (in 1743). Two separate images of the object are formed in the same field of view and means are provided for moving (or "shearing") the two images across each other (Fig. 10) with a suitable scale to indicate the amount of shear. This principle was applied to the microscope by Timbrell (1952) who used a vibrating mirror to produce the double image (p. 56). McGinn (1956)

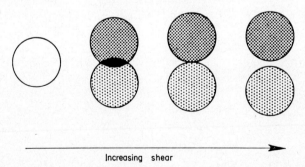

Increasing   shear

Fig. 10. The principle of image-shearing. As the images move apart, a black line appears just before the images separate. This disappears at the point of contact and is replaced by a bright line as the images separate.

used birefringent elements which introduced some aberration and gave only a small amount of shear. Barer (1960) and Dyson (1960, 1961) devised simple optical systems which gave adequate shearing without the need for relatively complicated electrical accessories. Barer's instrument (Fig. 11) consists of two beam-splitting prisms, P_1 and P_2,

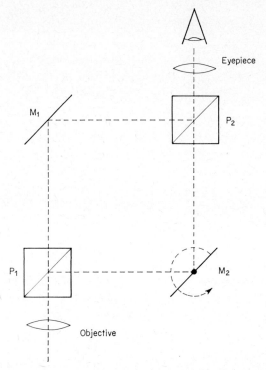

FIG. 11. The optical system of Barer's (1960) image-shearing micrometer microscope.

a fixed mirror, M_1, and a moving mirror, M_2. The mirror M_2 can be rotated through a small angle by means of a differential screw micrometer, producing a sheared image in one azimuth. The instrument is constructed as an attachable body that fits just above the objective carrier and can be rotated about the optical axis to allow the determination of shear in any direction. Dyson's instrument (developed in collaboration with Vickers Instruments Ltd.) also uses prisms to split the beam of light into two rays which, in the absence of shearing, are reunited in the microscope eyepiece (Figs. 12a, 13). The separation of the images is, however, achieved by rotating the prisms about a vertical axis. This movement is provided by a micrometer screw, the amount of shear being directly proportional to the movement of the screw. The instrument is constructed as an eyepiece attachment for use with any conventional microscope having a standard R.M.S. eyepiece tube diameter and with at least 4·5 in unobstructed length.

The image-shearing eyepiece marketed by W. Watson & Sons Ltd., is similar in principle to the devices described by Barer and Dyson.

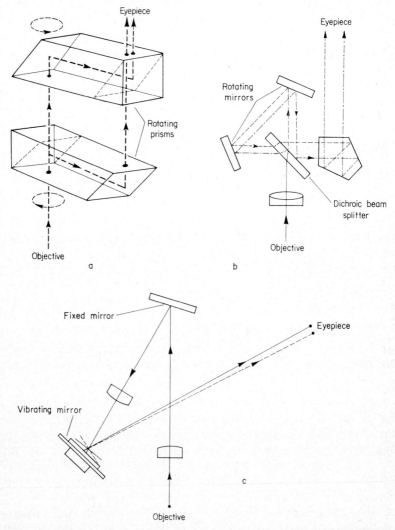

FIG. 12. a, Image-shearing by moving prisms (by permission of Vickers Instruments Ltd.); b, image-shearing by moving mirrors (by permission of W. Watson & Sons, Ltd.); c, image-shearing by vibrating mirror (by permission of Fleming Instruments Ltd.).

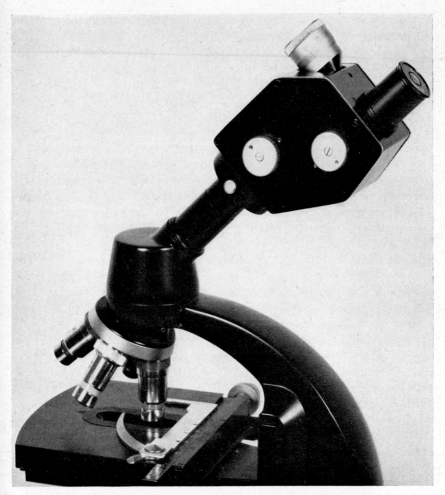

Fig. 13. Vickers–A.E.I. image-splitting eyepiece fitted to a standard microscope
(by permission of Vickers Instruments Ltd.).

The separation of the images is, however, brought about by the movement of two mirrors rotating about a horizontal axis (Figs. 12b, 14).
In place of the thimble used for position indicating and measuring
used in the Dyson instrument, the Watson eyepiece uses a "cyclometer" type mechanical counter.

In each of these instruments colour filters (usually red and green)
can be placed in the beams to aid in distinguishing the two images.

A high degree of accuracy is claimed for image-shearing eyepieces but as in the case of eyepiece graticules, the instruments must be calibrated before use by means of a stage micrometer.

A method of partially automating counting is to set the micrometer to a predetermined size and to count the grains larger than this size (i.e. those which are incompletely sheared). Repetition at various sizes makes possible a full grain size distribution analysis (Dyson and Noble, 1962).

Two attempts have been made to automate image-shearing eyepieces. Whitby and Vomela (1965) coupled a helical potentiometer to the Vickers eyepiece which produced a d.c. voltage proportional to the micrometer setting. This voltage was recorded as a pulse by a strip-chart recorder, the height of the pulse indicating the size of the particle. It was, however, necessary to count and classify the pulses to determine the particle size distribution. Schubel and Schiemer (1967) have eliminated the strip-chart recorder and have devised an electronic analogue-digital converter by means of which the signal from the potentiometer is made to operate the appropriate counter in a bank of sixteen. Each counter corresponds to a certain particle size interval, the exact value being dependant on the microscope magnification. The sixteen classes increase exponentially in size.

Powell and Errington (1963) have shown that for the mechanical type of image shearing eyepieces, in particular the Dyson instrument, an increase in accuracy can be achieved by separating the images first in one direction and then in the other, so that the position of the sheared images can be determined at two different micrometer readings. The two readings are nominally equidistant from the unsheared position, but it appears that the micrometer reading for this central (unsheared) position wanders erratically by about 0·1 units. These authors claim a precision of about 0·03 micron in the measurement of a bacterium, but Ross and Galavazi (1965) using interference microscopy believe that for bacteria an accuracy of better than 0·1 micron cannot be achieved. Nevertheless, they accept that the image shearing eyepiece has an instrumental accuracy of 0·03 micron but doubt whether the parameters actually measured truly represent the size of the object being investigated.

c. *The Timbrell microscope.* This instrument (Timbrell, 1952) also makes use of two identical images arranged to touch each other, and in this sense is also an image shearing device. However, the method by which shearing is achieved and the method of measuring the shear are entirely different from the instruments described above.

In this device the light from the objective is deflected by a small mirror inclined at 45° into a horizontal eyepiece. The mirror is attached

Fig. 14. Watson image-shearing eyepiece (W.I.S.E.)
(by permission of W. Watson & Sons, Ltd.).

to the diaphragm of a horn-type loudspeaker and can be made to vibrate by passing an alternating current of about 50 c/s through the loudspeaker coil. The microscope lamp is made to "flash" when the mirror is at the extremities of its vibration, the duration of the flash being short compared with the period of vibration. Because of the persistence of vision, an observer sees two images of each particle. By changing the current through the coil the amplitude of the vibration can be varied, thus the two images can be made to move apart. The separation between the images is proportional to the energizing current and therefore when the images are just touching each other, the coil current is proportional to the size of the particle. It is claimed that 1 micron particles can be measured with an accuracy of at least $\pm 3\%$. The maximum size of particle that can be measured appears to be about 120 micron. Particles can be classified by size and recorded by electro-mechanical counters. The size-range of each class can be predetermined by the operator. A disadvantage of this instrument was that it could be used only in conjunction with a specially modified microscope.

d. *Fleming particle size micrometer and analyser type 526.* This instrument was developed by Fleming Instruments Ltd., Stevenage, Herts., in conjunction with the N.R.D.C. The writer is indebted to Messrs Fleming for permission to describe this instrument. In some respects similar to the Timbrell instrument, this device does not require a special microscope and can be fitted as an eyepiece unit to most microscopes. The image is sheared as in Timbrell's instrument by a mirror attached to a coil (Fig. 11c) and caused to vibrate by the application of a variable current of square waveform, which eliminates the necessity for the flashing lamp. As before persistence of vision allows the eye to see two images. The amplitude of the current through the vibrator can be adjusted until the image of a particle is just sheared, when the size is proportional to the current. The range of size that can be measured is 1·0 to 250 micron (or in special circumstances 0·5 to 400 micron). The device can also be used for grading particles into size groups (up to 10 in number) whose limits may be preset to any desired value.

The grain diameter measured by these devices which utilize the principle of image-shearing depends on the orientation of the grain and does not in general correspond with any of the statistical linear measures described earlier (Fig. 15). However, by rotating the eyepiece type instruments in the body tube of the microscope it is possible to measure the long axis of a grain. It is preferable to use a microscope with a circular stage to rotate the grain, thereby minimizing wear on the

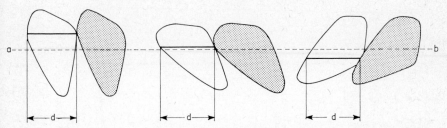

FIG. 15. Grain images as produced by image-shearing devices. Note that the measured diameter (d) does not correspond to any of the statistical linear measures shown in Fig. 3.

body tube. This type of instrument is especially suited to the size determination of roughly spherical particles and to the measurement of the diameter of fibres and wires. It appears to be less well suited to measurement of irregularly shaped grains because of its inability to measure the statistical linear measures, other than the long axis, as already noted.

One other major disadvantage of all types of image-shearing eye-pieces is that their application is limited to the measurement of particles which are isolated from their neighbours. Any attempt to measure grains in close proximity leads to an overlap of the image of the grain being measured and the adjacent grains. This leads to considerable confusion and consequently to operator fatigue. Thus the measurement of particle size in thin sections of rocks or tissues is extremely tedious with this type of instrument and liable to gross errors.

e. *The Lark semi-automatic particle counter*. The instrument described by Lark (1965) is unlike any other semi-automatic particle counter in that the recording of sizes is done by pricking holes in a paper chart. The device (Fig. 16) consists of an adjustable slotted eyepiece containing in its focal plane a fixed hairline and a second movable hairline. This second line is moved by an external mechanical link attached to a lever arm at a point very close to the pivot. The further end of this lever has a knob which can be depressed to make a pinpoint mark on a chart $3\frac{1}{2}$ inches wide. As this knob which is spring-loaded, rises from the chart it activates a bar and ratchet which advances the chart by $\frac{1}{16}$ inch and also operates an electro-mechanical counter to sum the total number of particles counted.

Since the chart recording unit is too large to be supported by the microscope, it is necessary to use a microscope of the stage-focusing fixed limb type to avoid strain in the operating linkage.

The chart is calibrated by a stage micrometer. The particles to be measured are moved across the field of view by a square mechanical

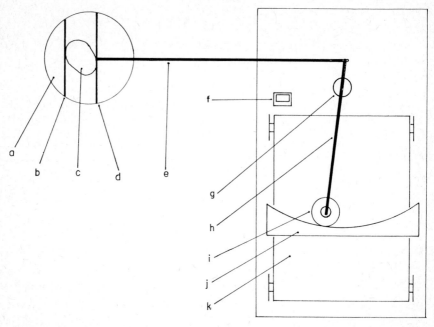

F<small>IG</small>. 16. Lark's (1965) semi-automatic particle counter showing the principle of operation (not drawn to scale): a, slotted eyepiece; b, fixed hairline; c, grain being measured (Feret's diameter); d, moving hairline; e, connecting link; f, electromechanical counter; g, pivot for operating arm; h, operating arm; i, marker knob; j, plate actuating chart drive; k, chart.

stage, the diameter measured being Feret's. As each particle is sized the knob is depressed and thus the record of the analysis consists of a series of pinholes in the chart. By ruling lines on the chart corresponding to a scale of sizes and counting the pinholes between these lines, a size frequency distribution can be determined. About 1000 grains per hour can be measured.

Although this instrument was devised for measuring individual grains in loose powders, it can equally well be used for indurated materials and continuous networks of cells, since no confusion of images is involved.

f. *The Humphries eyepiece micrometer* (Humphries, 1966a). This eyepiece in its original form made use of a fixed and a movable hair line, but unlike the Lark instrument is small enough to be attached to the microscope in place of the normal eyepiece and can therefore be used with any type of microscope. The eyepiece was subsequently modified (Figs. 17, 18) in collaboration with Mr. H. M. Malies so that both hairlines moved symmetrically about the centre of the field of view. The

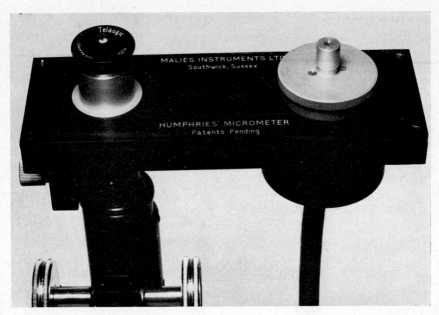

FIG. 17. Humphries (1966a) semi-automatic eyepiece micrometer for classifying and recording particle sizes.

hairlines are attached to sliding frames each with a small follower wheel in contact with the edge of a cam. The cams are designed so that for 20° of rotation the hairlines move a distance directly proportional to a $\sqrt[4]{2}$ scale. A contact arm attached to the cam spindle moves over a series of 16 small electrical contacts each of which is connected to an electrical counter. Depression of a knob in the centre of the wheel operating the cams closes a contact and operates the counter corresponding to a particular particle grade size. The boundaries of each grade size are determined by the points of a crown wheel beneath the contact arm. In the event of a particle size being such that the contact arm is over a point of the crown wheel, a knife edge on the contact arm deflects it to the adjacent fixed contact.

This device classifies particles into 16 size classes and records the total in each class. A seventeenth counter sums the total number of grains counted. The scale of sizes chosen allows a range of sizes with a ratio of 16 : 1, equivalent to 4 ϕ units of Krumbein's phi-scale (1934) to be measured at each objective magnification. The scale of sizes is made exact either by adjusting the tube length of the microscope or by placing an adjustable corrector ring between the objective and the nosepiece. Thus no conversion factors have to be applied and the totals

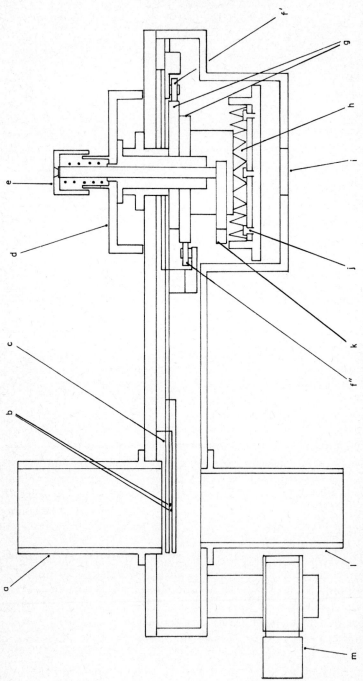

FIG. 18. Cross-section of Humphries (1966a) eyepiece micrometer: a, eyepiece tube; b, moving hairlines; c, hairline carriage; d, hand-wheel; e, push-button; f′, f″, cam followers; g, cams; h, crown wheel; i, cable outlet; j, fixed electrical contacts; k, moving electrical contact; l, body tube for attachment to microscope; m, clamp-screw.

recorded by the counter are a true record of the numbers of grains in each class of an exact scale of sizes.

The rate of counting and classifying particles depends largely on the dimension chosen for the analysis. With a square mechanical stage about 1000 grains an hour can be counted. Using a circular stage and measuring the long or intermediate axis reduces the rate to about half this value. Since the operator has no need to remove his eye from the eyepiece until the completion of the analysis, fatigue and eyestrain is much reduced and counting can continue for long periods.

As in the Lark instrument, loose grains and continuous networks of cells and metal or rock grains can be classified.

The range of sizes measured can be extended by the use of suitable objectives. For example, with a $95\times$ objective, the range is $62.5\ \mu$ to $3.9\ \mu$ and with a $3\times$ objective, it is 1.68 mm to 0.105 mm. Using corrector rings each of a series of objectives could be adjusted to the various points of a $\sqrt[4]{2}$ progression of size classes. With a suitable switching device attached to the nosepiece and an extended bank of counters a very considerable range of particles could be counted directly without reverting to the multiple counting procedures (B.S. 3406: Pt. 4: 1963) that have now to be employed. Consideration is also being given to recording the data directly on punched tape in order to further accelerate the process of collecting particle size measurements.

This Humphries' eyepiece is manufactured by Malies' Instruments Limited of Southwick, Brighton.

2. Semi-automatic nominal projection diameter measuring devices

Of the two devices noted here, one is applicable only to photo-micrographs, the other is a true microscope attachment.

a. *Zeiss-Endter particle size analyser*. This semi-automatic instrument made by Carl Zeiss (Oberkochen) was designed by Endter and Gebauer (1956) for the size classification of particles recorded photographically by electron microscopy. It may, of course, also be used for photo-micrographs of particles at optical microscope magnifications. In this instrument, an iris diaphragm, illuminated from one side, is imaged by a lens on to the plane of a plexiglass plate. An enlargement of the micro-graph on transparent paper is put on this plate. By adjusting the iris diaphragm the diameter of the sharply defined circular light spot appearing on the enlargement can be changed and its area made equal to that of the individual particle. If particles deviate from a circular shape, the image of the iris is so adjusted that the total area of pro-truding portions of the particle image becomes equal to that of the re-entrant ones (cf. Fig. 8). The different diameters of the iris are correlated, via a collector ring, with a number of electro-mechanical counters, each one corresponding to a certain size range of the iris diameter. In this instrument particles can be classified into 48 size classes, which may be of equal width or of exponentially increasing width.

Since the size category into which each particle is placed depends both on the original microscope magnification and on the photographic enlargement, the counted totals cannot be used as a basis for computation of size distribution parameters. Instead it is necessary to plot the data graphically and adjust the size scale according to the total magnification. From this it is possible to determine graphical parameters (e.g. quartile measures) or to extract data for moment measures (cf. p. 84).

The principal criticism of this and any other technique using photographs is that only those grains in good focus can be measured. In a mixture of sizes, it is highly probable that many grains, often of a particular size, are completely out of focus. Thus the resultant analysis may be seriously biased.

b. *The Hörnsten instrument.* This instrument designed by Hörnsten (1960) is perhaps the most sophisticated of all the semi-automatic devices. As well as grain size, it can be used to measure grain shape and roundness and mineral volume frequency. The system is based on the superimposition of a circular field of light on the image of the particle being examined The diameter of the light spot is controlled by a 12-bladed iris diaphragm, the image of which is projected into the microscope eyepiece by a semi-reflecting mirror. The intensity of this light spot can be varied by altering the voltage across the lamp by a rheostat. The light spot can also be moved to any position in the field of view. The aperture of the iris diaphragm is controlled by a gear and chain mechanism to which is attached a series of contacts which for grain size analysis divide the size scale into 10 classes in a 2 : 1 ratio (ϕ-intervals). Hörnsten has included in the apparatus a switching device attached to the objective nosepiece which automatically connects the contacts to the appropriate set of electro-mechanical counters. For mineralogical frequency analysis the specimen is moved by a point-count mechanical stage and the identity of the mineral recorded manually. At the same time the size can be recorded automatically. The shape and roundness can be measured by adjusting the size of the light circle to the nominal sectional diameter and then to the diameter of the smallest circumscribed circle, the diameters being read from the drum on the iris control. The ratio of these two diameters gives Wadell's (1933, 1935) two dimensional sphericity. The sphericity can then be added into the recorder by a manual switch. In all, 100 counters are used in the recorder unit and the author suggested that a record should be kept of the progress of the analysis by photographing the recorders at frequent intervals.

Despite the apparent complexity of this instrument its use would enable a tremendous amount of data to be accumulated relatively quickly.

3. *Mechanical stages*

Although not necessarily essential equipment there have been described a number of mechanical stages for the microscope which can facilitate grain size measurement.

The standard square stage and circular stage fitted with a square stage are sufficiently familiar that further comment is hardly necessary. A criticism of some stages is the small size of the control knobs and the present writer has found it advantageous to replace the horizontal traverse knob with as large a wheel as possible without obscuring any part of the field of view.

Where loose grains are to be measured it is essential that the movement of the stage should be quite free from jerkiness otherwise the grains tend to migrate off the slide. One such device is a hydraulically-operated stage (Humphries, 1964) in which a foot-operated control unit pumps oil to and from a small slave cylinder attached to the stage (Fig. 19). The use of the feet leaves the hands free for focusing the microscope and operating a measuring device. Other stages have been devised using small electric motors.

In using the various forms of eyepiece graticule it is common practice to measure grains in randomly selected fields rather than to measure all the grains on the slide. This selection can be made using the grid which is a common factor of most globe and circle graticules or the stage can be moved in a systematic manner so that the fields of view are arranged in a rectangular grid. Provided the first part of the grid is randomly placed on the slide, the other points of the grid will also be randomly placed. The positioning of the slide can be achieved using a standard mechanical stage with micrometer screws or verniers. A fully automatic stage which can displace the section by a preset distance has been described by Freere and Weibel (1967).

C. *Measurement of Vertical Dimensions of Particles*

Where grains are large enough to be handled individually and mounted in plastic rods (cf. p. 36) the measurement of the vertical dimension presents no difficulties. However, for very fine grained

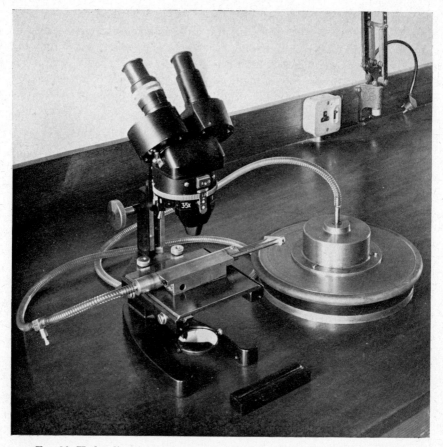

Fig. 19. Hydraulic microscope stage for counting and sizing loose particles in reflected light (Humphries, 1964).

materials and for measuring the depth of corrosion pits in crystals this method is not applicable.

A possible method is to use the fine adjustment of the microscope, provided it is graduated and an objective of small depth of focus. Care should be taken to avoid errors due to "backlash" in the screw mechanism.

If a vertical measurement is made within a transparent mounting medium or within the object, the apparent thickness must be multiplied by the refractive index of the substance to give the true thickness.

The accuracy of vertical measurements using the fine adjustment has been discussed by Addey (1922), John (1923), Metzner (1928) and Cantu (1956).

Another method which has been proposed by Fraser and Rogers (1954) is to shadow the particles as is done in electron microscopy and measure the length of the shadow.

The thickness of transparent objects can also be determined by measuring the optical path difference between the object and surrounding medium using the transmission interference microscope. If T is the thickness and μ_0 and μ_m are the refractive indices of the object and the medium, respectively, then the optical path difference is equal to $T(\mu_0 - \mu_m)$. Since the refractive index of the object may be unknown, the thickness and the refractive index may be determined simultaneously by measuring the optical path difference with the object successively mounted in media of two different refractive indices. The pair of equations thus obtained can be solved simultaneously for T and μ_0 (Barer, 1956).

Goldstein (1967) has proposed a method whereby the thickness and refractive index may be determined by measuring two optical path differences, one for axial light and the other with an oblique beam. The author calls this the "two-aperture" method, but says that with present equipment the method is probably too insensitive to be usefully applied to most biological objects. However, he believes that the position is likely to change radically when interference microscopes of greatly increased precision become available.

The depth of surface depressions on a variety of substances, but mainly crystals including diamonds, has been determined with a very high degree of precision by Tolansky (1948, 1953, 1955) using the methods of two-beam and multiple-beam interferometry.

D. *Measurement of Areas*

It may on occasion be necessary to determine precisely the area of an individual particle. In the study of the proportions of heterogeneous mixtures it was formerly considered necessary to determine the area occupied by each component, but as will be shown later, simpler methods can be employed. In particle size analysis, the nominal projection area is often determined by the subjective method of comparing the particle with circles of various areas. To check the accuracy of such comparative methods, it is obvious that means should be available of measuring the true area. The methods adopted for microscopy are essentially those commonly used in mensuration.

Thus the area of an object of simple geometrical shape may readily be determined by measuring its linear dimensions. A close approximation to the true area of irregular particles may be obtained by superimposing over the image a grid ruled with a network of small squares

and counting the number of squares occupied by the particle (Fig. 20).
Such a grid has to be calibrated using a stage micrometer. Since the
grid is placed at the focus of the eyepiece the area of even very small
particles can be determined in this way. The accuracy of this method
depends on the degree of irregularity of the boundary of the particle,
since it is necessary to estimate fractions of squares adjacent to the
grain boundary. Hally (1964) has shown that the squares can be

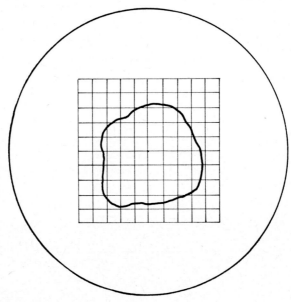

FIG. 20. Determination of grain area by counting squares of a calibrated grid.

replaced by points, each point being regarded as occupying the centre
of the square. By reducing the size of the squares or the spacing of the
points, a closer approximation to the true area can be obtained.
However, it would seem that as the size or spacing is decreased, so the
error in counting them increases.

An extension of this method is to draw the images by means of a
camera lucida on squared paper or to superimpose a transparent ruled
scale over a photograph. The area of the photographic image or drawing
may also be determined by a planimeter. Another method of determining the area from a photograph or a drawing is to cut out the
image with fine scissors and to weigh it. From the weight per unit area
of the paper, the area of the cut-out portion may be calculated. If
metal foil is used instead of paper considerable accuracy can be

achieved. This method was probably first used by Delesse (1847, 1848) on polished rock surfaces and later by Sorby (1853, 1856) who first used it as a basis of a method for determining the proportions of components in thin sections of rocks.

IV. Modal Analysis

The determination of the frequency of occurrence of the components in a mixture is a problem which frequently can only be resolved by microscopic methods. For example, in the analysis of a rock which is a heterogeneous mixture of minerals, chemical analysis will give only the composition in terms of chemical elements or radicals. It will give only an approximate indication of the mineral composition and indeed the interpretation of a chemical analysis in terms of mineral composition requires not only considerable skill but also considerable intuition. Other examples which may be cited include mixtures of natural products such as foodstuffs, paper or spices or materials such as metal alloys or ceramics. Especially problematic are instances of adulteration of high grade substances with inferior or deleterious matter.

This type of analysis has become known as modal analysis since it is concerned with the typical or modal value of the composition of a mixture of substances.

Delesse and Sorby intuitively accepted that the area frequency of a component in a mixture was a direct measure of the volume frequency. Given the density of each component, the volume frequency could be converted to a weight frequency. A fully rigourous proof of the area–volume relationship is probably impossible since this is essentially a statistical problem. Nevertheless it can be shown, as Chayes (1956) has done, that the ratio of the area occupied by one component to the area occupied by a second component is a *consistent estimate* of the volume ratio of these components.

Rosiwal (1898) showed that the volume proportions are equal to the lineal proportions intercepted by the minerals on a random line passed through the structure (Fig. 21a, c). The substitution of points (Fig. 21b, d) for lines is a further development and was probably first suggested by Glagolev (1933). At the present time most modal analyses, certainly in the field of geology, utilize the point-counting technique. A brief history and bibliography of the method has been given by Larsen and Miller (1935) and by Howard and Cohen (1947). A detailed discussion of the basic theory has been given by Chayes (1956).

Although the basis of modal analysis was announced 120 years ago, it is only in the last thirty years that the method has been fully accepted and its use become widespread.

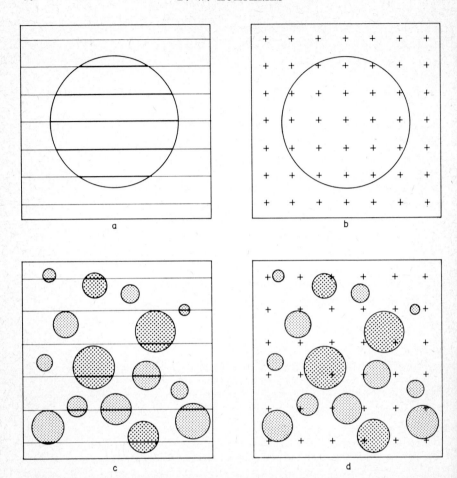

FIG. 21. Linear and point-count analysis: a, b, applied to the area measurement of a single grain; c, d, applied to the modal analysis of a mixture of components. In practice, the grids would be applied repeatedly to increase the total linear measurement or number of points counted. In the example shown with a single application of the grid, the following ratios have been calculated:

a, b, Ratio $\dfrac{\text{area of circle}}{\text{area of square}}$ = 0·43 (by direct measurement)

$$= 0\text{·}39 \text{ (by linear measurement)}$$
$$= 0\text{·}36 \text{ (by point count)}$$

c, d, Ratio $\dfrac{\text{area of light component}}{\text{area of dark component}}$ = 1·3 (by direct measurement)

$$= 1\text{·}1 \text{ (by linear measurement)}$$
$$= 1\text{·}0 \text{ (by point count)}$$

In c, d, the number ratio of light to dark components is 2·75 : 1, compared with a true area ratio of 1·3 : 1, hence counting the number of individual grains of components is not a true estimate of their volume frequency (cf. p. 72).

Early attempts to justify the method were based on somewhat crude experiments on synthetic mixtures. Subsequently attempts were made to prove the basic assumptions geometrically and to determine theoretically the accuracy of the method. Hilliard and Cahn (1961) have calculated the standard deviations to be expected in the measurement of volume functions by areal analysis, lineal analysis and by four point-count procedures. They conclude that a point-count using a two dimensional grid is the most efficient method providing the grid spacing is coarse enough (i.e. larger than the largest discrete patch of any component).

As noted earlier, modal analysis is a statistical problem and is essentially an exercise in sampling. It should be noted that in the case of area analysis, the analysis is an estimate of the proportions of the components in the population of the sample from which the thin section or polished surface was made, whereas in lineal analysis or point-count analysis, the total linear intercepts or the numbers of points are strictly only estimates of the population of the particular thin section or surface. If, therefore, the intercepts or points are to be used as estimates of the population from which the slide was made, the slide must be made at random from the original sample. Failure to accept that modal analysis was a sampling problem, led early workers to use samples which were too small and which were therefore unrepresentative of the parent population from which the sample was taken. Thus, it is apparent that the accuracy of the analysis will depend on the size of the sample actually analysed. It will also depend on the assumption that the components of the material are homogenously distributed. Since this is probably never the case, the accuracy will depend on the uniformity of distribution of *each* component. Thus a material in which the components are segregated into bands or lenses (i.e. ovoid patches) cannot be analysed with any great accuracy unless the dimensions of the segregations are small compared with the area of the surface being analysed. Even so it must be realized that a *single* random section taken from such banded material may be parallel to the banding. However, as Chayes (1956) has shown, the error introduced by banding may be reduced by analysing a sufficient number of *random* sections. The problem of banding is probably much less serious than is commonly believed, provided its presence is appreciated and that the basic procedures of sampling are thoroughly understood.

Preferred orientation of non-spherical particles, even though they are not segregated into bands may also cause bias in an analysis. As in the case of banding, the bias may be reduced by using adequate numbers of random samples.

Although from a theoretical standpoint it is necessary to analyse a number of thin sections to remove bias due to banding, in practice sufficient material may not be available to permit this. In this case the section should be made perpendicular to the banding and as large as possible to permit measurement over a number of bands.

The foregoing discussion has been restricted to the modal analysis of continuous aggregates of particles as in rocks and metals. The method can also be used to measure proportions of components when one of the components is continuous (e.g. a glassy matrix) or when one of the components is a hole in the material (e.g. in the measurement of porosity).

The modal analysis of mixtures of loose powders can be treated in the same way as for metals and rocks. In this case, it must be appreciated that one of the components (the mounting medium) is continuous though it need not be included in the analysis.

It is important to remember that counting the total numbers of grains of each component in a loose mixture is not a measure of the volume proportions of each component (Fig. 21) unless all the grains of all the components are exactly the same size and shape. As in consolidated rocks, the areas, linear intercepts or points of a grid falling on the particles must be measured. This commonly means that for fine powders determined by point-counting, relatively large numbers of slides must be prepared or the same slide must be counted repeatedly with a different setting of the grid for each count to obtain an adequate number of counts. Area measurement is not readily applied to fine powders since the error in measuring a small area is generally proportionately large.

Although modal analysis was first applied to the study of the mineralogical composition of rocks and subsequently to metals, it has in recent years found increasing application in the biological sciences. Hennig (1956, 1957, 1959), Hennig and Meyer-Arendt (1963) and Weibel (1963a) have discussed the techniques and their application in the field of medicine.

V. TECHNIQUES OF MODAL ANALYSIS

As in the determination of grain size, the methods used for modal analysis fall into two groups. The first utilizes eyepiece scales or grids, the second, semi-automatic devices which perform the necessary summation as analysis proceeds. Unlike the semi-automatic grain size devices which measure the enlarged image of the grain the instruments used for modal analysis are essentially mechanisms for moving the object across the field of view. For this reason, the eyepiece scales are generally preferred when high magnification is necessary, for example, in some metallurgical applications. In geology, however, where moderately coarse grained rocks are commonly encountered, the semi-automatic devices have completely superseded the use of graticules. Indeed, the development of semi-automatic devices has been closely associated with the needs of petrographers.

The determination of component areas is a tedious method prone to inaccuracy and is currently rarely employed. The methods used are basically those described earlier (p. 67) for the areal measurement of individual grains and will not to be discussed further.

A. *Graticules for Modal Analysis*

For lineal analysis, the ordinary eyepiece linear scale may be used in conjunction with a mechanical stage. As the slide is traversed, each component is identified and its intercept on the horizontal crosswire of the eyepiece measured and recorded. The stage is then traversed again at a distance from the previous traverse slightly greater than the average size of the particles.

Instead of measuring the intercepts of each component along a line, the number of intersections of each component with a line of known length may be used. The mathematical proof of this method is given by Rogers (in Short (1950)).

This method has also been used by Richardson (1953) and by Hennig (1956, 1959) from which was developed the Zeiss Integrating Eyepiece II (Fig. 23b). Trowell and Westgarth (1959) showed that this method could be used with a circular line as well as a straight one. In fact, it can be used with a line of any form.

For point-counting the grid usually consists of a square grid of lines placed at the focus of the eyepiece. The intersections of the grid lines falling on each component are counted or a mechanical recorder having a separate key for each component may be used. The grid size should be such that the intersection points have a spacing four or five times greater than the mean size of the particle image. Sufficient random fields spread uniformly over the slide are counted to yield either a grand total of counts or to indicate the localized variation or composition within the slide. Using a graticule having 100 lines in each direction, ten thousand points can be superimposed on each field of view. However, where there are more than two components or the two components are present in comparable amounts, it is hardly possible to count the points falling on each component with any accuracy. Nevertheless, the square grid is invaluable for rapid counting of the number of points falling on a single component which is present in small proportions in a two component system; the second component being determined by difference. Similarly a single minor component can be determined in a multicomponent mixture. If such a component is present in relatively large grains (i.e. it is not uniformly distributed through the field of view), it is relatively easy to place the grid on the slide in a 10 × 10 square grid pattern and effectively count one million points (Fig. 22).

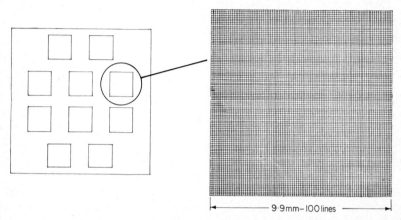

9·9mm–100 lines

FIG. 22. Ten thousand point square grid for rapid estimation of minor component in two-component mixture. Placing the grid ten times (left) gives a count of 10^5 points 10^6 points when placed in a 10 × 10 array.

A somewhat different pattern of point-counting grid designed by Hennig (1959) has been marketed by Carl Zeiss (Oberkochen). In this (Fig. 23a) the graticule has 25 points asymmetrically arranged within a circle which limits the counting field. The points are joined by straight lines to facilitate counting. The procedure for using this graticule is similar to that outlined above for the square grid.

Geologists and metallurgists have used the regular array of points as described above. Although the arrays are regular they are nevertheless random in relation to the slide as a whole. Biologists have used regular grids but have also used irregular arrays, apparently in the belief that this achieved a closer approach to randomness. Chalkley (1943) employed a grid (Fig. 23c) in which the ends of four lines were taken as the randomly arranged points; a fifth line served for setting the array. Curtis (1960) produced a grid (called by him the "Modified Chalkley array") in which randomly arranged points were obtained by plotting random numbers from a table alternately on one axis and the other on graph paper (Fig. 23d). For grains or cells arranged at random,

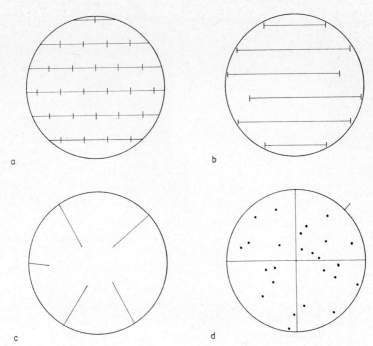

Fig. 23. Grids for modal analysis. a, Zeiss Integrating Eyepiece I (Hennig, 1959); b, Zeiss Integrating Eyepiece II (Hennig, 1959); c, irregular line array (Chalkley, 1943); d, modified Chalkley array (Curtis, 1960). Fig. 23d is reprinted from "Medical and Biological Illustration 1960", Vol. 10, pp. 261–266, by permission of the Author, Editor and Publishers.

this type of array appears to have little advantage over the regular net and is probably more difficult to count accurately. On the other hand, if the cells being counted tend to fall into a regular net, then the irregular array may have the virtue that points seen on the counting array do not coincide with rows of cells in the specimens.

B. *Semi-automatic Modal Analysis*

Both lineal analysis and point-counting have been adapted to semi-automatic devices. Most of the instruments described and marketed have been based on the principle of keeping the point of observation fixed (by the cross hairs of the eyepiece) and measuring the distance traversed by the stage as each component has been moved along the horizontal hairline. The summation of the distance moved by the stage for each component was achieved by one or more micrometer screw threads. Devices of this type were described by Shand (1916), Wentworth (1923), Hunt (1924), Thackwell (1933), Dollar (1937) and

FIG. 24. Point-counter stage (by permission of James Swift & Son).

Hurlbut (1939). These devices often required considerable manual
dexterity and are now rarely used.

Automated point-counting has now largely replaced lineal analysis.
In this method the screw-driven stage is replaced by a sledge moved
by an electromagnet. The distance moved is controlled by a ratchet
wheel which thus defines the spacing of the observation points along a
traverse. The components are counted on separate counters operated
by push-buttons. The operation of the button also causes the stage to
be stepped along to the next point. For each traverse the stage has to
be returned manually and also moved manually to the next line. The
grid of observation points on the slide may therefore be made a square
or rectangular grid as desired by the operator.

Glagolev's (1934) stage was apparently of this type except that the traversing of the sledge was achieved mechanically by pressing any one of the keys on the counting box. Modifications to this type of stage were made by Barringer (1953). Ford (1954), Chayes (1949) and Rosenfeld (1954) have also devised point-counter stages. Perhaps the best known at the present time is that manufactured by Messrs. J. Swift & Son, London. In this instrument (Fig. 24) the length of step can be changed by replacing certain gears in the driving mechanism of the sledge. A maximum of thirteen components can be counted and a tally is kept of the total number of points counted. With a little practice the keyboard can be operated by touch and 400–1000 "points" identified and counted in one hour.

VI. MEASUREMENT OF INTERNAL BOUNDARIES IN THREE-DIMENSIONAL STRUCTURES

In any network of cells, whether the "cells" be biological, metal-lurgical or petrological, the boundary of the individual cell is of fundamental importance, since any change in volume or composition must take place across that boundary. By modal analysis it is possible to determine the proportions of components in a mixture and by grain size analysis the size of each component grain can be determined. Thus, if the shape of each grain can be assumed, it is possible to compare the total surface area of each component. Such a procedure is tedious and open to considerable error on the grounds that rarely is the true shape of every grain known (or knowable).

Therefore any method which attempts to relate the surface area of a grain to its volume should not be dependant on any factor relating to the shape of the grain.

Two techniques for the solution of this problem have been devised by Chalkley et al. (1949) and by Smith and Guttman (1953). Both methods depend on counting the number of intersections between the grain boundaries and a randomly placed line.

Chalkley showed that if a short line (of known length) is placed at random in a three-dimensional space containing a closed body, then in a very large number of throws $rh/c = 4 \times$ volume/surface, where $r =$ length of line, $h =$ number of hits by the ends of the line on the body and $c =$ the number of times the boundary of the body cuts the line. If the randomly placed line is considered to occur in a randomly placed plane, then the method can be applied to thin sections of biological materials or rocks or to polished surfaces of metals. In this case the line is not applied repeatedly to the same grain but to a large number of grains. The resultant ratio is therefore an average value of volume to surface for all the grains examined, provided the individual grains have random orientation. Where more than one component is present, the number of "hits" and "cuts" for each component can be counted separately.

In practice this method may be applied using an eyepiece graticule having a pattern of short lines of equal length (Fig. 25). These lines need not be random and the regular pattern facilitates counting. For materials which are noticeably anisotropic, lines placed at random

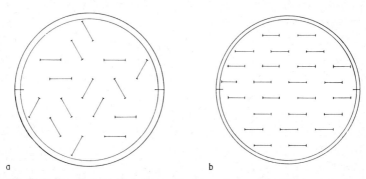

FIG. 25. Patterns of short lines for surface to volume estimation: a, random lines; b, regular pattern (after Weibel, 1963a). Note: the random pattern was devised specifically for the determination of wall thickness of cylindrical tubes, but is not limited to this usage.

might be used. Alternatively, these lines might be arranged in a circular pattern or as sections of a spiral. No investigation by this method of materials showing preferred orientation appears to have been made.

The method of Smith and Guttman (1953) is similar to that of Chalkley in that they also consider the results of placing a random line in three dimensional space. However, in the application of their method they use a long line in a continuous three dimensional structure and count the number of intersections of grain boundaries with this line. While this furnishes an average grain size, these authors show that the number of intersections for unit length is exactly half the true ratio of surface to volume. This assumes that the boundaries are shared between adjacent grains. The ratio of unshared surface to volume is therefore four times the number of intersections for unit length.

This method is most readily applied to single component polycrystalline materials if the measurement of the length of the intercepts on each of several components is to be avoided. A suitable eyepiece graticule consists of a number of equally spaced parallel lines of known length (Fig. 23b) or a circle with a number of parallel lines inscribed across it and placed asymmetrically with respect to the centre of the circle (Fig. 26). Smith and Guttman recommend a graticule with coarsely spaced lines placed repeatedly in the field of view in different orientations.

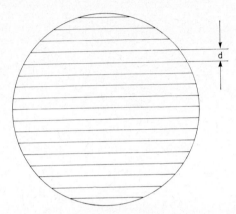

Fig. 26. Line and circle graticule for surface to volume estimation
(after Smith and Guttman, 1953).

It may be noted that in these two methods there is no substantial difference between the authors' conclusions, since if Chalkley's short line becomes longer, the number of "hits" decreases and the surface to volume ratio of unshared boundaries approaches 4 × number of intersections/length of line.

It is apparent that the short line graticule could also be used as a point-count graticule if the ends of the lines are taken as the "points". Freere and Weibel (1967) and Weibel et al. (1966) have described such a multipurpose graticule (Fig. 27) consisting of a square frame enclosing 21 lines of equal length Z. These are arranged in parallel rows, the distance between the ends of the lines being Z in any direction. The 42 end points form a lattice for modal analysis, while the 21 lines provide the probes necessary for surface estimations. The square frame delimits the test area for counting the particle sections. The graticule can also be used for area estimation by Hally's (1964) method since each point (end of line) has an area value of $Z^2 . \sqrt{3}/2$. This graticule is used in conjunction with the automated stage noted earlier (p. 65). The electric counter unit for recording the data can be connected to an automatic print-out facility and to a card puncher for computing analyses.

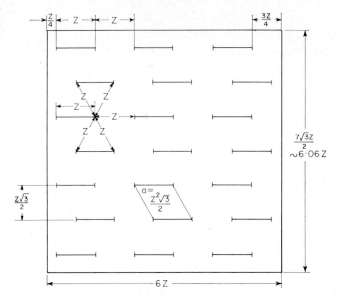

Fig. 27. Multipurpose graticule (Freere and Weibel, 1967; Weibel *et al.*, 1966) for point-counting, surface to volume ratio, area measurement, etc.

The method of estimation of surface/volume ratios is obviously not limited to single grains or cells, but can be applied to a wide variety of structures provided they can be sectioned and the sections of the structures can be differentiated from their surroundings. The realization that much could be learnt of the morphology of structures by simple counting techniques has led to the rapid development of "stereology" or the description of three-dimensional structures from two-dimensional sections. It is perhaps a little surprising that geologists, having played the principal role in the development of volumetric analysis, have largely neglected this extension of the linear and point-counting methods and it has been in the fields of metallurgy (e.g. Saltykov, 1958) and medicine (e.g. Weibel and Gomez, 1962; Weibel, 1963a, 1963b; Ebbesson and Tang, 1965; Weibel *et al.* 1966)), that the methods of stereology have been most extensively applied.

VII. WEIGHT AND VOLUME DETERMINATIONS

The volume of microscopic particles is readily determined if they are of simple geometric shape and if their density is known, the mass can readily be found. This method of mass determination as a substitute for weighing in assaying is very old and may be very accurate if the particles are perfect spheres. The method may also be applied to the determination of the volume and mass of gas bubbles (Chamot and Mason, 1958, p. 432).

An ingenious method for determining the average weight of particles in powders has been devised by Wallis (1919, 1957). A known weight of lycopodium spores is added in a small proportion (e.g. 5%) to the powder. The two components are thoroughly mixed and a small portion placed on the microscope slide. The number of lycopodium spores and particles are counted. Wallis states that 1 mg of lycopodium contains 94,000 spores and hence knowing the proportion of spores in the mixture and their weight, the weight of powder can be determined. From the count of the number of particles, the average weight per particle can be found. Wallis has used this method extensively in the examination and characterization of foods, spices and drugs.

The total dry mass of biological materials can be determined by interference microscopy (Barer, 1952; Davies and Wilkins, 1952). The method depends upon the determination of the relative retardation of light by the object when placed in a suitable immersion medium. The method is now well established, yielding accurate results especially in the case of isolated, well-defined structures such as cells, nuclei or bacteria. Galjaard and Szirmai (1965) have extended the method to tissue sections. They employ a Leitz double beam interference microscope which gives a separation of the interfering beams sufficient to avoid the formation of ghost images. The optical path difference is determined from densitometric measurements of photographs.

VIII. Angular Measurements

The use of the circular stage for the determination of the angles of crystals, extinction angles or refractive indices is familiar to most microscopists (cf. e.g. Hartshorne and Stuart, 1960; Saylor, 1966). In the absence of a circular stage, angular measurements may be made with an eyepiece graticule with a protractor ruling.

Large numbers of angular measurements are rarely required, but there are, however, two fields of study in which they play an important role. One is concerned with the orientation of particles resulting from fluid flow; the other is associated with the angles between the sides of polygons in topological studies of metals and rocks.

Schwarzacher (personal communication) has devised a circular microscope stage in which the positions of the stage can be recorded on electromagnetic counters. This device can be used to measure the position of the long axis of particles relative to a fixed direction and to classify the directions in $5°$ sectors. A special eyepiece devised by

Smith (1960) has a moving arm which rotates a graticule ruled with parallel lines. One side of the angle to be measured is lined up with the vertical cross hair and the graticule turned to coincide with the other side of the angle. A push button and a series of contacts actuates one of a number of counters. The contacts are spaced at 5° intervals and overlapping of the fixed contacts by the moving contact is prevented by knife edges between the fixed contacts.

IX. The Arithmetic of Mensuration Methods

A. *Grain Size Measurement of Loose Grains*

The term "arithmetic" has been deliberately used here in place of the more usual term "statistics", since it is not possible to discuss fully the application of statistical methods to microscopic measurements in the space available.

The problem of shape in relation to the size of microscopic particles has been discussed earlier. It is apparent that, except in the case of spherical particles, a single size measure is an inadequate statement of the true size of a particle. Each of the grain size parameters described is thus only an approximation to the true size. Subsequent calculations relating to the average size and the spread of sizes of the particles in a powder are therefore in error by an amount by which the measured size fails to record the true size. Since particles, even in the same powder may show a variety of shapes, especially if the range of sizes is considerable, the measured size appears to become even less meaningful. However, this extremely pessimistic viewpoint is not entirely justified since one of the purposes of the application of statistical procedures is the characterization of powders and the prediction of their behaviour in relation to other samples. The fact that standard statistical procedures give usable measures for comparative purposes suggests that the size parameters employed are satisfactory and acceptable.

For particles which look similar in size and shape, the size of all grains might be satisfactorily described by the size of one. This is often true of plant seeds and spores. Usually, however, a large number of grains must be measured and an average size calculated. This may be a weighted average of the actual sizes as measured by a linear scale. It is easier and less fatiguing merely to classify the particles according to some predetermined scale of sizes. Despite argument to the contrary, no scale of sizes is more correct than any other, though one scale may be more convenient mathematically or it may indicate the distribution of particle sizes more clearly. The class intervals, that is the intervals into which the scale of sizes is divided, should be narrow enough to distinguish maxima in the size distribution, but not so narrow that every grain falls into a different size category.

Where the range of particle size is small an arithmetic scale is sometimes employed. The principal objection to this, however, is that in general if the classes are small enough to give an adequate description of the finest particles, then the total number of classes becomes excessive. Furthermore, if the total number of classes is kept small, particles with a large ratio of sizes are grouped together and the ratio between classes is not constant. For example, if the class interval is $1\,\mu$ and the overall range is $10\,\mu$, particles in the range $1\,\mu$ to $2\,\mu$ (ratio $2:1$) are grouped together, while the $9\,\mu$–$10\,\mu$ particles with a ratio of only $1\cdot11:1$ are also grouped together. To overcome these objections a size scale with a constant ratio between classes is commonly used. The ratio may have any value, such as $2:1$. This gives rather wide classes and is often replaced by $\sqrt{2}:1$ or $\sqrt[4]{2}:1$ ratio. With class sizes based on ratios, it is convenient to have a common starting point for the scale of 1 mm. Thus the class limits less than the origin of these scales would be:

Scale of 2	0·2500			0·5000			1·000 mm
Scale of $\sqrt{2}$	0·2500		0·3536	0·5000		0·7071	1·000
Scale of $\sqrt[4]{2}$	0·2500	0·2973	0·3536	0·4104	0·5000	0·5946	0·7071	0·8409	1·000

Unfortunately, graticules are usually described in relative dimensions instead of absolute ones and in use the graticule has an effective size dependent upon the optics of the system. The ultimate size classes, while having a constant ratio, are not, therefore, necessarily part of a unified scale. The virtue of such a unified scale is that by means of a simple transformation (Krumbein, 1934), the somewhat unwieldy numbers of the $\sqrt{2}$ and $\sqrt[4]{2}$ scales can readily be converted to simple numbers in arithmetic progression. The transformation takes the form: $\phi = -\log_2 \xi$ where ϕ is the transformed size and ξ is the size in millimetres. The $\sqrt[4]{2}$ scale above thus reads as follows:

Scale of $\sqrt[4]{2}$	0·2500	0·2473	0·3536	0·4204	0·5000 mm
ϕ units	2·00	1·75	1·50	1·25	1·00

In the size range of fine powders the $\sqrt{2}$ scale would be:

Scale of $\sqrt{2}$	0·00098	0·0014	0·0020	0·0028	0·0039 mm
ϕ units	10·00	9·50	9·00	8·50	8·00

The use of the ϕ-scale greatly simplifies the subsequent arithmetic of calculating means and standard deviations. The result in ϕ-units can be converted back to millimetres by application of the transformation formula or by reference to tables (e.g. Page, 1955). It must be borne in mind, however, that the mean so calculated will be the geometric mean and not the arithmetic mean; the standard deviation will also be in a geometric form.

The standard procedure in size analysis is to allot each particle to its appropriate size class and from the resultant data calculate or determine graphically such parameters as will adequately describe the size distribution. These parameters normally comprise a mean or average size and a measure of spread of sizes often represented by the standard deviation. Other parameters such as skewness and kurtosis may also be determined but as their reliability depends largely on the extremes or "tails" of the distribution which in turn demands that a large number of grains be counted, they are not infrequently neglected.

The mean size of a distribution can be calculated (as a moment measure) from the formula

$$M = \frac{\sum fm}{\sum f}$$

where f is the frequency by number in each class and m is the mid-point of the size classes regardless of whether the classes are equal or unequal.

The standard deviation (σ) is based on the second moment measure and may be calculated as follows:

$$\sigma = \sqrt{\frac{\sum f(m - M)^2}{\sum f}}$$

The values thus calculated are based on the size distribution by number. If the particles all have the same density the mean and standard deviation on the basis of size distribution by weight can be determined by substituting m^3 for m and M^3 for M in the equations given above.

In place of the mean and standard deviation determined as moment measures and utilizing the whole of the observational data, graphical measures can be used. These are often referred to as "quartile" or "percentile" measures and make use of only the central part of the size distribution, the extreme portions being neglected. Quartile measures may be based on arithmetic, geometric or logarithmic frequency classes (as may moment measures) and are calculated directly from the cumulative size frequency distribution curves.

The "median" is that diameter larger than 50% of the diameters in the distribution and smaller than the other 50%. It is that diameter which corresponds to the point where the 50% line crosses the cumulative curve. The quartile deviation is a measure of spread of sizes about the median. The quartiles lie on either side of the median and are the sizes corresponding to the frequencies of 25 and 75%. The simplest form of quartile deviation is the arithmetic quartile deviation which is a measure of half the spread between the quartiles. Geometric and logarithmic quartile deviations may also be determined. To express more closely the form of the cumulative curve which in general tends to be sigmoidal, deviations based on size frequencies other than the quartiles are sometimes used. These frequencies are referred to as "percentiles".

One of the advantages of quartile measures is that they can be read directly from a cumulative curve and that the arithmetic involved is negligible. Their principal disadvantage, however, is that they cannot be manipulated algebraically. Thus it is not possible to calculate the average size of a group of samples from the medians of the individual samples.

The number of particles counted materially affects the values of the distribution parameters. The British Standard Specification 3406: Part 4: 1963 recommends that the total number of grains counted should not be less than 625. Fairs (1951) has tabulated the number of particles to be counted to achieve any given accuracy on the basis of weight percentage and recommends that for a size range containing 20% by weight of the total, 400 particles in that class should be counted for an expected accuracy of 1%. To achieve an accuracy of 0·1% would require the counting of 40,000 particles. It appears, therefore, that very little increase in accuracy can be expected when very large numbers of grains are counted.

With coarser-grained materials, such as sands, 400–1000 grains can be accommodated under a $\frac{7}{8}$ inch square cover slip and all the grains should be counted. For very fine grained materials the numbers present on the slide will be greatly in excess of this value. Although it is often assumed that the grains on a slide are randomly scattered, it is better to assume that they are not and to sample the slide, counting perhaps 40 grains in each field. The central grids of the "globe and circle" graticules described earlier facilitate the selection of random fields.

A general account of statistical measures applied to loose grains is given by Krumbein and Pettijohn (1938) and by Chamot and Mason (1958). A more detailed account, including a discussion of the various forms of distribution curves is given by Herdan (1953).

B. *Grain Size Measurement in Thin Sections and Polished Surfaces*

The actual measurements and their classification may be made in exactly the same way as for loose grains, as also may the statistical calculations. The parameters determined are not, however, the same as would be obtained if the grains were isolated from each other before measurement. This is a direct consequence of sectioning the material with the result that the size measured will be less than the true size of the original particle (Fig. 28). Numerous authors have considered this problem from various aspects. Wicksell (1925, 1926) has examined the problem of sectioning spherical and ellipsoidal corpuscles embedded

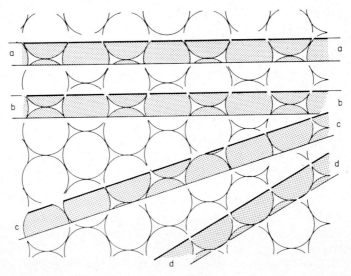

FIG. 28. The effect of sectioning a close packed array of regular spheres. Note that the size frequency distribution is dependent on both position (e.g. a—a and b—b) and direction (e.g. c—c and d—d) of section.

in tissue. Hagerman (1924), Fisher (1933), Krumbein (1935), Greenman (1951a, b), Chayes (1954) and Packham (1955) have discussed the effects of sectioning rocks, while Rutherford, Aborn and Bain (1937), Johnson (1946), Cahn and Fullman (1956) and DeHoff (1962, 1964, 1965) have considered the effects of sectioning metals. Rosenfeld, Jacobsen and Ferm (1953) and Friedman (1958, 1962) have derived empirical equations relating thin-section size analysis of rocks to the sieve-size distributions.

From a theoretical standpoint, the shape of the particles is again a major problem and authors have generally considered the effects of sectioning relatively simple shapes such as spheres and ellipsoids. Krumbein (1935) has shown that for spheres having an arithmetic-normal size frequency distribution, the arithmetic mean size for the thin section is $\pi/4$ times the mean size for the spheres from which the section was cut. For random sections of uniform spheres of radius r Fullman (1953) has shown that the average area is $2/3(\pi r^2)$ and the average random linear intercept is $4/3(r)$. Hilliard (1962) also discusses the problem of sectioning spheres showing a range of sizes and considers the errors introduced by the overlap of large particles over small ones when the thickness of the section is greater than the diameter of the smallest particles. Krumbein (1935), Wicksell (1925, 1926) and others have succeeded in relating moments of the true size distribution to the thin section distribution assuming that the original distribution was normal or lognormal in form. Roethlisberger (1955) has given simple graphical methods for transforming chord measurements into grain size cumulative frequency distributions. In this method the author uses a point-counter stage to select the grains to be measured. In this way he randomly samples the grains instead of measuring all of them. DeHoff (1965) has adopted a new approach in that he assumes a general mathematical form for the size distribution which is described by two parameters (as the normal distribution is described by assigning values to the mean and standard deviation) and then estimates these two parameters from simple counting measurements. The introduction of a third counting measurement permitted the evaluation of the number of particles per unit volume. In this method it is necessary to determine (by direct counting) the three measures N_A, the number of particle sections observed in unit area, N_L, the number of intercepts which unit length of random test line makes with particle outlines in the structure and P_P, the fraction of points in a randomly placed grid of test points which lie in the phase of interest in the microstructures. DeHoff takes as an illustration the lognormal distribution since it is commonly observed that many empirical size distributions are well fitted by this functional form. The two quantities μ_g (geometric mean) and σ_g (geometric standard deviation) define a distribution of this form and these may be determined from the equations:

$$\ln \mu_g = -\frac{5}{2} \ln N_A + 4 \ln N_L - \frac{3}{2} \ln P_P + \ln \left(\frac{16 k_1^{2/5} \cdot k_3^{3/2}}{k_2^4} \right)$$

and

$$\ln {}^2\sigma_g = \ln N_A - 2 \ln N_L + \ln P_P + \ln \left(\frac{k_2^2}{4 k_1 \cdot k_3} \right)$$

The total number of particles per unit volume is given by:

$$\ln N_V = 3 \ln N_A - 3 \ln N_L + \ln P_P + \ln \left(\frac{k_2^3}{8 k_1^3 \cdot k_3} \right)$$

In these equations k_1, k_2 and k_3 are shape factors related to the average distance between tangent planes (or grain diameter—D_V), the average particle surface area (S) and the average particle volume (V) respectively. Thus for a sphere of radius (r) where $D_V = 2r$, $k_1 = 2$; $S = 4\pi r^2$, $k_2 = 4\pi$, $V = 4/3(\pi r^3)$, $k_3 = 4/3(\pi)$. DeHoff (1964) has discussed the quantitative estimation of shape of particles of various forms. In order to apply the above equations to real particles it is necessary to determine or assume the shape of the component grains and their corresponding shape factors. As a first approximation it would appear reasonable to assume that the grains are spherical and to use the values for k given above.

Although the basic technique of DeHoff is the simple one of counting, certain assumptions regarding grain shape have still to be made. Nevertheless, the method represents a considerable advance towards a more precise determination of grain size distributions from thin sections.

The most recent contribution to the literature of grain size distribution from thin section size data (Sahu, 1967) makes use of the Gram-Charlier approximation for the conversion of phi-size distribution moments (duly corrected for random sectioning) to cumulative frequencies. This author bases his method on the assumption that the size distribution of sediments is approximately phi-normal. There is, however, no indication of the parameter used to describe the particle size, though by inference from an earlier contribution (Sahu, 1964) it is the nominal sectional diameter.

This emphasizes the necessity for clearly stating the method by which size analyses are performed and the measure used to describe the grains. It also points to the necessity for further investigation of the inter-relationship between grain size parameters, shape coefficients and the information deduced from the analysis by statistical methods.

C. *The Errors of Grain Size Measurement*

It has been shown repeatedly that the shape of grains, whether loose or in thin section, introduces a major uncertainty in the determination of true grain size. The actual sectioning of a grain introduces a further uncertainty since the precise position of the plane of sectioning with respect to the individual grain is unknown. There are, however, other features which affect the measurement of size which become especially significant as the particle size diminishes. These effects are due to the index of refraction of the mounting medium, the focus of the microscope and its aperture and resolution. A further error is related to the slope of the sides of opaque grains in thin-section, well known as the Holmes effect (Holmes, 1927).

Saylor (1965) has investigated the error in the measurement of microscopic spheres and has shown that the principal uncertainties originate in the geometrical optics of the object and that resolving power has less, but by no means negligible importance. Saylor states that the most reliable methods of determining the real diameter of a transparent sphere is to immerse it in a liquid of the same refractive index as the sphere itself, so that it becomes virtually invisible. Under this condition the very fine dirt particles on the surface of the sphere are faintly visible and the circle of maximum diameter as the focus is changed is a very close approximation to the true diameter of the sphere.

A further source of error stems from the inability of the eye to distinguish accurately the position of the boundary between areas of high and low luminance due to the occurrence of light and dark bands at the boundary. These bands are known as the Mach bands and are apparently a purely physiological phenomenon. There is no evidence that they are present in the luminance distribution presented to the eye. The effect of the Mach bands is to enhance the sharpness of the edge between light and dark areas, but the position of this subjective edge may not coincide with the position of the true edge. Welford (1968) has discussed the significance of this effect in relation to particle size determination and has shown that its magnitude, in linear dimensions, is of the same order as the resolution limit of the microscope objective. Thus, the measured size of particles less than about 2μ diameter is likely to be subject to considerable error. Furthermore, the presence of Mach bands may lead to the "recognition" of non-existent detail in the object, such as a surrounding membrane (Watrasiewiez, 1966). Since the Mach bands appear to be, at least in part, a function of the brightness contrast between the object and its surroundings, it may be deduced that the level of illumination used should be as low as possible especially when opaque grains are to be measured.

The Holmes effect is more usually associated with errors in modal analysis, but is relevant to errors in measuring sizes of particles in thin section, where it is important that all the measurements are made in the same plane, e.g. in size distribution studies. The effect arises from the fact that the edges of a sectioned particle are rarely perpendicular to the plane of sectioning. Thus if an opaque grain is adjacent to a transparent grain (Fig. 29) in a section of finite thickness the true diameter (in the upper surface of the section) will be smaller than the apparent diameter of the grain if the sides of the opaque particle slope outwards towards the bottom of the section. This error may be negligible in many instances, but where large amounts of opaque minerals are present as very small grains they may be over-

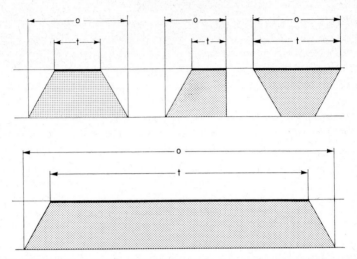

Fig. 29. Holmes effect (i). The apparent size of opaque grains (stippled) in transparent media or adjacent to transparent grains depends on the slope of the grain boundary: t = true dimension; o = observed dimension. The effect is of maximum significance when the grain size is comparable to the grain thickness (top) and becomes less important as the grain size increases (bottom).

estimated by a factor of 2·5 or more. A further difficulty arises of particles small enough to be contained within the thickness of the slide which are not sectioned, but are nevertheless visible (Fig. 30). This particular error appears not to have been investigated, but it emphasizes that size or modal analysis of transparent substances containing minute opaque grains should be accepted cautiously.

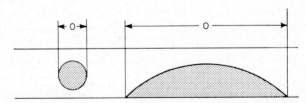

Fig. 30. Holmes effect (ii). Particles smaller than the thickness of the section may be visible and therefore counted, but are not in plane of counting (o = observed dimension; true dimension is zero).

D. *The Calculations and Errors of Modal Analysis*

The calculations of modal analysis merely comprise the conversion of total areas, total lengths or total point-counts for each component into percentages of the area measured, length of line measured or number of points counted. It should be remembered that these values are volume percentage frequencies. To determine weight percentage frequencies each volume must be multiplied by the density of the component and the percentage of the total recalculated.

The simplicity of the calculations should not, however, be allowed to mask the fact that unsatisfactory techniques or sampling which is inaccurate or inefficient can lead to grossly inaccurate results. Nevertheless, the method is potentially accurate and the basic theory relating area to volume entirely justified (Chayes, 1954).

The sources of errors in modal analysis fall into three principal groups:

> (a) Errors due to mechanical deficiencies of the measuring apparatus.
> (b) Operator errors.
> (c) Sampling errors.

A source of error which may be termed the "counting" error is sometimes invoked as a further group. Since, however, the term may be used in relation to failure of the mechanical device or of the operator to count accurately and also as a measure of the inadequacy of sampling of the thin section or polished surface, it will not be isolated as a specific error.

Errors due to mechanical deficiencies are relatively rare and are largely under the control of the operator. Certain types of integrating stage were prone to errors of this sort. Especially troublesome was the Dollar stage (Dollar, 1937). This simple and ingenious device stored the linear measurements by means of a series of nuts on a common threaded axle. The nuts were prevented from rotating except when actually recording by friction stops. Unfortunately these stops sometimes failed to hold the nuts and occasionally adjacent nuts locked against each other. The operator's attention therefore had to be divided between the analysis and the stage. Another source of mechanical error sometimes occurs in the operation of electromechanical counters, which either fail to record or record twice when the operating button is pressed. Fortunately the errors so introduced are insignificant.

Operator errors are of rather greater importance, though they too can be minimized. The chief error here is mis-identification of the component being measured. Errors may be also introduced in linear or area analysis by difficulties in determining the exact position of grain boundaries. As noted earlier, this error becomes important with very small grains. It may also occur where the boundary between components is diffuse as when minerals such as felspars are partially decomposed and it is desired to know the proportions of the fresh mineral and its decomposition products. It has also been noted earlier that for strict accuracy all measurements should be made in the same plane. The operator must, therefore, be careful to maintain a fixed focus on the surface of the thin section and not be tempted to readjust the focus for grains within the thickness of the section.

Although the errors so far discussed may be significant in certain circumstances, the main errors are those due to sampling.

The term sampling is here used to include the selection of the block of material from which the thin section or polished surface will be made, the choice of a particular section from this block and the particular field of view in this section. The sampling error is also concerned with the size of the sample and it is in this connection that the term "counting error" is sometimes used.

There are thus three levels of sampling and deductions about each population from which the sample is taken depend upon the accuracy of the analysis at successively lower levels. However, the problems of sampling must here be restricted to the evaluation of the thin-section or polished surface. For the significance of modal analysis in problems relating to a parent population which comprises a volume of rock measured in cubic miles, see, for example, Whitten (1961a, 1961b).

In the determination of the volume-fraction of components from a thin section or polished surface, it is desirable to know which procedure is most efficient, what are the conditions for maximum efficiency and under these conditions how many measurements are required for a given precision.

All methods of testing the result of an analysis must depend on the supposition that the components in a mixture are randomly distributed *provided* a large enough number of grains is measured. For very small numbers of grains (i.e. small samples) the frequency of each component will vary from sample to sample. Therefore the problem becomes one of predetermining an acceptable level of variation and estimating the number of grains that will give a value equal to or less than this level.

Hilliard and Cahn (1961) have examined the various methods of modal analysis theoretically and have concluded that the most efficient method is by point-counting using a two-dimensional grid. They stress that the spacing of the grid points should be such that not more than one point should fall on each grain. Providing this condition is satisfied, the relative standard deviation (i.e. σ/μ where σ is the standard deviation; μ is the mean value of the volume fraction) in the volume fraction will be approximately $1/\sqrt{n}$ where n is the number of points falling on the components concerned. Thus to improve the accuracy of measurement by a factor of 2 (i.e. to halve the error) it is necessary to increase the number of counts by a factor of 4. As an example, suppose a component is present in the proportion of 10% of the total mixture and it is desired to estimate this quantity with an accuracy of $\pm 1\%$ (i.e. $\pm 10\%$ of the quantity present), then the number of grains to be counted will be 100. On the other hand, for a component forming 50% of the mixture a count of 100 grains will give an estimate with an accuracy of $\pm 5\%$ (equivalent to 10% of the quantity present). To determine a 50% component with an accuracy of $\pm 1\%$ demands the counting of 2500 grains. Thus having counted a number of grains in a section it is possible to estimate the error of each component and reduce it to any desired value by increasing the number counted. By this method it is apparent that very large numbers of grains must be counted to achieve an accuracy better than $\pm 1\%$. Furthermore, in this method experimental errors are ignored.

The accuracy of modal analysis has been discussed by Chayes (1956), Gladman and Woodhead (1960) and by Gladman (1963) as well as by others. Most authors have based point-count analyses on a grid that is coarse enough for only one point to fall on each particle and have suggested that the accuracy of point-counting falls off rapidly as the grid spacing is decreased. Solomon (1963) has examined experimentally a theoretical study by Hasofer (1963) of some of the problems of point-counting in which an attempt was made to relate the grid spacing, grain radius, the volume fraction of a given component and the area measured to the total variance arising from counts of different sizes. According to these authors the total variance will be equal to or less than

$$\frac{0 \cdot 44 \, pa^3}{RA} \left[1 + 5 \cdot 8 \left(\frac{R}{a} \right)^3 \right]$$

where A = measurement area, a = grid spacing, R = grain radius and p = the fraction of the particular mineral in the rock. Solomon recommends that for a rock with average grain size of 0·2 mm ($R = 0\cdot1$ mm) and $p = 25\%$, the grid spacing should be 0·5 mm and 1300 points counted covering an area (A) of 400 mm². Where grains depart markedly from being equidimensional, the variance may be greater and the number of points counted increased.

By the methods outlined above some measure of the accuracy being achieved can be determined and greater reliance placed upon the results. This is particularly important when attempting to estimate the parameters of parent populations.

E. *Other Mensuration Methods*

The calculations involved in the determination of grain boundary parameters have been described earlier. To date no detailed consideration appears to have been given to the magnitude of the likely errors. They are, however, closely associated with problems of sampling and the foregoing discussion of modal analysis is probably relevant. Thus the spacing of the short line grid (p. 98) should preferably be such that each line cuts at least one boundary, possibly two or three, but not more, and that each grain is cut by a single line or less. In the case of grain boundary calculations by the long line method (p. 79), the longer the line, the greater the accuracy, but in the absence of a theoretical treatment, the precise accuracy cannot be predicted. The experimental approach suggests that the short lines should be increased in number and the long line increased in length until with each successive increase no significant alteration in the result is apparent.

Errors in angular measurements and the distribution of errors likewise appear not to have been investigated.

The errors relating to determination of weight and volume are closely related to those associated with the determination of grain size and the shape of the particle.

X. Conclusion

The large number of techniques outlined indicates the versatility of the microscope as a measuring tool and show that it is not restricted to simple linear dimensions. However, to achieve a high degree of accuracy, strict consideration must be given to the character and attributes of the parameter being determined. To many of these measurements it is necessary to apply the methods of statistics in order to reduce a large amount of data to useful and usable information.

The methods of particle size analysis are well known and extensively used, those of modal analysis are rapidly growing in importance, especially in the geological and metallurgical field. Grain boundary methods have had some application in metallurgy and biology, but almost none in geology.

Further advances in the use of the microscope in mensuration now demand a greater degree of automation of a relatively simple and inexpensive kind. Many laboratories possess or can afford a microscope, but its use in mensuration is in danger of being frustrated if the ancillary equipment becomes so large and complex that the cost makes its purchase prohibitive.

Closely associated with advances in techniques must come further refinements in theory especially in relation to the determination of the shape of particles and the distribution of shapes within any powder. While much of present-day theory is adequate for the purposes of a specific industry or discipline, a unification of methods, terminology and understanding is long overdue.

Whatever other methods may be used to determine the size and shape parameters and composition of powders the properties of the individual particles can only be precisely determined when the particle can be seen—under the microscope.

ACKNOWLEDGEMENTS

The writer is indebted to the following for permission to reproduce text-figures: Professor R. Barer, Professor A. Curtis, Professor W. C. Krumbein, Professor C. S. Smith, Professor Dr E. R. Weibel, Dr S. Guruswamy, Dr R. J. Hamilton, Dr K. R. May, Dr D. A. Robson, Mr P. D. Lark, Mr H. M. Malies, Mr J. H. Bassett (James Swift & Son Ltd.), Firth-Brown Tools Ltd., Sheffield, Fleming Instruments Ltd., Graticules Ltd., Vickers Instruments, Ltd., W. Watson & Son Ltd., Carl Zeiss, Oberkochen.

Thanks are also due to the Editors and Publishers who have given permission for the reproduction of figures previously published in their Journals.

Finally, the writer is most grateful to Professor R. Barer for inviting him to undertake the task of reviewing the methods of mensuration available to the microscopist.

REFERENCES

Addey, F. (1922). *J. Queckett microsc. Club* (2) **14**, 279.

Aschenbrenner, B. C. (1956). *J. sedim. Petrol.* **26**, 15–31.

Barer, R. (1952). *Nature* (Lond.) **169**, 366–367.

Barer, R. (1956). "The Interference Microscope in Quantitative Cytology". C. Baker of Holborn, Ltd., London, England.

Barer, R. (1960). *Nature*, **188**, 398–399.

Barringer, A. R. (1953). *Trans. Instn Min. Metall.* **63**, 21–41.

Beirne, T. and Hutcheon, J. M. (1954). *Br. J. appl. Phys.*, Suppl. No. 3, S76–81.

Cahn, J. W. and Fullman, R. L. (1956). *J. Metals, N.Y.* **8**, 610–612.

Cantu, —. (1956). *Bull. Microsc. appl.* (2), **6**, 199–216.

Chalkley, H. W. (1943). *J. natn. Cancer Inst.* **4**, 47–53.

Chalkley, H. W., Cornfield, J. and Park, H. A. (1949). *Science* **110**, 295–297.

Chamot, E. M. and Mason, C. W. (1958). "Handbook of Chemical Microscopy", Vol. I, 3rd Edition, Wiley, New York, U.S.A.

Chayes, F. (1949). *Am. Miner.* **34**, 1–11.

Chayes, F. (1954). *J. Geol.* **62**, 92–101.

Chayes, F. (1956). "Petrographic Modal Analysis". Wiley, New York, U.S.A.

Curtis, A. S. G. (1960). *Med. biol. Illust.* **10**, 261–266.

Davies, C. N. (1964). *Nature* (Lond.) **201**, 905–907.

Davies, H. G. and Wilkins, M. H. F. (1952). *Nature* (Lond.) **169**, 541.

DeHoff, R. T. (1962). *Trans. metall. Soc. A.I.M.E.* **224**, 474–477.

DeHoff, R. T. (1964). *Trans. metall. Soc. A.I.M.E.* **230**, 764–769.

DeHoff, R. T. (1965). *Trans. metall. Soc. A.I.M.E.* **233**, 25–29.

Delesse, A. (1847). *C.r. hebd. Sèanc. Acad. Sci., Paris* **25**, 544–545.

Delesse, A. (1848). *Ann. des mines* **13**, 379–388.

Dollar, A. T. J. (1937). *Mineralog. Mag.* **24**, 577–594.

Dyson, J. (1960). *J. opt. Soc. Am.* **50**, 754–757.

Dyson, J. (1961). *AEI Engineering* **1**, 13–17.

Dyson, J. and Noble, P. J. W. (1962). *Jl. R. microsc. Soc.* **81**, 95–99.
Ebbesson, S. O. E. and Tang, D. (1965). *Jl. R. microsc. Soc.* **84**, 449–464.
Endter, F. and Gebauer, H. (1956). *Optik* **13**, 97–101.
Fairs, G. L. (1943). *Chemy Ind.* **62**, 374–378.
Fairs, G. L. (1951). *Jl. R. microsc. Soc.* **71**, 209–22.
Feret, L. R. (1931). *Assoc. International pour l'Essai des Mat. Zurich* 2D.
Fisher, G. (1933). *Jb. preuss. geol. Landesanst. Berg Akad.* **54**, 320–343.
Ford, I. H. (1954). *J. scient. Instrum.* **31**, 164–165.
Fraser, R. D. B. and Rogers, C. E. (1954). *Biochim. Biophys. Acta.* **15**, 146–148.
Freere, R. H. and Weibel, E. R. (1967). *Jl. R. microsc. Soc.* **87**, 25–34.
Friedman, G. M. (1958). *J. Geol.* **66**, 394–416.
Friedman, G. M. (1962). *J. sedim. Petrol.* **32**, 15–25.
Fullman, R. L. (1953). *Trans. metall. Soc. A.I.M.E.* **197**, 447–452.
Galjaard, H. and Szirmai, J. A. (1965). *Jl. R. microsc. Soc.* **84**, 27–42.
Gladman, T. (1963). *J. Iron Steel Inst.* **201**, 1044–1049.
Gladman, T. and Woodhead, J. H. (1960). *J. Iron Steel Inst.* **194**, 189–193.
Glagolev, A. A. (1933). *Trans. Inst. Econ. Min., Moscow* 59.
Glagolev, A. A. (1934). *Engng. Min. J.* **135**, 399.
Goldstein, D. J. (1967). *Nature* (Lond.) **213**, 386–387.
Greenman, N. N. (1951a). *J. Geol.* **59**, 268–274.
Greenman, N. N. (1951b). *J. Geol.* **59**, 447–462.
Guruswamy, S. (1967). "Particle Size Analysis". Proceedings of a conference. Soc. for Analytical Chemistry, Loughborough, 1966, pp. 29–31.
Hagerman, T. H. (1924). *Geol. För. Stockh. Förh.* **46**, 325–353.
Hally, A. D. (1964). *Q. Jl. microsc. Sci.* **105**, 503–517.
Hamilton, R. J., Holdsworth, J. F. and Walton, W. H. (1954). *Br. J. appl. Phys.*, Suppl. 3, S101–S105.
Hartshorne, N. H. and Stuart, A. (1960). "Crystals and the Polarizing Microscope". Edward Arnold, London, England.
Hasofer, A. M. (1963). *Aust. J. appl. Sci.* **14**, 168–179.
Hausner, H. H. (1967). "Particle Size Analysis". Proceedings of a Conference. Soc. for Analytical Chemistry, Loughborough, 1966, pp. 20–28.
Hennig, A. (1956). *Mikroskopie* **11**, 1–20.
Hennig, A. (1957). *Mikroskopie* **12**, 174–202.
Hennig, A. (1959). *Zeiss-Werkz.* **6**, 78.
Hennig, A. and Meyer-Arendt, J. R. (1963). *Lab. Invest.* **12**, 460–464.
Herdan, G. (1953). "Small Particle Statistics" Elsevier, New York, U.S.A.
Heywood, H. (1933). *Proc. Instn mech. Engrs* **125**, 383.
Heywood, H. (1937). *Chemy Ind.* **56**, 149.
Heywood, H. (1938). *Proc. Instn mech. Engrs* **140**, 257–347.
Heywood, H. (1946). *Trans. Instn Min. Metall.* **55**, 1–14.
Heywood, H. (1947). "Symposium on Particle Size Analysis", Supplement, *Trans. Instn. chem. Engrs* **25**, 15.
Heywood, H. (1954). *J. imp. Coll. chem. Engng Soc.* **8**, 25–33.
Heywood, H. (1961). "Powders in Industry", Soc. chem. Ind. Monograph, No. 14, 429–440.
Heywood, H. (1963). *J. Pharm. Pharmac.* **15**, 56T–74T.
Heywood, H. (1967). "Particle Size Analysis". Proceedings of a Conference. Soc. for Analytical Chemistry, Loughborough, 1966, pp. 355–359.
Hilliard, J. E. (1962). *Trans. metall. Soc. A.I.M.E.* **224**, 906–917.
Hilliard, J. E. and Cahn, J. W. (1961). *Trans. metall. Soc. A.I.M.E.* **221**, 344–352.

Holmes, A. H. (1927). "Petrographic Methods and Calculations", Murby, London, England.
Hörnsten, Å. (1960). *Bull. geol. Instn Univ. Uppsala* **38**, 105–137.
Howard, R. T. and Cohen, M. (1947). *Trans. Am. Inst. Min. metall. Engrs* **172**, 413–426.
Hulbe, C. W. H. (1955). *J. sedim. Petrol.* **25**, 302–303.
Humphries, D. W. (1964). *Mineralog. Mag.* **33**, 918–923.
Humphries, D. W. (1966a). *Microscope* **15**, 267–280.
Humphries, D. W. (1966b). *Sedimentology* **6**, 241–245.
Hunt, W. F. (1924). *Am. Miner.* **9**, 190–193.
Hurlbut, C. (1939). *Am. J. Sci.* **237**, 253–261.
John, O. (1923). *Z. wiss. Mikrosk.* **46**, 395.
Johnson, W. A. (1946). *Metal Progress* **49**, 89–92.
Krumbein, W. C. (1934). *J. sedim. Petrol.* **4**, 65–77.
Krumbein, W. C. (1935). *J. Geol.* **43**, 482–496.
Krumbein, W. C. (1941). *J. sedim. Petrol.* **11**, 64–72.
Krumbein, W. C. and Pettijohn, F. J. (1938). "Manual of Sedimentary Petrology". Appleton-Century-Croft, New York, U.S.A.
Lark, P. D. (1965). *Microscope* **15**, 1–6.
Larsen, E. S. and Miller, F. S. (1935). *Am. Miner.* **20**, 260–273.
Martin, G., Blyth, C. E. and Tongue, H. (1923). *Trans. Br. Ceram. Soc.* **23**, 61–109.
May, K. R. (1945). *J. scient. Instrum.* **10**, 187.
May, K. R. (1965). *J. scient. Instrum.* **42**, 500–501.
McGinn, J. H. (1956). U.S. Patent 2,730,008.
Metzner, P. (1928). "Das Mikroskop". Leipzig.
Packham, G. H. (1955). *J. Geol.* **63**, 50–58.
Page, H. G. (1955). *J. sedim. Petrol.* **25**, 285–292.
Patterson, H. S. and Cawood, W. (1936). *Trans. Faraday. Soc.* **32**, 1084–1087.
Powell, E. O. and Errington, F. P. (1963). *Jl. R. microsc. Soc.* **82**, 39–49.
Powers, M. C. (1953). *J. sedim. Petrol.* **23**, 117–119.
Richardson, K. C. (1953). *J. Endocr.* **9**, 170–184.
Robins, W. H. M. (1954). *Br. J. appl. Phys.*, Suppl. No. 3, S82–S85.
Robson, D. A. (1958). *J. sedim. Petrol.* **28**, 108–110.
Roethlisberger, H. (1955). *J. Geol.* **63**, 579–584.
Rose, H. E. (1953). "The Measurement of Particle Size in Very Fine Powders". Constable, London, England.
Rosenfeld, M. A. (1954). *Am. Miner.* **39**, 834–836.
Rosenfeld, M. A., Jacobsen, L. and Ferm, J. C. (1953). *J. Geol.* **61**, 114–132.
Rosiwal, A. (1898). *Verh. geol. Reichsanst. (St Anst./Landesanst.)*, Wien 143–175.
Ross, K. F. A. and Galavazi, G. (1965). *Jl. R. microsc. Soc.* **84**, 13–25.
Rutherford, J. J. B., Aborn, R. H. and Bain, E. C. (1937). *Metals Alloys* **8**, 345–348.
Sahu, B. K. (1964). *J. sedim. Petrol.* **34**, 768–773.
Sahu, B. K. (1967). *Sedimentology* **8**, 329–336.
Saltykov, S. A. (1958). "Stereometric Metallurgy", Moscow, U.S.S.R.
Saylor, C. P. (1965). *Applied Optics* **4**, 477–486.
Saylor, C. P. (1966). "Advances in Optical and Electron Microscopy", Volume 1, 41–76. Academic Press, London and New York.
Schubel, J. R. and Schiemer, E. W. (1967). *Sedimentology* **9**, 319–326.
Shand, S. J. (1916). *J. Geol.* **24**, 394–404.

Short, R. H. D. (1950). *Phil. Trans. R. Soc.* (B) **235**, 35–87.
Smith, C. S. (1960). *Trans. Am. Inst. Min. metall. Engrs* **218**, 58–62.
Smith, C. S. and Guttman, L. (1953). *Trans. Am. Inst. Min. metall. Engrs* **197**, 81–87 and 1561.
Solomon, M. (1963). *J. Petrol.* **4**, 367–382.
Sorby, H. C. (1853). *Q. Jl. geol. Soc. Lond.* **2**, 344–346.
Sorby, H. C. (1856). *Phil. Mag.* **11**, 20–37.
Thackwell, F. E. (1933). *Econ. Geol.* **28**, 178–182.
Timbrell, V. (1952). *Nature* (Lond.) **170**, 318–319.
Tolansky, S. (1948). "Multiple Beam Interferometry", Clarendon Press, Oxford, England.
Tolansky, S. (1953). *Symposium on the Properties of Metallic Surfaces.* Institute of Metals, London, England, pp. 1–22 and pp. 298–299.
Tolanksy, S. (1955). "Microstructures of Diamond Surfaces", N.A.G. Press, London, England.
Trowell, O. A. and Westgarth, D. R. (1959). *Anat. Rec.* **134**, 463–471.
Wadell, H. (1932). *J. Geol.* **40**, 443–451.
Wadell, H. (1933). *J. Geol.* **41**, 310–331.
Wadell, H. (1935). *J. Geol.* **43**, 250–279.
Wallis, T. E. (1919). *Pharm. J.* **103**, 75.
Wallis, T. E. (1957). "Analytical Microscopy", 3rd edition, Churchill, London, England.
Watrasiewiez, B. M. (1966). *Microscope* **15**, 281–283.
Watson, H. H. (1952). *Br. J. ind. Med.* **9**, 80–82.
Watson, H. H. and Mulford, D. F. (1954). *Br. J. appl. Phys.*, Suppl. No. 3, S105–S108.
Weibel, E. R. (1963a). *Lab. Invest.* **12**, 131–155.
Weibel, E. R. (1963b). "Morphometry of the Human Lung". Academic Press, New York, U.S.A.
Weibel, E. R. and Gomez, D. M. (1962). *J. appl. Physiol.* **17**, 343–348.
Weibel, E. R., Kistler, G. S. and Scherle, W. F. (1966). *J. Cell Biol.* **30**, 23–38.
Welford, W. T. (1968). "Advances in Optical and Electron Microscopy", Vol. 2, 41–76, Academic Press, London and New York.
Wentworth, C. K. (1923). *J. Geol.* **31**, 228–232.
Whitby, K. T. and Vomela, R. A. (1965). Particle Technol. Lab., Dept. Mech. Eng., Univ. Minn., Publ., 86 : 83 pp.
Whitten, E. H. T. (1961a). *J. Geol.* **69**, 619–646.
Whitten, E. H. T. (1961b). *Bull. geol. Soc. Am.* **72**, 1331–1360.
Wicksell, S. D. (1925). *Biometrika* **17**, 84–99.
Wicksell, S. D. (1926). *Biometrika* **18**, 151–172.
Wood, J. G. and Marriner, R. S. (1966). *Metallurgia* **73**, 297–300.

Microincineration Techniques for Electron-microscopic Localization of Biological Minerals

RICHARD S. THOMAS

*Western Regional Research Laboratory, Agricultural Research Service,
United States Department of Agriculture, Albany, California, U.S.A.*

I. HISTORICAL INTRODUCTION AND LITERATURE REVIEW

A. *Microincineration for Light Microscopy*

MICROINCINERATION was first described more than a century ago by the French botanist and pioneer histochemist, Raspail (1833). He found that thin preparations of plant material, such as onion epidermis, mounted on glass slides, could be burned over a flame to a red glow without destroying the microscopically-visible organization of the tissue. A burned preparation quickly dissolved if a drop of dilute acid was added to the slide, however. Evidently the tissue structures were represented merely by ash from the mineral elements they contained, but the pattern of ash showed accurately where the mineral had been. This simple experiment is a primitive but adequate prototype for all subsequent elaborations of the technique.

The method was independently rediscovered several times in later years (see Horning, 1942 and Hintzsche, 1956); but never came into much use until the persistent efforts of Policard in the 1920's and later (Policard, 1923, 1929, 1942). Earlier workers apparently regarded the technique mostly in terms of their own special problems, whereas Policard championed its *general* usefulness for histochemical localization of heat-stable mineral substances. At the same time, he made improvements in specimen preparation and temperature control to make the procedure reproducible. A wave of interest followed this work during which the method was further perfected by Scott and others and was applied to a wide range of biological materials, both normal and pathological (Scott, 1933a, 1933b, 1937; Scott and Packer, 1939; Horning, 1942; Hintzsche, 1956; Kruszynski, 1966).

Ash patterns, in general, could be expected to contain such minerals as Na_2O, CaO, MgO, Fe_2O_3, SiO_2, $Ca_3(PO_4)_2$, $Mg_3(PO_4)_2$ and other heat-stable metallic oxides, phosphates and mixed compounds (see Kruszynski, 1966). Attempts were made to extend the microincineration technique to identify or exactly localize these individual minerals in the ash pattern. This met with only limited success, however (see Hintzsche, 1956; Kruszynski, 1966), owing to the chemical complexity of the ash and the poor spatial resolution of the histochemical tests, which was usually far inferior to the spatial resolution of the ash patterns. With the best procedures, this ash pattern resolution ultimately approached the resolution limit of the light microscope.

Use of the technique continued high until the start of the Second World War, and again shortly after, but seems to have declined in the last few years. Recently, Kruszynski (1963a, 1966) published a comprehensive bibliography of nearly 500 references and also an extended review article. An excellent monograph on microincineration has been written by Hintzsche (1956).

B. *Microincineration for Electron Microscopy*

Unlike the light microscopic technique, microincineration for electron microscopy has never experienced any progressive development or wide use and there are only isolated reports of it in the literature. Some of these were reviewed by Kruszynski (1963a, 1966). A more extensive review is attempted here, but no claim can be made for exhaustive coverage of the literature.

Strictly speaking, the very first use of an electron microscope with the microincineration technique was by Scott and Packer in 1939; they constructed a thermionic emission instrument for selectively demonstrating calcium and magnesium in ash patterns. Specimens ashed on a heated cathode were visualized by the thermal electrons they emitted. The instrument was limited by its special purpose, however, and its resolution did not exceed that of the light microscope.

The first use of a conventional electron microscope with microincineration may have been by Fernández-Morán in 1948. This was before ultrathin sectioning and he tried burning smears of tissue mounted on grids simply as a way to thin them. Results were rather artifactual, judging by modern standards, but the experiments are still interesting for their technical details. The problem of thin specimen supports stable to heat and oxidation was solved with vapor-deposited films of aluminum or beryllium. Specimens were burned not only by direct heating outside the microscope but also within the electron microscope, either on a hot stage, or by the energy of the electron beam. Some of the residues were crystalline and gave characteristic electron diffraction powder patterns.

Draper and Hodge (1949, 1950) independently described a technique of burning the specimen by high beam current in the electron microscope. Using isolated fibrils from skeletal muscle, mounted on silicon monoxide, collodion, or Formvar membranes, they showed organized detail in the incinerated residues with resolution down to about 100 Å. Their successful use of organic support films suggests, however, that the residues may have been carbonized, rather than totally ashed. König (1951) clearly demonstrated that collodion membranes and polystyrene latex particles could be converted to carbon under the electron beam without any change in their outward appearance.

Yasuzumi and Sawada (1950) studying squash preparations of chromosomes, and Policard and Bessis (1952), using intact leucocytes, carried out microincineration in the traditional way on a solid support and then made pseudoreplicas of the ash for electron microscopy. Higher resolution viewing of the ash patterns showed artifacts in greater detail, but of significant structural features little more could be seen than in the light microscope. Recently, a similar technique has been used by Garamvolgyi and Kerner (1962) on whole-mounted muscle fibrils, with similar results, and by Vose (1963) on bone surfaces.

In another early experiment, Williams (1952) attempted to localize nucleic acid in tobacco mosaic virus particles by the phosphorus remaining after microincineration. The particles were sprayed on silicon monoxide membranes, together with colloidal gold to serve as permanent marker particles. Nothing of the virus was left after 400°, however. The mineral apparently volatilized. Recently, experiments along a similar line have been undertaken by Bendet and Trontyl (1963) on T-2 phage particles, with more success. Again the phosphorus volatilized, but, by using heat-stable iron or uranium as a stain for the nucleic acid, they obtained a residue which was localized, if not to the precise site of the nucleic acid, at least to the core of the virus.

The very first attempt to apply microincineration to ultrathin sections was probably by Fernández-Morán in 1952. These were experimental, frozen sections, however, and difficulties with the preparation, such as contamination with extraneous salt, precluded useful results. In recent times, Desler and Pfefferkorn (1962) showed the practicability of incinerating conventional ultrathin sections by using model preparations of fine silicon dioxide particles embedded in methacrylate. Similar experiments were done by Arnold and Sasse (1963) on thin sections of various rat organs, including lung tissue containing titanium oxide dust. The organic material was burned away cleanly, but the mineral grains remained, apparently undisturbed.

Quite recently, Drum (1967) reported ultramicroincineration of whole-mounted fragments of a siliceous, freshwater sponge. Practically no details were given, however.

Many of our own microincineration results will be described in Section III.A. Studies on calcium-loaded mitochondria, shown there, have recently been extended by Greenawalt and Carafoli (1966) to strontium-loaded mitochondria.

C. *Low-temperature Incineration, Macro and Micro*

Of importance to the present and future development of microincineration for electron microscopy of biological specimens is another technique which in the past has been applied primarily to microscopic non-biological specimens or to chemical analysis of minerals in larger biological and organic samples. This is the low-temperature combustion of solid organic substances by gaseous oxygen activated in an electrical discharge. Burning of specimens at low temperatures—e.g. below 100°C—offers the possibility, both theoretical and real, of greatly improving the definition of ash patterns (see Sections II.C and III).

The technique of low-temperature incineration first came to our attention in 1962 through the work of Gleit and co-workers (Gleit and Holland, 1962; Gleit et al. 1963; Gleit, 1963, 1966, 1967), but a somewhat earlier history is now known to us. Turkevich and Streznewski (1958), Streznewski and Turkevich (1959), and independently, Black-wood and McTaggart (1959) and Hennig *et al.* (1958), reported that elemental carbon could be burned near room temperature by atomic oxygen produced in an electric discharge. Turkevich and Streznewski in many of their incineration experiments used submicron soot particles mounted on silicon monoxide-filmed grids and observed the partially burned remains in the electron microscope. The similarity of the work to biological microincineration is obvious, and indeed, Turkevich (1959) suggested using low-temperature combustion for this purpose.

Independently Jatopic (1961) and Spit (1961), following the work of Mahl (1945), Grasenick (1957), Kassenbeck (1958) and others, also described devices and procedures for using a low-temperature oxygen plasma to treat electron microscope specimens. The procedures have been applied to inorganic and non-biological organic specimens in a variety of ways:

1. production of metal oxide replica films by oxidation of metal surfaces;
2. etching of organic specimens to produce surface detail;
3. burning of organic residue from silicon monoxide replica films of organic polymer surfaces;
4. treatment of various surfaces to make them hydrophilic;
5. thinning of organic polymer specimens for transmission viewing in the electron microscope;
6. burning of organic specimens mounted on silicon monoxide films to liberate inorganic inclusions for electron microscopic study.

These applications and the history of the development have recently been reviewed by Aldrian *et al.* (1967) and Geymayer (1966).

A recent monograph by McTaggart (1967) covers the broad subject of plasma chemistry in electrical discharges and contains many useful references.

The technique of low-temperature ashing independently developed by Gleit and co-workers has been used primarily for the liberation of minerals for chemical analysis from bulk samples of organic material. To some extent it has also been used to free mineral particles from filter paper and other organic matrices for microscopic examination (see recent reviews by Hollahan, 1966, and by Bersin *et al.* 1966). In a couple of instances it has been used as a biological microincineration tool:

1. to free pathological mineral deposits in lung tissue sections for light microscopic examination (Berkeley *et al.* 1965);

104 RICHARD S. THOMAS

2. to test the mineral nature of fossilized bacteria observed with the electron microscope (Doberenz and Wyckoff, 1967). The technique can be performed with commercially available devices, and we have used one of these in our experiments. The device will be briefly described in Section II.C.

While this manuscript was in press, a brief report appeared describing the application of our low-temperature microincineration techniques to electron-microscopic thin sections of avian cells (Hohman and Schraer, 1967).

II. Electron Microscopic Techniques

A. *Specimen Grids and Support Films*

In our experience, ordinary copper grids are quickly oxidized and become fragile if heated to high temperature in the presence of oxygen, but platinum, gold and stainless steel grids can easily withstand these conditions. Gold grids soften and warp above 600°C, but stainless steel grids can be used to at least 1000°C.

Titanium grids eventually oxidize but are usable if the time and temperature are not too great. An interesting possibility for very high temperatures is ceramic grids (Williamson *et al.* 1966). High-temperature incineration with nickel grids has been reported (Streznewski and Turkevich, 1959), but nickel is not much more resistant than copper.

For low-temperature ashing, titanium grids are completely inert and stainless steel nearly so, but platinum, gold, nickel and copper are generally unsatisfactory since, at all but the lowest power levels, catalyzed recombination of atomic oxygen at the surfaces of these grids heats them to high temperatures (see Greaves and Linnett, 1958; Myerson, 1965; McTaggart, 1967). For most of our experiments with both high- and low-temperature ashing we have used 200 mesh grids of stainless steel. Hohman and Schraer (1967) have used molybdenum grids for their low-temperature incineration experiments.

As support film, carbon could be used for heating in vacuum (König, 1951), but, in the presence of oxygen, inorganic materials such as aluminum oxide, beryllium oxide, silicon dioxide or silicon monoxide are required. The last mentioned has been the most common choice of previous investigators. (Beryllium is highly toxic, and satisfactory silicon dioxide membranes are difficult to prepare.)

Thin silicon monoxide films are easily made by vacuum evaporating the substance (Bradley, 1961) onto grids covered with a thin collodion membrane and then either dissolving the collodion in acetone or burning it away. The latter method is easiest and cleanest. Also, if any silicon is deposited along with the silicon monoxide (Williams, 1952), burning converts it to the oxide. Measurements on shadowed fragments (see Fig. 1), indicate the films we use are about 175–350 Å thick. They are quite resistant to temperatures up to at least 1000°C and are very stable in the electron beam, but they are mechanically fragile and sometimes break in the course of picking up thin sections.

Fig. 1. Fragments (one on top of the other) of silicon monoxide membrane, sprayed with 0·088-μ polystyrene latex (PSL) particles and uranium shadowed. From the shadows, the membrane is about 250 Å thick. To make the membrane, 4·3 mg SiO were evaporated at normal incidence onto a collodion-filmed, gold grid from a tungsten wire basket at 12 cm. The collodion was then burned off at 600°C. The membrane was broken with a hair tip and fragments dispersed to adjacent, unbroken grid squares. Reverse contrast print (RCP), × 17,000.

To circumvent this difficulty the specimen can be mounted on a silicon monoxide-collodion film; the collodion on the back side is simply burned off when the preparation is incinerated. A minor disadvantage of the films is that they are not completely flat; thus in a shadowed preparation undulations in the film produce variations in the local shadow angle.

B. *Preparation of Specimens*

Specimen preparation for microincineration studies should ideally preserve not only organic fine structure but also all of the mineral constituents in an undisturbed state. Unfortunately, no generally valid and practical procedures which accomplish this completely exist today, so for the present, we have accepted the limitations of standard, or only slightly modified techniques, and have chosen our material and the aims of investigations accordingly. Various exotic techniques which partially avoid the hazards of standard methods are discussed in Section IV.B.

a. *Unfixed whole mounts.* Whole mounts of unfixed material are, in general, the only preparations likely to retain all their mineral content intact. We have prepared virus particles and bacterial spores by simply spraying them from distilled water or dilute neutral buffer onto the grids and either air-drying or freeze-drying (Williams, 1953), (see Figs 10a, 11a and 17a). Silicon monoxide films are quite hydrophilic and so it is easy to disperse the particles well. To avoid contamination with salts, the buffer must be volatile, e.g. ammonium acetate, or ammonium bicarbonate.

b. *Fixation.* Most specimens cannot be satisfactorily prepared as whole mounts and must be fixed for embedding and sectioning. As fixative we have generally used formaldehyde rather than osmium tetroxide or other metallic reagent, to avoid introducing extraneous mineral into the specimen. Glutaraldehyde or acrolein should also be satisfactory. To avoid introducing mineral with the buffer used in the fixative, we have simply neutralized the formalin with a few drops of ammonium hydroxide. In the preparation of virus particles for sectioning, the fixation step was omitted altogether; the particles were effectively fixed by ethanol during the dehydration, and the result was satisfactory for our purposes (see Fig. 12a). This procedure is probably not generally valid, however.

Theoretically, osmium tetroxide might be used without introducing extraneous mineral in the final preparation. Reduced osmium could be re-oxidized to osmium tetroxide during the ashing and would vaporize. Gleit (1967) has, in fact, found that OsO_2 and Na_2OsO_4 are completely lost from a specimen during low-temperature, excited-oxygen incineration. Arnold and Sasse (1963) show osmium tetroxide-fixed tissue sections incinerated at 450°C, and the ash patterns seem to contain considerably less residue than would be likely if the osmium were largely retained. But we have obtained some results (unpublished; mentioned in Thomas, 1967) on 600°C, and also low-temperature-ashed, sections of osmium tetroxide-stained human hair compared to identical preparations unstained which indicate considerable retention of osmium in the ash. Disulfide-rich keratin is very heavily stained with osmium tetroxide, however. It may be that osmium retention in this case results from the presence of a large amount of fully reduced osmium, rather than the osmium dioxide which may be more common in fixed tissue cells (Riemersma, 1963). Preliminary experiments (unpublished) on osmium compounds indicate that fully-reduced osmium black is relatively resistant to incineration.

Any aqueous chemical fixation will very likely leach some inorganic elements out of the specimen, and so one must be content to study only insoluble "structure-bound" minerals. Table I shows the effect of

TABLE I

Mineral Elements in *Bacillus megaterium* Spores†

Mineral element	Amount (percent native spore dry wt.)	
	Native	Formalin-fixed
Potassium	3·4	0·8
Calcium	2·6	2·5
Manganese	1·6	1·4
Phosphorus	1·5	1·4
Magnesium	0·24	0·24
Sodium	~ 0·1	(undetectable)
Copper	0·04	~ 0·005
Iron	0·01	0·01

† Data taken from Thomas (1964).

formalin fixation on the mineral content of bacterial spores. Evidently in this case most of the mineral, including calcium, manganese, phosphorus, magnesium, and iron, is "structure-bound". Only potassium and traces of sodium and copper are largely lost.

c. *Embedding and sectioning.* As embedding medium we have used either methacrylate or Epon, and it seems likely that any of the commonly used embedments would be satisfactory. In any case, they can be burned away together with the organic portion of the specimen. Methacrylate may cause extreme "explosion" damage in specimens fixed only by formalin or other organic reagent, but this can be partially controlled by using azodiisobutyronitrile as catalyst for u.v. polymerization (Watson and Aldridge, 1961), or by using prepolymerization. Offsetting its disadvantage, methacrylate can be readily removed from the sections—e.g. by benzene—to increase contrast of the unstained material for initial viewing under both the light and electron microscopes.

Mineral constituents may be lost during dehydration and embedding, but perhaps the most dangerous step in the procedure is floating the

sections onto a water surface as they are cut. Examples of this problem
are shown in Figs 2 and 3. Losses during sectioning are particularly
annoying since they cannot be easily quantified by chemical analysis.
The absolute amounts of material involved are too minute. It is not
routinely practical to eliminate the water in sectioning (see Section
IV.B), but mineral losses can sometimes be reduced by controlling the
pH of the water. We now cut sections onto 0·001 M ammonium
bicarbonate, pH 7·5. The problem of mineral loss in sectioning has
been discussed by Boothroyd (1964).

Sections suitable for incineration are usually about 40–70 mμ thick,
but the optimum depends on the material and the method of incineration (see Section III.B). Sections should be mounted on the grid free
of wrinkles, if possible, since good contact of the specimen with the
support film is necessary to minimize migration of the ash. With
methacrylate sections, poor contact can be remedied by exposure to
benzene vapor or by simply immersing the grids briefly in benzene to
dissolve out the methacrylate.

To facilitate locating the often nearly invisible residues of the sections
after microincineration, it is useful to remove the silicon monoxide
film from extraneous areas of the grid beforehand. This is conveniently
done by brushing the grid with a hair tip under a dissecting microscope.

C. *Devices and Procedures for Incineration*

a. *High-temperature ashing.* A number of special furnaces for microincineration have been described (Scott, 1937; Hintzsche, 1956;
Kruszynski, 1966), but for our experiments an ordinary electric muffle
furnace has been quite satisfactory. The specimen grids are placed in a
small porcelain crucible, partly covered to keep out dust, and this in
turn placed on a stainless steel block in the furnace. A thermocouple
embedded in the block gives a more accurate measurement of the
specimen temperature than does the furnace thermostat. If required, a
silica slide bearing a light-microscope preparation or a second crucible
containing a bulk sample for chemical analysis can also be placed on the
block.

Single grids can be conveniently microincinerated on a simple
heating stage in the vacuum evaporator (Fig. 4). It consists of a
platinum ribbon mounted horizontally in the filament holders of the
evaporator. A thermocouple junction is spot-welded to the under-
surface at the center of the ribbon, and the specimen grid is placed on
the upper surface directly over the junction. Gold or platinum grids
are especially suitable for this device because at elevated temperatures
they will lightly adhere to the platinum surface and insure good

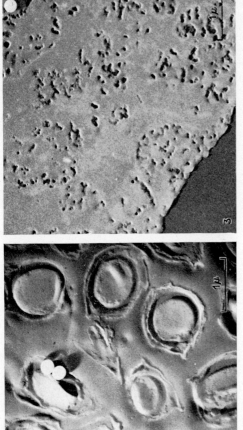

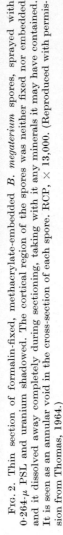

Fig. 2. Thin section of formalin-fixed, methacrylate-embedded *B. megaterium* spores, sprayed with 0·264-μ PSL and uranium shadowed. The cortical region of the spores was neither fixed nor embedded and it dissolved away completely during sectioning, taking with it any minerals it may have contained. It is seen as an annular void in the cross-section of each spore. RCP, × 13,000. (Reproduced with permission from Thomas, 1964.)

Fig. 3. Thin section of isolated rat liver mitochondria which originally contained calcium phosphate granules. The granules dissolved away during sectioning onto distilled water, leaving holes in the section, (sectioning onto dilute neutral buffer prevents this loss. See Figs 6–8.). The unstained mitochondria are themselves not visable ownig to low contrast. Formalin fixation, Epon embedding, section sprayed with 0.264-u PSL and shadowed. RCP, × 13,000.

thermal contact. The thermocouple can be calibrated by the melting points of various salts placed on the center of the ribbon. Adjustment of the temperature is rapid and reproducible but requires fine control of the filament current. For this purpose a supplemental fine rheostat can be installed in the power supply of the vacuum evaporator.

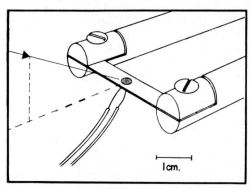

FIG. 4. Heating stage in vacuum evaporator. The specimen grid is seen on the platinum ribbon filament directly over the thermocouple junction. The arrow indicates a possible direction of shadowing. (Reproduced with permission from Thomas, 1964.)

Concerning procedures of microincineration there is a vast literature for the light microscope to which we have referred in devising our own techniques (see Hintzsche, 1956). A few workers have advocated using special gas mixtures for incineration. So far we have followed the majority and simply burned our specimens in air. Using the vacuum evaporator heating stage it would be easy, however, to introduce any specified gas into the bell jar, and the specimen could also, of course, be incinerated under vacuum. Interestingly enough, Williams (1952) found no difference between electron microscope specimens incinerated in air, or under vacuum.

Most classical workers have stressed the importance of raising the temperature gradually, especially below 150°C to minimize heat-induced contraction of the specimen. In our experience to date, specimens introduced directly into the preheated furnace have come out looking not much different than those heated gradually. Perhaps the relatively greater force of adhesion to the substrate in our very thin preparations completely overrides contracting forces in the material.

There are many recorded opinions on the best sustained temperatures and the times to insure complete ashing, but most workers have favored long times at relatively low temperatures, rather than the converse, in order to reduce losses of volatile minerals (such as sodium and potassium chlorides), and have rarely used higher than 650°C. Hintzsche claimed that at least 500°C was usually necessary for complete incineration, and he maintained his specimens at 520°C for at least 40–60 minutes. We have arbitrarily used 500–600°C for 10–30 minutes, realizing, however, that shorter times and/or lower temperatures would often suffice for our very thin specimens. Fortunately, the ash patterns seem to be relatively insensitive to overtreatment.

We have occasionally worried over whether our thin specimens were completely ashed, in spite of the fact that they had reached an endpoint where further treatment produced no significant further change in appearance in the electron microscope. One useful approach here has been to treat in parallel a *thick* preparation for light microscopy (ashed thin preparations are invisible in the light microscope) and examine it after ashing for absence of carbon black, for solubility in acid, etc. This has set a conservative standard for the thinner preparation. More conservative still, a multimilligram sample of the material could be similarly treated and then chemically analyzed for residual carbon. Table II shows the results of such an experiment on bacterial spores.

TABLE II

Total Ash and Residual Carbon of *B. megaterium* Spores after Incineration at 600°C†

Sample no.	Initial total wt. (mg)	Time at 600°C (min)	Ash wt. (percent initial total wt.)	Acid insoluble residue (visual estimate)	Carbon wt. (percent initial total wt.)
1	29·49	10	11·46	+++	0·05
2	28·43	30	11·50		
		90	11·50	++	0·02

† Data taken from Thomas (1964).

A very slight carbon residue remained after both 10 minutes and 90 minutes at 600°C, but examination in the light microscope showed this to be simply a few carbonized spores, well shielded in the center of ash aggregates. No carbonized spores were seen in aggregate-free preparations on slides, even if the treatment was so little as 1·5 minutes.

After incineration, some of the ash may take up water from the atmosphere and alter distribution in the ash pattern (Kruszynski, 1955; Hintzsche, 1956). To guard against this, we have routinely protected the specimen by shadowing it immediately after incineration.

If the vacuum evaporator heating stage is used, the specimen need not be transferred, and can even be shadowed while still warm. If the ash is not hygroscopic, as seems to have been the case with our specimens, shadowing is still a valuable procedure for increasing the visibility of very slight ash deposits and for showing the three dimensional shape of the ash in general.

   b. *Low-temperature ashing.* We have experimented with low-temperature, active-oxygen microincineration using a single-sample, modified. prototype version of the Tracerlab† Low-Temperature Asher, model LTA 500, described by Gleit (1963). It is shown diagrammatically in Fig. 5. The device consists essentially of a glass tube through which

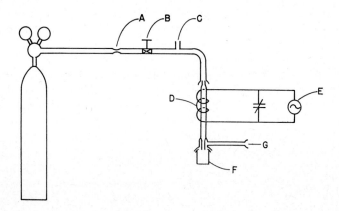

Fig. 5. Schematic of the low-temperature asher. Molecular oxygen from the tank passes through a small leak, A, and a three position valve, B. Pressure is measured by a Hastings gauge attached to sidearm, C. The gas then passes into a borosilicate glass chamber, D, where it is activated in a discharge produced by inductive reaction with a field generated by the radio frequency oscillator, E. The active oxygen passes over the specimen contained in the beaker, F, and the products of oxidation and unreacted oxygen are removed by a vacuum pump attached to the exhaust tube, G. (Reproduced with permission from Gleit, 1963.)

passes a stream of oxygen at a pressure of about 1 mm Hg. and a flow rate of about 50 cc/min (S.T.P.). At the upstream end, a coil surrounding the tube imposes a high voltage, radiofrequency electromagnetic field on the gas, producing an electrodeless ring discharge. Atomic oxygen and other highly reactive species of oxygen are created in the plasma and are seen as a pink glow, which extends a considerable distance down-

   † Reference to a company or product name does not imply approval or recommendation of the product by the United States Department of Agriculture to the exclusion of others that may be suitable.

stream from the coil. The specimen is placed in this glow at the down-stream end.

Energy input is largely confined to intramolecular excitation rather than thermal agitation of the gas molecules; thus, ambient temperature at the specimen is not greatly above that of the room. If the instrument is operated at low power level, as is the case for microincineration experiments, the temperature rise in the specimen owing to exothermal reactions is also slight. The exact temperature of electron microscope grids and other specimens during the ashing process can be conveniently measured with an infrared radiation pyrometer which can "see" objects through the glass wall of the specimen chamber (e.g. the Infrascope, Mark I, model 3-1L-02, manufactured by Huggins Laboratories, Inc., Sunnyvale, California. It has a temperature range of 65–300°C and a minimum viewing field of 3 mm diameter at a distance of 15 cm). Grid temperatures in most microincineration experiments have not exceeded 80°C.

Use of the LTA-500 is not confined to microincineration experiments and similar microscale procedures; operated at higher power levels, it can ash samples of up to a gram or more. It was, in fact, designed primarily for such use. A particular advantage of the instrument and others like it, in macroscale applications, is that losses of volatile inorganic substances which may occur during high-temperature ashing are minimized or eliminated. Table III, taken from Gleit (1966), shows the retention in ashed, multimilligram samples, of a number of inorganic compounds after both low-temperature, active-oxygen incineration and conventional, high-temperature, muffle-furnace ashing. The much better retention by low-temperature ashing is amply demonstrated. Another advantage of the low-temperature technique is that the original state of a mineral—e.g. calcite ($CaCO_3$), kaolinite ($Al_2O_3 . 2SiO_2 . 2H_2O$) pyrite (FeS_2)—can often be retained without alteration in the ash (Gluskoter, 1965). A disadvantage of the technique in macroscale applications is the relatively poor efficiency of ashing, particularly for bulky, mineral-rich samples with a low surface-to-volume ratio. The diffusion of oxygen into the specimen is much slower than for high temperature incineration and an insulating layer of ash forming on the surface can be an important diffusion barrier and deactivation surface for the excited gas (Bersin et al. 1966). This inefficiency often necessitates use of high power levels, with attendant higher temperature, and ashing times of many hours for multimilligram samples.

Thin specimens for microincineration experiments, having very high surface-to-volume ratios, are burned very efficiently by the low temperature procedure, and only short times at low power levels are required

TABLE III

Recovery of Radioactive Tracers From Ashed Blood[†]

Nuclide	Tracer	Percent recovered after ashing	
		Low-temperature asher	Muffle furnace (700°C)
Sb^{124}	$SbCl_3$	99	35
As^{76}	H_3AsO_3	100	0
Cd^{109}	$Cd(NO_3)_2$	99	—
Cs^{137}	$CsCl$	100	—
Co^{60}	$CoCl_2$	102	67
Cu^{67}	$CuCl_2$	101	87
Cr^{51}	$CrCl_3$	100	85
Au^{198}	$AuCl_3$	70	0
Fe^{59}	$FeCl_3$	101	52
Pb^{210}	$Pb(NO_3)_2$	100	—
Ho^{166}	$HoCl_3$	100	—
Mn^{54}	$MnCl_2$	99	85
Hg^{203}	$Hg(NO_3)_2$	92	0
Re^{186}	$HReO_4$	98	—
Mo^{99}	$(NH_4)_2MoO_4$	100	—
Ag^{110}	$AgCl$	72	45
Na^{22}	$NaCl$	100	—
Ta^{182}	$K_8Ta_6O_{19}$	102	—
Tb^{160}	$Tb(NO_3)_3$	100	—
Zn^{65}	$ZnCl_2$	99	69

[†] Data taken by permission from Gleit (1966). The muffle furnace data comes originally from Pijek et al. (1960). Radioactive tracer was added to citrated blood, the solution allowed to stand for a minimum of 24 hours, dried in a desiccator, and ashed.

for complete ashing. It has been found important to use only low power levels, since specimens ashed at high power show some indications of the melting which is characteristic of high-temperature ash patterns (see Section III.A, B). An indirect measure of power input on our instrument is obtained by monitoring the plate current of the final stage amplifier. Maximum power reads 300 mA; microincineration experiments have usually been done at 20–30 mA, with treatments of 10–30 min. To follow the course of incomplete incineration of thin sections, even lower power levels and shorter times have been used.

Since power input in our instrument is known only in arbitrary terms, it has been useful for comparison with other instruments to determine the burning rate at various power levels using a standard specimen. Thin carbon films vapor-deposited on glass cover slips are convenient objects for this purpose; the film thickness before and after exposure to the plasma can be readily determined by measuring the optical density of the film in a spectrophotometer (Streznewski and Turkevich, 1959). The burning rate is found to increase with increasing time periods of treatment, perhaps due to a rise in temperature of the specimen during treatment (Gleit *et al.* 1963). Nevertheless, useful ranges of values for different power levels have been obtained and are shown in Table IV. Semiquantitative estimations of burning rate from

TABLE IV

Combustion Rates of Thin Carbon Films in the Low-temperature Asher

Power level (plate mA)	Treatment interval (min)	Carbon removal rate†	
		O.D. units/min	Ångstroms/min
10	10	0·0010	0·7
	60	0·0016	1·1
20	5	0·0044	3·0
	15	0·014	9·4
30	2	0·014	9·4
	6	0·050	34
40	1	0·021	14
	3	0·13	88

† Optical density, O.D. of the carbon films was measured at 400 mμ. For the films used, O.D. ranged up to 0·5. The thickness of the films was calculated from the data of Streznewski and Turkevich (1959); according to their figures (also determined at 400 mμ), for optical densities below 0·5, 0·1 O.D. unit equals 69 Ångstroms of carbon.

the appearance of partially-ashed thin sections (e.g. see Figs 9a–c) indicates that the thin sections burn away considerably faster than do the carbon films.

The usual criterion for determining complete ashing of our electron microscope specimens has been the observation that further treatment produced no significant further change in their appearance. In some cases, we have verified complete ashing by showing that the residue produced by low-temperature treatment could subsequently withstand heating to 600°C (see Section III.A, mitochondria). Occasionally, we have included a thick specimen for light microscopic examination in the low-temperature ashing chamber and tested its solubility in acid after incineration. Unfortunately, its color could not be used as a criterion for absence of carbon since materials do not char under low-temperature treatment. It is not generally feasible to use trace carbon analysis on microchemical-scale samples as a control for complete ashing since such large specimens are ashed so much less efficiently than the thin electron microscope specimens.

After incineration, the electron microscope specimens are usually transferred without delay to the vacuum evaporator and shadowed.

D. *Examination of the Same Specimen Before and After Incineration*

Unlike most other histochemical procedures, microincineration can sometimes be carried out successfully on specimens which were previously viewed under the electron beam. Exposure to the beam certainly alters the specimen's reactivity to stains and other subtle reagents, but this is inconsequential compared to the drastic treatment of burning. The main problem in previewing is contamination from the electron beam. Low-temperature ashing and mild high-temperature treatments, which are sufficient to burn the thin specimen completely, are usually not adequate to remove an overlying contamination film, and the resultant shadowed ash pattern has a "muddy" appearance. Thirty minutes at 600°C does remove the contamination, however, and the ash pattern is indistinguishable from one not previewed (see Figs 6 and 13). Use of presently available anti-contamination devices in the electron microscope should greatly decrease the problem, and should make previewing a generally applicable procedure for microincineration experiments.

In order to return to the same field of view after incineration it is usually necessary to map the specimen grid. Special gold finder grids with numbered and lettered grid squares have recently become available commercially† and may greatly simplify the problem when gold grids can be used. With stainless steel grids, a workable procedure is to cut a reference notch extending into the center far enough that it can be seen under the electron beam. The center of the grid with thin sections or other specimens on it is then photographed under phase contrast at low magnification in the light microscope so as to include the notch in the field. With the optical micrograph as a survey map, and the notch apex as an initial reference point, the grid is scanned under the electron beam, and areas of interest are photographed at a series of magnifications taking care to include any natural features such as membrane tears, grid wire edge contours, or section edges that will persist after incineration and serve as secondary reference points. Section edges are usually permanent features since even if the section contains little ash,

† Manufactured by Graticules, Ltd. London, England. Available in the United States from E. F. Fullam, Inc. Schenectady, N.Y.

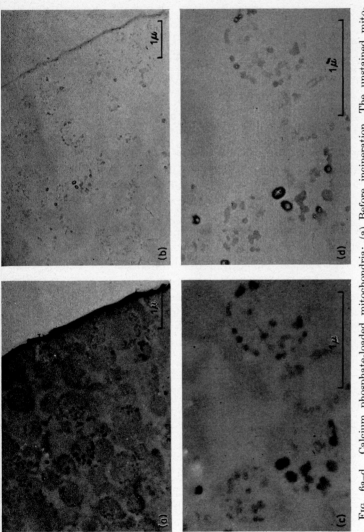

Fig. 6a–d. Calcium phosphate-loaded mitochondria: (a) Before incineration. The unstained mitochondrial cross-sections are faintly visible, and dense granules within them stand out clearly. × 8700. (b) Same area as Fig. 6a, but after 30 min at 600°C. Except for a line (presumably contamination) tracing the edge of the section, nothing remains but the dense granules. Lightly shadowed, × 8700. (c) Area selected from Fig. 6a, enlarged to show granules in more detail, × 26,000. (d) Same area as Fig. 6c, but after 30 min at 600°C. The residues correspond exactly to the dense granules and only to the granules. The larger residues contain a bubble, however, suggesting melting and some decomposition. Lightly shadowed, × 26,000. (Reproduced with permission from Thomas and Greenawalt, 1968.)

the edge will show a residue from various slight contaminants of the block surface (see Fig. 6b).

If the area of interest is lacking in permanent markers, these may be provided by initially spraying the back side of the grid with mineral particles (Thomas and Greenawalt 1968). A suitable preparation of sub-micron silicon dioxide particles is easily made by ball-milling diatomaceous earth (e.g. Johns-Manville Celite analytical filter-aid), suspending it in water or ethanol and centrifuging out the larger diatom fragments. Spraying from ethanol improves the particles' dispersion on the grids.

III. Some Results and Discussion

A. *The Accuracy Obtainable in the Ash Pattern: Some Examples*

Microincineration is such a drastic procedure, removing as it does the supporting organic framework of the specimen, that it is easy to imagine all sorts of migration of the liberated mineral. The aim of the present section is to show that the mineral can, in fact, stay close enough to its origin that ash patterns are worth viewing with the resolution of the electron microscope. Some of the factors involved will be discussed in the next section.

a. *Mineral deposits in mitochondria.* Dense mineral deposits in organic specimens are good test objects for the technique since their easily recognized, electron-opaque images in the intact material can be directly compared with the residues after burning. Desler and Pfefferkorn (1962) and Arnold and Sasse (1963) exploited this in their experiments, mentioned in Section I.B. Our own experiments of this sort have been done on dense, noncrystalline mineral deposits found in isolated rat liver mitochondria which were incubated *in vitro* to accumulate calcium phosphate metabolically (Greenawalt *et al.* 1964). Unincubated mitochondria afforded a valuable control. We have used both conventional high-temperature ashing and the new active-oxygen, low-temperature technique.† (Thomas and Greenawalt, 1964, 1968.)

Figures 6–8 show a thin-sectioned pellet of the isolated mitochondria containing calcium phosphate deposits. The mitochondria were incubated to accumulate the mineral and were then fixed in formalin, embedded in Epon and sectioned onto 0·001 M ammonium bicarbonate pH 7·5.

Figures 6a–d show the same section before and after incineration for 30 min at 600°C. Beforehand (Figs 6a, c), dense mineral granules are easily visible in the less dense matrix of the unstained mitochondria.

† Blocks of embedded mitochondrial material for these experiments were provided by Drs J. W. Greenawalt, C. Rossi and F. D. Vasington.

After burning (Figs 6b, d), the embedding Epon and all of the mito-chondrial substance other than the granules is completely absent, but the latter stand out sharply and appear nearly unchanged. The only evident alteration in the granules is a bubble-like appearance of the larger ones, suggesting some melting and decomposition. It is well seen in Figs 7b and 8b, which were chosen to show it. Higher magnification of an untreated section, Fig. 8a, suggests a reason for this decomposi-tion; the granules look diffuse and seem to be an agglomerate of much smaller mineral grains, held together in some sort of matrix. Presumably, then, the granules as a whole are partly organic in nature. (See also Greenawalt et al. 1964; Weinbach and von Brand, 1965, 1967.)

When low-temperature incineration is applied to the sections (Figs 7a and 8c) the ashed granules no longer look bubbly but rather have a finely porous texture (Fig. 8c) which seems to correspond to the diffuse distribution of mineral in the intact granules. Apparently, the organic matrix of the granules is burned out, as before, but there is now no melting which could allow gross distortion of the mineral structure as the gaseous products leave. Interestingly enough, these low-temperature ashed granules can now withstand 600°C with little or no alteration. Evidently the melting during high-temperature incineration involves some intermediate product rather than the final inorganic ash.

Another difference between the high- and low-temperature ash preparations is seen in Fig. 7a. In addition to the dense granules, a fine tracery of ash is sometimes seen outlining what was initially the rest of the mitochondrion. Evidently this non-granule ash is volatilized during high-temperature incineration; it is never seen in ash patterns of mitochondria by that technique.

Unincubated control mitochondria (Fig. 9a) are devoid of dense granules, and when incinerated at 600°C they show no ash residue what-soever. (This agrees with previous findings; see Kruszynski, 1966.) When they are incinerated by the low-temperature procedure (Figs. 9c, d), however, they show in considerable abundance the same non-granule ash residue seen faintly in the low-temperature-ashed, calcium phos-phate-loaded mitochondria. Evidently, the non-granule mineral is mostly lost from the latter during incubation for calcium phosphate uptake. That the non-granule residue is an inorganic ash can be shown by heating it to 600°C; it is unaltered by this treatment.

The distribution of the non-granule ash suggests that it may repre-sent the membranes of the mitochondria. The pattern is rather "sketchy" however. Attempting to gain further information, we have also examined partially incinerated preparations (Fig. 9b); the emerging pattern of what will become the final ash suggests even

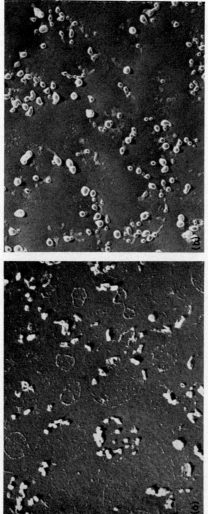

Fig. 7a, b. Calcium phosphate-loaded mitochondria. Thicker sections, showing a greater number of granules, after ashing. Shadowed, RCP, × 19,000. (a) A section after low-temperature ashing for 30 min at 30 mA. The granules do not look decomposed. In addition to the granules, a slight residue apparently corresponding to the rest of the mitochondrion is visible in some cases. (b) A section after 30 min at 600°C, showing decomposition of granules and absence of ash other than from granules.

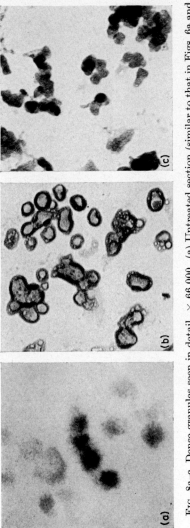

Fig. 8a–c. Dense granules seen in detail, × 66,000. (a) Untreated section (similar to that in Figs. 6a and 6c). The native granules look somewhat diffuse; they apparently are aggregates of much smaller particles. (b) A section after 30 min at 600°C, showing the decomposed appearance of the granules. (c) A section after low-temperature ashing, 30 min at 30 mA. The granule residues show a fine porosity which seems to correspond to the diffuse appearance of the granules before incineration.

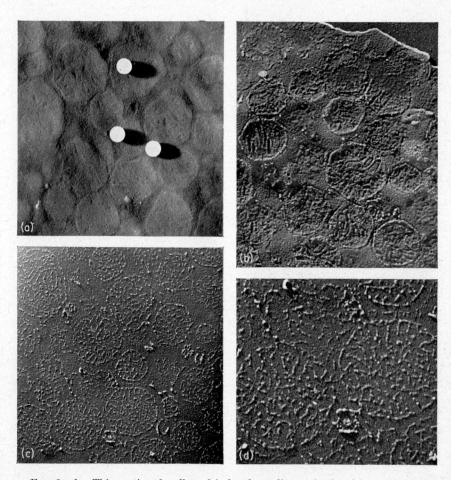

Fig. 9a–d. Thin-sectioned pellet of isolated rat liver mitochondria, unincubated control preparation. Formalin-fixation, Epon embedding, sections cut onto 0·001M ammonium bicarbonate. Shadowed after treatment, RCP: (a) Thin section sprayed with 0·264-μ PSL, but otherwise untreated. The mitochondria are visible partly by their inherent contrast, but also by surface detail. The latter apparently arises during sectioning owing to the differing compressibilities of the mitochondria and the embedding medium. × 16,000. (b) A section after low-temperature ashing for 5 min at 10 mA. Both the Epon and the mitochondria are partially etched away, revealing what may be the outer membranes and cristae. × 16,000. (c) A section after low-temperature ashing for 20 min at 10 mA. This treatment was sufficient for complete ashing since the section is indistinguishable from more extensively treated (e.g. 30 min at 30 mA) preparations. The pattern of ash is similar to the etch pattern in Fig. 9b. × 16,000. (d) Area selected from Fig. 9c and enlarged to show the ash grains in more detail, × 32,000. (Reproduced with permission from Thomas and Greenawalt, 1968.)

more strongly that we are looking at membranes. This could very well be the case, since mitochondrial membrane structures even if depleted of lipid by the fixing and embedding procedures we have used (Ashworth *et al.* 1966), would still survive (Fleischer *et al.* 1967).

b. *Virus particles.* Stimulated by the experiments of Williams (1952), and Bendet and Trontyl (1963), (see Section I.B), we have tried microincineration on particles of *Tipula* irridescent virus (TIV) to see if the known localization of phosphorus in the virus core could be directly demonstrated by ash patterns (Thomas, 1965; Thomas and Corlett, 1969).

TIV is a good test object because it is relatively large, crystallizes easily (Klug *et al.* 1959), is well characterized chemically (Thomas, 1961) and topochemically (Thomas and Williams, 1961), and contains enough phosphorus to leave a detectable residue. The particles are icosahedral with a minimum diameter of about $130\,m\mu$, (Williams and Smith, 1958, and see Fig. 11a), and have a core about $90\,m\mu$ in diameter (Thomas and Williams, 1961, and see Fig. 12a), containing nucleoprotein. The latter accounts for most of the phosphorus in the virus. The physical distribution of phosphorus in the particles is shown in Table V. Allowing a roughly 3-fold greater ash weight than phosphorus

TABLE V

Physical Distribution of Phosphorus in TIV

Total phosphorus content of virus	$16\cdot0$ μg/mg virus†
Fraction of total phosphorus in core	$0\cdot89$†
Fraction of total mass in core	$0\cdot33$†
Phosphorus concentration in core $\left[\dfrac{16\cdot0 \times 0\cdot89}{0\cdot33}\right]$	43 μg/mg core
Phosphorus concentration in coat $\left[\dfrac{16\cdot0 \times (1-0\cdot89)}{1-0\cdot33}\right]$	$2\cdot6$ μg/mg coat

† Data taken from Thomas and Williams (1961).

weight (e.g. $Mg_2P_2O_7/2P = 223/62 = 3\cdot5$), ash of a core could be easily more than 10% of original core mass whereas coat ash would be considerably less than 1% of original coat mass.

Figures 10a–c show sprayed, dried-from-liquid preparations, either untreated, or after high- or low-temperature ashing. The untreated particles (Fig. 10a) have dried down in close-packed hexagonal arrays and are somewhat flattened by surface tension. After high-temperature incineration, a slight ash residue remains, as seen in Fig. 10b. This was somewhat unexpected, considering the complete volatilization of virus mineral previously reported (Williams, 1952; Bendet and Trontyl, 1963). More residue remains after low-temperature ashing, however (Fig. 10c), indicating that at least some of the TIV mineral is volatilized by high temperature.

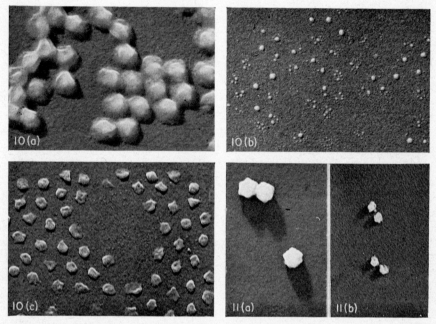

Fig. 10a–c. Purified *Tipula* iridescent virus (TIV), unfixed, sprayed on grid while suspended in 0·001 M ammonium bicarbonate, and allowed to dry from the liquid. Shadowed after treatment (if any). RCP, × 38,000. (a) Untreated control. (b) A preparation after 30 min at 600°C. (c) A preparation after low-temperature ashing for 30 min at 30 mA.

Fig. 11a, b. Purified TIV, unfixed, sprayed on grid while suspended in 0·001 M ammonium bicarbonate and freeze-dried. Shadowed after treatment (if any). RCP, × 38,000. (a) Untreated control. (b) A preparation after low-temperature ashing for 30 min at 30 mA. (For description, see text.)

The high-temperature ash has a droplet appearance quite different from the angular, finely porous low-temperature deposits. This difference apparently reflects melting in the former case, since neither ash is very hygroscopic. Both on this count, and on its low volatility, the ash is evidently not phosphorus pentoxide, but it may be a metallic phosphate, or a non-volatile polyphosphate.

The overall distribution of ash in both high- and low-temperature preparations (Figs 10b–c) reflects the hexagonal close-packed spacing of the original particles, but the individual residues or residue patterns, much smaller than the original particles, now no longer touch each other and are confined to the virus centers. This suggests that the ash is, indeed, derived from the virus core alone.

Figures 11a and 11b show spray freeze-dried preparations of TIV, either untreated or after low-temperature ashing. The untreated control particles (Fig. 11a) are not flattened by surface tension and the hexagonal profile corresponding to their icosahedral shape is readily apparent. After low-temperature ashing (Fig. 11b) the residue is a three-dimensional, somewhat porous particle about 60 mμ in diameter. This is smaller than the virus core (90 mμ) and suggests either that the ash has contracted during incineration or that the mineral is found in a region less than the whole core.

Thin sections of a crystallized pellet of TIV give further evidence on mineral localization. Figures 12a and 12c show an unincinerated section about 40 mμ thick (i.e. about 1/3 virus diameter) cut along a (100) crystal plane (Klug et al. 1959). As seen in Fig. 12a, the transected particles were not perfectly preserved, but as a result, the coat can usually be distinguished from the core by slight separation, due to swelling during fixation and embedding. In Fig. 12c, note that the crystal plane undulates somewhat, so that there are regions in which the crystal plane goes out of register with the plane of the section. Here the virus particles are cut through the periphery and only coat or outer core material is found in the section. Figures 12b and 12d show a similar section including the same crystal plane, after low-temperature ashing. Ash particles, about 50–60 mμ in diameter, are seen in regular array with very similar spacing (Fig. 12d). Interspersed blank areas evidently correspond to the out-of-register zones of the crystal plane which contain only peripheral virus material. Their occurrence provides further evidence that the ash derives solely from the central region of the particles. As seen in Fig. 12b (and to a lesser extent in Fig. 10c), some of the residues have a dimple in the center. This suggests that the actual distribution of mineral in TIV may be a shell structure within the core, with an empty center and a radius about two-thirds that of the core.

It may well be that the ash residues are a faithful representation of the localization of nucleic acid in the virus particle. The nucleic acid could leave a phosphate ash equal to at least 30% of the original mass of the constituent. That the nucleic acid could be localized to a shell structure within the core is consistent with the calculated volume that the nucleic acid could occupy (Thomas and Williams, 1961). A shell localization of nucleic acid is also consistent with recent findings on some other isometric virus particles (Anderegg *et al.* 1963; Kaiser, 1966; Finch and Klug, 1967).

c. *Bacterial spores.* Most bacterial spores have a rather high mineral content; *Bacillus megaterium* spores, for example, yield an ash representing 11 to 12% of the dry weight (see Table II). Some of the mineral

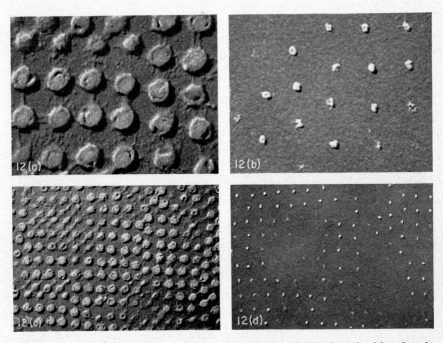

Fig. 12a–d. Purified TIV crystalline pellet fixed and dehydrated with ethanol, embedded in methacrylate, and sectioned at about 40 mμ. Shadowed after treatment, RCP: (a) Unincinerated control, with methacrylate removed by benzene, $\times$ 38,000. (b) Section (with methacrylate retained) after low-temperature ashing for 30 min at 30 mA. $\times$ 38,000. (c) Low-magnification micrograph of the field from which Fig. 12a was selected. $\times$ 13,000. (d) Low-magnification micrograph of the field from which Fig. 12b was selected. The crystal plane is similar to that of Fig. 12c. $\times$ 13,000. (For description, see text.)

elements contributing to this ash are listed in Table I. We became interested in the physical distribution of the mineral in spores because some of it, particularly calcium, is intimately involved in the remarkable resistance of these organisms to environmental adversity. A full account of this work has been presented elsewhere (Thomas, 1962, 1964).

Spores do not represent a test object for the accuracy of the microincineration technique in the sense that ash patterns can be compared with known information on mineral distribution; actually, very little was known before. Nevertheless, some indication of probable accuracy is given by the inherent resolution of the patterns.

Figures 13, 14 and 16 show thin-sectioned *Bacillus megaterium* spores formalin-fixed, pelleted in gelatin, and methacrylate-embedded, either before incineration or after high- or low-temperature ashing. The transected spores lost some of their mineral during fixing (see Table I),

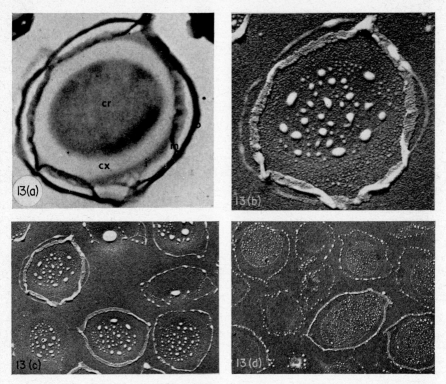

Fig. 13a–d. Thin-sectioned *Bacillus megaterium* spores. (a) Cross-section, about 70 mμ thick, of single spore before incineration, with methacrylate removed by benzene. The coat of the spore has been split into three layers by methacrylate "explosion": o, outer coat, m, middle coat (seen crossing from the outer to the inner coat layer at the point marked); i, inner coat. Inside the coat is the empty space of the extracted cortex, cx; and innermost is the structureless core, cr. × 35,000. (b) Same area as Fig. 13a, but after 30 min at 600°C, and shadowing. (See text for description.) RCP, × 35,000. (c) Lower-magnification view of the field from which Fig. 13b was selected (the spore at upper left). Lower left is a spore which had lost its coat and thus yielded ash only from the core. At upper center is a spore which was poorly cut and had a thick, displaced section of core, the ash from which formed a single, large droplet. RCP, × 13,000. (d) A thinner section (about 40 mμ thick) on the same grid as that of Fig. 13c. The ash patterns of the spore cores show a more uniform distribution of finer droplets than in Fig. 13c. RCP, × 13,000. (Reproduced with permission from Thomas, 1964.)

embedding, and sectioning. In particular, the spore cortex and any mineral associated with it was lost during sectioning (see Fig. 2). Consequently, the ash patterns represent only "structure-bound" mineral. Figure 13a shows a sectioned spore, typical by our techniques, before incineration. Three layers of the spore coat can be distinguished owing to their artifactual separation during embedding. Inward from the coat is an empty space where the cortex once was, and in the center is the dense structureless core. (The core contains the nucleic acid and other dormant biochemical machinery but this is not reflected in visible structures.) The same sectioned spore after 30 min at 600°C is shown in Fig. 13b. Both the coat and the core leave an ash, the latter seen as a pattern of droplets.

The droplets are apparently an artifact of melting since the ash is not hygroscopic. Their size and distribution depend on section thickness as can be seen by comparing Figs 13c and 13d.

More interesting than the core ash, in Fig. 13b, is the residue of the coat layers. The inner layer apparently leaves no ash and the outer, relatively little. The previously unobtrusive middle layer, however, yields a very prominent residue. Striations in it suggest the existence of fine structure, albeit poorly preserved. A more convincing demonstration of structure here is obtained by incinerating at 600°C for only 10 min rather than 30 min (see Fig. 14). The middle layer ash now shows regular arrays of fine fibrils, with spacing of about 100 Å!

We were amazed to see this fine structure and doubts arose as to whether it really is an ash pattern and not an organic residue. The experiment summarized in Table II suggests that it is carbon-free. That it is no artifact of crystallization is indicated by electron diffraction; the mineral comprising it is not crystalline. The structure is also found in unfixed specimens and by low-temperature ashing. Figure 15 shows an unfixed, isolated fragment of the middle layer after this treatment. Apparently the ash structure does reflect pre-existing fine order in the specimen. Our attempts to see it in intact, unashed specimens were not successful, but recently the structure has been demonstrated in spores partially degraded by chemical treatment (Rode and Williams, 1966). We do not yet know its functional significance.

Figure 16 shows an entire spore cross-section after active oxygen incineration. The ash pattern is similar to that of spores treated at high temperatures—the fine structure of the coat middle layer is readily apparent, as would be expected from Fig. 15—but there are significant differences. The core ash, rather than droplet-like, now is a reticulum of fine grains. Its general character is not unlike that seen in mitochondria (Figs 9c–d); whether its texture is related to pre-existing structure is less clear in this case, however. The outer coat ash now seems more abundant than in high temperature incineration, and the ash of both outer and middle coats is strikingly three-dimensional.

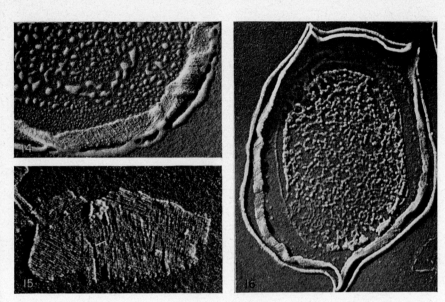

Fig. 14. Part of a spore cross-section, treated similarly to those of Figs. 13b–d except that incineration at 600°C was for only 10 min. Detailed fine-structure is now evident in the ash of the coat middle layer, with a periodic spacing of about 100 Å. RCP, × 58,000. (Reproduced with permission from Thomas,1964.)

Fig. 15. Fragment of *B. megaterium* spore coat middle layer found fortuitously after low-temperature ashing and shadowing of unfixed, whole spores sprayed on the grid. Note the many different orientations of the 100-Å fibrillar arrays. RCP, × 58,000. (Reproduced with permission from Thomas, 1964.)

Fig. 16. Spore cross-section (similar to that of Fig. 13a except that the methacrylate was not removed) after low-temperature ashing and shadowing (see text for description). RCP, × 41,000. (Reproduced with permission from Thomas, 1964.)

The preservation of three-dimensional structure in the low-temperature ash patterns of thin sectioned spores encouraged us to try the technique on whole spores. Figure 17a shows a whole mount preparation of a *Bacillus cereus* spore. Spores survive this spray-mounting treatment with no apparent damage, either chemical, morphological, or biological. A similar spore after low-temperature ashing is seen in Fig. 17b, at higher magnification. The ash is, indeed, three-dimensional. A delicate, free-standing ash skeleton from the spore coat remains precisely in place. Outside the coat, on the support film, lies the slight mineral residue of the spore exosporium and inside the coat is an

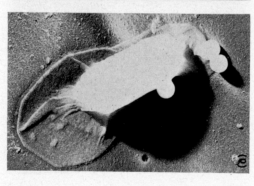

FIG. 17a, b. Whole, unfixed, *Bacillus cereus* spores sprayed on grid while suspended in distilled water and allowed to dry from liquid. Shadowed after treatment. RCP. (Reproduced with permission from Thomas, 1964.) (a) Preparation sprayed with 0·264-μ PSL but otherwise untreated. Typical example. The spore body was little, if at all, flattened by surface tension during drying. The peripheral flattened structure is the exosporium, a membraneous sac which surrounds the spore body and is characteristic of this species $\times$ 18,000. (b) A spore after low-temperature ashing. Selected example (see text for description). $\times$ 30,000.

opaque mass of ash apparently representing the core. There is some ambiguity in interpreting the latter residue because the core and cortex may have contracted together during ashing (see Section III.B). It is easiest to believe that the cortex left little ash, however, since this would explain the clean separation of the coat ash from the central ash mass. This preparation is especially significant since *all* of the native minerals were retained. Using it, we hopefully foresee localizing experimentally-induced alterations in the mineral content of native spores.

B. *Factors Limiting Ash Pattern Accuracy*

a. *Ash particle formation by high temperature incineration.* One of the most important limitations on accuracy for both high- and low-temperature ashing, our results show, is the tendency of the ash to deposit in discrete, artifactual particles obviously coarser than the true *in vivo* distribution of mineral. With high-temperature ashing, these are often relatively large and appear as droplets (e.g. in Figs 10b and 13b). Apparently, at some stage in the incineration process the specimen melts, and the liquid is subdivided by surface tension. Earlier workers also saw this on a gross scale (Policard, 1942; Policard and Bessis, 1952). The size and distribution of the droplets depends not only on the mineral concentration but also on specimen thickness (Figs 13c–d) as might be expected from surface energy considerations.

Melting may occur in some intermediate mineral-organic product of incineration rather than the final ash, as suggested by our experiments on the heat-stability of low-temperature-ashed dense granules in mitochondria (Section III.A). On the other hand, small particles or thin films of even "heat stable" minerals may appear to melt or sinter in the microincineration temperature range or below, even though this is far below their bulk melting point. The phenomenon is, again, due to their relative great surface energies and is well known in the electron microscopic study of metals and ceramics (see Jacobs and Pashley, 1962; Giovanoli *et al.* 1965; Moorthy *et al.* 1965; Pashley and Stowell, 1966; Wasserman and Hines, 1967; see also Section III.C).

Fortunately, not all ash structures melt, as shown by the middle layer of the spore coat (Figs 13b and 14), and herein lies the best hope for high resolution with the high temperature technique.

b. *Ash particle formation and migration during low-temperature ashing.* The ash can also deposit in artifactual particles in low-temperature ashing, but, rather than coarse droplets, one sees fine, non-contiguous grains or strands which are about 50–200 Å in diameter, as in the "sketchy" ash patterns of mitochondria (Figs 9c, d) or the spore core

(Fig. 16). The artifact-producing phenomenon, here, is evidently not melting in the usual sense but is probably a related micro-scale process induced by an inadequate local concentration of mineral; the ash tolerates only a certain minimum grain size, as required by surface energy considerations, and it migrates as much as necessary during incineration to form the grain. The approximate site of each grain is probably already determined during the late stages of ashing. The surface of the specimen by this time has become quite uneven owing to differential etching (see Fig. 9b). The rate at which organic material sublimes then depends not only on the inherent resistance of the various ultrastructures (the mineral content of the ultrastructure is an important factor in this resistance), but also on the somewhat fortuitous variations in the surface area of the resistant, emergent structures. Ultimately, differential sublimation rate gives rise to small islands of mineral-organic material, and as the remaining organic material is vaporized, the islands become small grains of mineral. If mineral content of an ultrastructure is high, as in the spore coat middle layer, the TIV core, or the mitochondrial dense granules, then only small scope for migration is afforded the mineral before it is condensed into the final ash.

In the absence of melting and gross coalescence, the size of low-temperature ash particles does not depend on specimen thickness. This permits successful microincineration of thick objects if the ash can form a coherent structure (e.g. the spore coat in Fig. 17b). If the ash is not coherent, however, another problem enters. The ash particles and strands are not supported as the thick structure burns away and they migrate as a whole to form an artifactually compact configuration. Figure 18 illustrates this migration with a low-temperature-ashed, one-micron section of mitochondria. As experience with low-temperature microincineration accumulates, mitochondria will probably prove more typical than spore coats, and specimens will usually have to be thin. There is also a lower limit to thickness, however; if the specimen is too thin, the ash grains will distribute too sparsely to form any pattern.

c. *Atmospheric moisture uptake and reaction with the support film.* These two factors have not yet caused us trouble, but both represent important potential hazards, depending on the chemical nature of the ash.

Atmospheric moisture uptake in the ash would presumably give droplet-like particles similar to those attributed to high-temperature melting. We have been able to distinguish between the two effects by covering the ash with a shadowing film before it comes in contact with

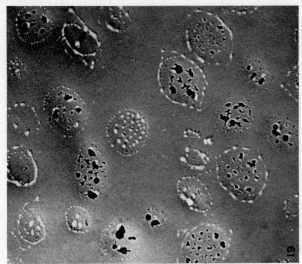

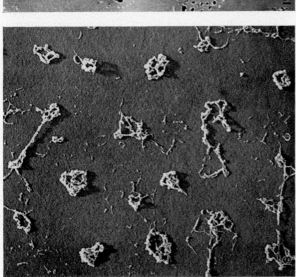

FIG. 18. Too-thick section of isolated rat liver mitochondria after low-temperature ashing. Preparation similar to that of Fig. 9c except that section was initially about 1·0 μ thick. The ash apparently aggregated into fine strands which, in the absence of support, contracted into configurations bearing little resemblance to the original distribution of mineral. Many of the strands do not touch the support film. Shadowed, RCP, × 22,000.

FIG. 19. Thin-sectioned *B. megaterium* spores (osmium-fixed, methacrylate-embedded, methacrylate removed from section) after 30 min at 900°C, and shadowing. Ash particles of the spore core have reacted with the silicon monoxide support film, producing holes in the film. RCP, × 11,000.

the moist atmosphere. The ash particles have always corresponded to their shadows, indicating no post-shadow changes, and have not differed from unshadowed controls. Confirming the absence of deliquescence, low-temperature ash patterns of the same preparations have never shown droplets. Our ashed specimens have probably not contained any large amount of sodium and potassium salts. These are reportedly major contributors to the dilequescent behavior of ash patterns (Kruszynski, 1955).

Ash particles can also react chemically with the specimen support (Hintzsche, 1956). We have encountered this trouble only when specimens were heated excessively. Figure 19 shows a thin section of bacterial spores which was microincinerated at 900°C. Reaction of the ash particles with the silicon monoxide support film made small holes in the latter. Similar results were obtained with a model preparation of a known compound, sodium borate. In this case, the reaction product, seen rimming the holes, was presumably a borosilicate glass.

Another possible problem with the support film is migration of the ash induced by surface irregularities in the film. Fernández-Morán (1948) recommended making pseudoreplicas of the specimen so that after incineration one could see not only the ash pattern but also the original form of the object preserved in the replica film. Our preliminary experiments and also those of Bendet and Trontyl (1963, oral communication) indicate that the ash tends to migrate into crevasses of the replica, producing a very artifactual pattern of distribution.

4. *Volatilization of mineral constituents.* The quantitative accuracy of the ash pattern in terms of original mineral elements in the specimen may be limited by evaporative loss of mineral substances, especially with high-temperature incineration. The most striking example of this in our experience so far is with thin-sectioned, control mitochondria (Figs 9a–d) which show no ash at all after 600°C burning, but a considerable amount after low-temperature ashing. To some degree, most specimens have shown less ash after high- than after low-temperature ashing.

The loss may be due to a macroscopically-unimportant, low volatility of the mineral itself, which, however becomes quite significant for very small particles. This is the case with sodium chloride (bulk boiling point: 1413°C) and potassium chloride (bulk sublimation temperature: 1500°C) which are usually lost from 600°C ash patterns (Grove *et al.* 1961; Hintzsche, 1956). The loss may also be due to the existence or formation during incineration of volatile mineral-organic complexes. This could be the case with the 600°C-incinerated, control mitochondria since mitochondrial ash initially produced by low-temperature incineration (Figs 9c–d) proves to be stable at 600°C. (Alternatively, the original mineral of the mitochondria may have been converted from a volatile into a non-volatile state by the low temperature oxidation; see Gleit, 1967.)

Low-temperature ashing is probably the best answer to the mineral volatility problem, but even here some losses may possibly occur through local heating by exothermic reactions, or ion bombardment of the specimen surface, and the necessity of working under vacuum. These possibilities could, and should, be checked by tracer experiments on microincineration specimens with incorporated radioactive mineral elements. Retention of specific minerals in macroscale specimens by low-temperature ashing has been discussed by Gleit and Holland (1962), Gleit (1963, 1966, 1967), Gluskoter (1965), Hollahan (1966), Mulford (1966) and Sanui and Pace (1966). The last mentioned workers were able to show in their specimens (rat liver microsomes) that the biologically important cations, sodium, potassium, calcium and magnesium were quantitatively retained.

C. Identification of Ash Minerals by Electron Diffraction

As mentioned in Section I.B, the possibility of identifying ash pattern minerals by their crystalline electron diffraction patterns was reported many years ago (Fernández-Morán, 1948). We have done a few experiments to see if this approach would have any merit in practice. We have finally obtained some fairly encouraging results (Thomas and Greenawalt, 1968), but have also encountered a couple of noteworthy problems.

a. *Results.* Our initial attempts to record crystalline diffraction patterns were not at all encouraging, for the simple reason that the ash, either by low-temperature- or even by 600°C-incineration, is almost never crystalline. Rather, it is usually laid down as a vitreous deposit, and in general, the better the definition of the ash pattern, the less likely that it is crystalline. Recent experiments show, however, that the ash can sometimes be crystallized by slow cooling from higher temperatures. Apparent melting, or remelting of the ash decreases the definition of the ash pattern but not to an extent which makes it unrecognizable.

Figure 20a shows a section of dense granule-containing mitochondria, similar to that of Fig. 6a, except thicker (about 0.5μ) which was first microincinerated for 25 min at 600°C, then examined in the electron microscope (it looked like that of Fig. 7b and was not crystalline), and finally heated briefly in air to 700°C and slowly cooled. Some melting of the ash is evident. The same field viewed under dark field conditions is

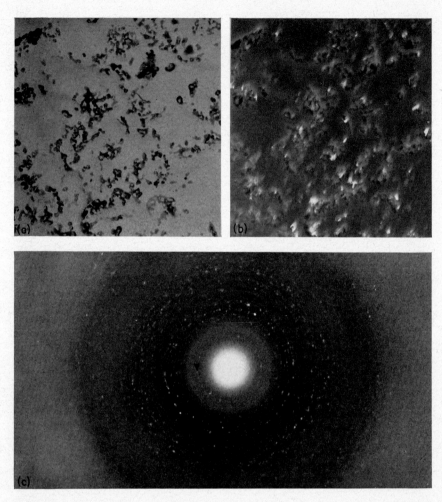

Fig. 20a–c. Ashed section (unshadowed) of isolated rat liver mitochondria containing crystallized calcium phosphate granules (for treatment see text). (a) Bright-field view of a selected area. (0·35 μ objective aperture centered.) The ashed granules look more melted than after 600°C treatment but are still recognizable. Although they have no angular, obviously crystalline contours, they show marked variations in opacity which are due to crystalline diffraction contrast. $\times$ 15,000. (b) Dark-field view of same area as Fig. 20a. (0·35 μ objective aperture off center.) Many granules appear bright, indicating that they contribute to the part of the crystalline diffraction pattern passed by the aperture. $\times$ 15,000. (c) Diffraction pattern from a 20 μ^2 area including that of Figs. 20a, b. The pattern was printed through a contrast control mask (out-of-focus negative in register with the positive plate; see Gonzales, 1962) to suppress background and enhance the visibility of the crystalline diffraction spots (for interpretation, see text). (Reproduced with permission of Thomas and Greenawalt, 1968.)

shown in Fig. 20b, and clearly indicates the crystallinity of the ash. The selected area diffraction pattern is shown in Fig. 20c. The powder pattern is very grainy owing to the large size and small number of crystals contributing to it, but some rings and arcs are sufficiently continuous to be recognized as such.

The pattern was calibrated by reference to the diffraction from a silicon monoxide membrane bearing vapor-deposited gold, and the lattice spacings computed for recognizable arcs. The four, apparently strongest, inner rings, marked in Fig. 20c, were found to represent spacings of 5·15, 3·18, 2·86 and 2·57 Å. These spacings, as well as others, agree fairly well with those expected for β-tricalcium phosphate, whitlockite (Brindley, 1957; Bale et al. 1945). This finding is reasonable in view of the presumed nature of the dense granules. The granules may well be a sub-crystalline precursor of calcium-deficient hydroxy-apatite, with a calcium/phosphate molar ratio of about 1·5 (Eanes et al. 1965), and this could dehydrate upon heating at 700°C to give β-tricalcium phosphate (Hodge et al. 1938; Trautz et al. 1954; Trautz, 1955; Neuman and Neuman, 1958).

A seeming discrepancy in this identification is the increased appearance of melting and sintering in the inorganic ash after heating to the relatively low temperature, 700°C; this temperature is far below the bulk melting points of hydroxyapatites or tricalcium phosphate (Bale et al. 1945). However, preliminary studies on model preparations of pure hydroxyapatites do, in fact, show melting or sintering of the mineral on the electron microscope grid in this same temperature range (Thomas and Greenawalt, 1968). A similar micro-sintering phenomenon evidently accounts for the sharper X-ray diffraction lines obtained from hydroxyapatite in calcified biological specimens after heating to 600°C (see Scott et al. 1962; Myers and Engström, 1965).

b. *Problems.* Contamination of the specimen with small amounts of extraneous mineral can be a serious problem because of the great sensitivity of the diffraction technique to very small amounts of well dispersed, highly crystalline material. In our first experiments with thin-sectioned mitochondria, the ash gave fine-grained powder patterns identified as iron oxide. The diffraction came only from selected areas which included the section, so we initially ruled out contamination as a possibility. Subsequently we found that traces of dissolved iron, picked up perhaps from the stainless steel grid or perhaps from razor blade fragments at the edge of the section, could be uniformly deposited under the section as it dried onto the support film from water. Heating the section crystallized not at all the mitochondrial ash, in this case, only the extraneous iron. In guarding against misinterpretations, it is helpful to use darkfield viewing of the ash to see from where and from what comes the diffraction pattern.

Another problem arises when one attempts to identify the mineral in a very small area of the ash pattern. Unambiguous identification of minerals usually requires a fairly complete powder pattern, since some indication of relative intensities for the various spacings is required (Bigelow, 1960). On this account, the grainy pattern of Fig. 20c is already marginal. If the $20 \mu^2$ area-selecting aperture used here is reduced to $1 \mu^2$, there remain only a few discrete spots in the diffraction pattern and the information content is inadequate for reliable identification. The difficulty here is, of course, too few crystals per unit area in the ash pattern. When the ash is heated to crystallize it, the mineral grains coalesce, and form a few large crystals rather than many small ones. With thicker specimens the amount of mineral per unit area is increased, but so is also the size of the coalesced crystals. This problem may be less pronounced with more favorable objects (e.g. see Rasmussen and Caulfield, 1960; Arstila et al. 1966) and with improved techniques of crystallization, but the crystal concentration will always set a lower limit to the spatial resolution. It seems likely to us that adequate powder patterns will only rarely be obtained on areas of ordinary tissue ash approaching one square micron.

IV. FUTURE APPLICATIONS AND DEVELOPMENTS

Microincineration for electron microscopy is still very much in the exploratory phase, and the full range of its capabilities and applicability to ultrastructural problems remains still to be determined. Most of our experiments, so far, have been confined to relatively simple objects—spores, virus particles, isolated mitochondria. Preliminary experiments, (unpublished mentioned in Thomas, 1967) on more complex objects, thin-sectioned plant cells, produced ash patterns suggesting membrane structures, as were seen in low-temperature ashed sections of isolated mitochondria (Fig. 9c). The patterns seen so far are quite sketchy, but it is to be hoped that better retention of mineral in the specimens (see Section IV.B) will improve not only the significance of the patterns but also their definition (Section III.B). If the interpretation of these ash patterns proves correct, then we may speculate that microincineration will ultimately prove a valuable tool for studying many important problems of ion binding and transport through cellular membranes. In considering the field of ultrastructural studies in general, we can envisage several general categories of application for the microincineration technique and also foresee some technical problems and some possible improvements in the method.

A. *Use of Microincineration to Demonstrate Total Mineral Distribution*

a. *Comparative studies.* Just as its light-microscopic predecessor, the high resolution technique will probably be most generally useful simply for showing the overall distribution of all mineral substances in the specimen, and its variations under controlled conditions. Of particular importance, here, will be the technique's unique ability to demonstrate small amounts of bound, as well as unbound minerals. Other electron microscopic techniques for localization of minerals require that the substance be free to react with precipitants (see, for example, Costantin *et al.* 1965, and Komnick, 1962) or that the bound mineral be sufficiently concentrated that it can be clearly recognized by its inherent electron opacity.

The microincineration technique's lack of specificity for individual mineral elements may be no disadvantage in exploratory experiments, where exactly what to look for has not yet been determined. In other applications, e.g. studies of calcified objects, lack of specificity will pose no problem because the dominant mineral constituent will be known. In many cases, the technique may be used with other, more specific cytochemical procedures and serve as a valuable control for them.

Among the obvious applications of the technique will be investigations of *in vivo* alterations in mineral content of cells and organelles with pathological conditions. The technique will be especially valuable here if it proves to be so that osmium is consistently lost from incinerated tissue specimens. The pathologist often has unique specimens, which, after fixation with osmium tetroxide in the usual way, prove to contain unusual, electron-dense bodies. Microincineration might be used, with before-and-after viewing of these same specimens, to determine whether the electron density is due to native mineral deposits or due to introduced osmium. Otherwise, microincineration may be used on thin sections of specimens fixed with aldehyde or other non-metallic fixative, or unfixed (see Section IV.B), to find variations in lesser mineral content incorporated into organic structures and not recognizable by electron opacities.

In vitro alterations in mineral content of specimens as the result of specific manipulation may also be studied. In dormant bacterial spores, for example, a fraction of the calcium on which depends the spores' heat-resistance can be reversibly removed by changing the pH (Alderton and Snell, 1963); the site of the removed calcium might be determined by comparison of ash patterns. The technique could also be used to localize incineration-resistant metallic fixatives, stains, and cytochemical precipitates and markers introduced into the specimen.

The true distribution of small amounts of heavy metals in specimens is often confused by inherent contrast that could be removed by incineration. Light metallic elements could also be localized, thus offering new possibilities for cytochemical reagents. Electron diffraction for the specific identification of the crystallized, cytochemical reaction product could be a useful adjunct to the microincineration procedure (see Arstila *et al.* 1966).

b. *Quantitative studies.* The value of the technique for comparative studies will be greatly enhanced if the amount of ash derived from a specimen can be determined quantitatively. Quantification was very difficult in the classical technique owing to inherent limitations of the light microscope (Kruszynski, 1963b, 1966) but prospects are encouraging with the electron microscope. As shown by Bahr and Zeitler (1965) and others, the mass per unit area of a specimen under the electron beam can be accurately measured from its electron opacity. The determination is insensitive to the chemical nature of the specimen since the effective total electron scattering cross-section per gram is nearly independent of atomic number. Thus, it should be possible to "weigh" intact objects from their micrographs, incinerate them, "weigh" them again, and compute their ash content. (For an analogous use of the quantitative electron microscopic technique, see Bahr *et al.* 1965.) With precautions against contamination, as discussed in Section II.D, all of this could be done on the same field of view. Valid "weighings" could not be obtained on crystalline material owing to the complications of diffraction contrast, but fortunately for this case the ash is usually not crystalline.

B. *The Problem of Retaining Mineral in the Specimen*

A major problem for many comparative studies and especially for quantitative work will be retention of mineral *in situ* in the specimen; either all of the *in vivo* mineral or, at least a well-defined fraction of it. Low-temperature ashing will minimize mineral loss during micro-incineration itself, but there will still remain the difficulty of initially preparing the specimen without translocations and losses. With very favorable mineral-rich objects, such as bacterial spores, the problem may be solved by resorting to relatively thick specimens: either whole-mounts or semi-thin (1 μ) sections of fresh, frozen material, cut in a cryostat, dry-mounted and subsequently freeze-dried (Stumpf and Roth, 1965). Usually, however, because of the complications of mineral migration during incineration and/or geometrical confusion of the electron microscopic image, the specimens will have to be prepared as ultra-thin sections.

At the present time, there does not seem to be any general, practical method for producing ultra-thin sections which is completely without hazard to the mineral content of the specimen. The Stumpf and Roth (1965) procedure has evidently not succeeded with sections which are ultra-thin ($< 0.1 \mu$). Also, it is not certain whether their procedure, developed for light microscopy, preserves most ultrastructures well enough to be an acceptable electron microscopic technique. Bernhard and Nancy (1964) and Bernhard and Leduc (1967) have had some success with an ultrathin frozen-sectioning procedure, but they found it necessary first to fix the specimen with glutaraldehyde and infiltrate with gelatin in order to minimize ice crystal artifacts and obtain good cutting qualities. These steps would, of course, extract water-soluble minerals. Also, the sections were collected on aqueous solutions, which even though maintained at $-$ 20°C, could still extract substances.

To avoid the extractions of the aqueous fixation and dehydration steps of conventional procedures, the specimens may be freeze-dried and fixed from the vapor phase (e.g. see Sjöstrand and Elfven, 1964). Extraction of lipid-bound minerals may still occur, however, when the specimen is infiltrated with the nonpolar embedding medium (Hyman, 1966), and further losses can occur when the specimen is sectioned in the usual way onto a water surface. Similar comments apply to freeze-substitution procedures (e.g. see Rebhun, 1965) and the recently described, inert-dehydration procedure (Pease, 1966a). To avoid lipid-bound mineral extraction the specimen may be infiltrated and embedded with water-soluble polymers such as gelatin (Gilëv, 1958). It is usually necessary to alter the specimen's permeability by prior fixation in order to get the gelatin in, however, and this also allows water-soluble mineral salts to leach out.

Borysko (1963), and Tranzer (1965) have described thin sectioning of tissue which was simply air-dried, thus escaping the extractions produced by conventional dehydration and embedding. It was first necessary to fix the tissue with aqueous aldehyde, however, and the sections were collected on a water surface. Koller and Bernhard (1964) sectioned fixed but unembedded tissue which was dried by the Anderson (1951) critical-point method. This produced better preservation of ultrastructure than did air-drying, but the liquid N_2O introduced into the fixed specimen may have produced additional extractions and translocations of substances. To avoid extraction during collection of the sections on a water surface, Koller and Bernhard dry-mounted the sections on the electron microscope grids with a novel device using a strong electrostatic field (Koller, 1965).

Dry-mounting of sections, completely avoiding the use of liquids in

142 RICHARD S. THOMAS

section collection, would seem *a priori* a better means of eliminating extraction of minerals during sectioning than substitution of non-aqueous liquids for water in the collecting trough. Usable liquids, such as ethylene glycol (Pease, 1966b), which have wetting and surface tension properties similar to water, also have, like water, an appreciable ability to dissolve mineral salts. Sections thin enough for electron microscopy can be dry-mounted on electron microscope grids even without the Koller device (Rode *et al.* 1962; Thomas, 1962) if the experimenter has sufficient patience and a steady hand. In our experience, thin methacrylate sections cut on a dry knife curl up badly, but

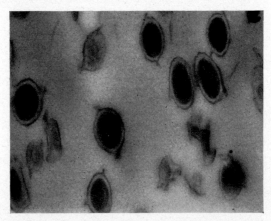

FIG. 21. Dry-cut thin section of unfixed *B. megaterium* spores. The spores were freeze-dried from distilled water, vacuum-infiltrated with methacrylate, and the polymerized block sectioned at 150 mμ with a dry diamond knife. With a hair tip, sections were transferred from the knife to a bare, adhesive-coated grid and mechanically flattened and caused to adhere. The grid was then mounted on a peg, a dry support film (carbon-collodion) lowered onto it from a ring, and the sections flattened onto the film with benzene vapor. The spores are remarkably well preserved; they show compression in the direction of sectioning, as would be expected, but there is no evidence of a methacrylate "explosion artifact" or other obvious disruption of structure. The relatively high opacity, except for the cortex, suggests that little, if anything, has been extracted. × 11,000. (Reproduced with permission from Thomas, 1962.)

they can be lifted off the knife with a fine hair tip and unrolled onto a bare grid previously coated with adhesive to stick them down. Sections as thin as 150 mμ have been handled this way. Figure 21 shows an example. The same unfixed material sectioned onto water mostly dissolves.

In view of the fact that all presently available routes to thin section production present some possibility of mineral extraction from specimens in general, the best course for microincineration studies, it would seem, is to choose special objects for study, and/or limit objectives of the study, so as to circumvent the technical shortcomings. Spores are an example of a special object; they can be sectioned even though they are only encapsulated but not infiltrated with embedding (see Figs 2 and 21; see also Rode *et al.* 1962). Thus gelatin embedding might be used without fixing the spores and with no penetration of the gelatin. This should be a completely physiological embedding procedure in which the spores would remain viable. Dry-sectioning would produce thin specimens which were completely intact chemically. With tissue cells, such an approach would not be possible. However, one could choose a method which preserved tissue lipid- and protein-bound minerals at the expense of unbound, water-soluble salts—such as one of the embedding-free methods (Borysko, 1963; Tranzer, 1965), together with dry sectioning (Koller, 1965)—and limit objectives to the study of membrane-bound and other structure-bound minerals. The loss of soluble minerals at only one step, initial fixation, would permit direct quantitative determination of the lost minerals by chemical analysis of the fixed specimens and the fixative. Loss of unbound minerals might actually be an advantage since, if they were retained, they might deposit artifactually on various ultrastructures in the dehydrated specimen. In applying these unorthodox methods, perfect preservation of ultrastructure would not necessarily be required since the objectives of the study would be primarily cytochemical rather than morphological. Interpretation of ash patterns could be aided by viewing the same area before and after ashing (Section II.D).

C. *Use of Microincineration for Structural and Chemical Simplification of Specimens*

a. *Unmasking of hidden ultrastructure.* The discovery of 100 Å fibrils in the ash of spore coats (Figs 14–16) and the dimpled configuration of ash in thin-sectioned TIV cores (Fig. 12b) illustrates a somewhat different way in which the microincineration technique can be used: to demonstrate hidden ultrastructural organization by its mineral residue. The early experiments of Fernández-Morán (1948) as well as those of Williams (1952), Bendet and Trontyl (1963) and Vose (1963), were undertaken with this aim. Success of the approach in any instance depends, of course, on the presence in the structure of sufficient mineral to form a coherent, well-defined ash skeleton, as discussed in Section III.B. If sufficient native mineral is lacking, it should be possible in some cases to build up the mineral content by specific *in vitro* treatment. Bendet and Trontyl (1963), seeking to demonstrate the organization of

DNA in phage particles by their ash patterns, found no heat-stable native mineral at all after incineration, but they were able to create an ash skeleton by introducing a metallic stain, either uranyl acetate or ferric chloride, which specifically bound to the nucleic acid.

To prevent gross loss of detail by melting or mineral volatilization, the low-temperature ashing technique will be the method of choice for ultrastructural unmasking, and its present limit of resolution, about 50–100Å owing to grain size, may be somewhat lessened by technical improvements. It should be possible to ash not at room temperature but at −20°C (Aldrian et al. 1967) or even lower temperature to reduce thermal agitation and migration of the ash. Also, it may be that bombardment of the ash with charged species in the plasma induces migration or volatilizes mineral; these ions could be screened out, permitting combustion solely by atomic oxygen (Gleit et al. 1963). If moisture uptake in the ash proves a problem, the low-temperature ashing could be done directly in a modified vacuum evaporator, to allow immediate stabilization of the ash by deposition of a protective film.

b. *Liberation of recognized mineral deposits.* The use of microincineration to liberate mineral granules from thin-sectioned mitochondria (Figs 6a–d) illustrates yet another application of the technique which should be generally useful. The granules were recognized as mineral deposits in the intact section by their high, intrinsic electron opacity, but encased in the surrounding organic material, they were inaccessible to experimental manipulations. Free, they could be heated and crystallized, and presumably they could be subjected to various chemical or physical tests *in situ* (see Section IV.D). High-temperature ashing may be especially valuable for liberating such mineral deposits if, as in the case of the mitochondrial granules, it produces a "clean" preparation by volatilization of other ash. Such a preparation would, of course, be an easier object for any subsequent analysis. Low-temperature ashing, on the other hand, may have a special advantage for analysis of some mineral deposits where the original and exact chemical form of the mineral must be preserved. Carbonate minerals, for example, should be retained as carbonates (Gluskoter, 1965) and could presumably be recognized as such by appropriate analysis in the absence of tissue carbon.

The ashed thin sections containing mineral deposits, besides providing mineral material for *in situ* analysis, may also be used to clarify the meaning of gross analysis of macroscale samples of ashed material. For example, the finding of nothing but dense granule residues in high-temperature-ashed thin sections of calcium phosphate-loaded mitochondria suggests that analytical results on the high temperature ash of multimilligram samples of the same material would pertain largely, if not exclusively, to the dense granules.

D. *Identification and Localization of Specific Minerals in the Ash*

The possibility of using electron diffraction to identify minerals in ash patterns was described and discussed briefly in Section III.C. As indicated there, unaided identifications by electron diffraction will usually require fairly sizeable, polycrystalline fields of ash which can produce good powder patterns. Owing to the coarsening of the ash texture by fusion during crystallization, this minimum necessary field may often exceed several square microns in area. Such a limit on resolution evidently means that successful electron diffraction analysis will usually be confined to extended, topochemically simple arrays of ash such as the dense granule residues of mitochondria, or to individual, compact, multicrystalline deposits of pure minerals which have not fused (Rasmussen and Caulfield, 1960; Galle, 1962; Arstila *et al.* 1966). With small complex objects, such as spores, the smallest, potentially-analyzable area of ash will usually exceed greatly the domain of a single mineral compound, and the composite powder pattern will probably be undecipherable. In some cases, of course, it may turn out that only one of the many minerals in the ash has crystallized. Then the analysis would again become manageable, and the sites of this crystallized mineral could be discovered by darkfield examination.

One can speculate on other means of identifying minerals in the ash, but they are much less specific than electron diffraction and are more in the nature of clues. For example, the melting point, crystallizability, and volatility of the mineral at elevated temperatures might be valuable information, and even reaction with the support film might provide a useful indication. These observations would have to be compared with the behavior of model systems of known mineral, however, since the small particles of the ash act differently than bulk material (Sections III.B, III.C). Deliquescence of the ash might also be a clue, and extending this, one can envision selective solubility experiments. The ash, perhaps protected by an overlying permeable membrane, could be washed with various solvents or saturated solutions. Arnold and Sasse (1963) have apparently pursued this approach. Specific precipitation reactions from solution, such as hexahydroxyantimonate for sodium (Komnick, 1962), may be a possibility, but, since the substrate mineral is not bound, the localization might be rather inexact. The ideal specific reactant would be gaseous, e.g. hydrogen sulfide (Tada, 1926). Another interesting possibility for a gaseous reagent is atomic hydrogen (Bergh,

1965; McTaggart, 1967) which could be produced in the Low Temperature Asher. The susceptibility to reduction of the various oxides in the
ash patterns, and the characteristics of the products, might provide
evidence as to their chemical nature. Silicon monoxide support films
could not be used, however, since they would be reduced and destroyed
(McTaggart, 1964). The action of other electrically-activated, low-
temperature gases such as nitrogen, halogens and organic vapors could
also be explored (McTaggart, 1967).

High resolution microincineration may also be useful in more
precisely localizing minerals identified by quite other techniques. The
electron microprobe (see Birks, 1963; Tousimis, 1963) can now identify
individual elements in areas down to about one square micron, and in
quantities down to about 10^{-14} grams. Microprobe analysis of suitably
thick and extended specimens, coupled with electron microscopic ash
pattern displays of thin preparations of similar specimens, might push
the effective cytochemical discrimination down to a few hundred square
millimicrons and quantities of 10^{-17} to 10^{-18} grams or less. (For
example, the amount of phosphorus in the readily visualized ash of one
TIV particle should be 3×10^{-17} grams; see Thomas, 1961.) Microincineration, of sorts, has already been used as a preparative method for
microprobe specimens (Albright, 1965).

E. Conclusion

As with other methods, fruitful use of microincineration for electron
microscopy will depend on recognizing the limitations of the procedure
and choosing material and problems for its application accordingly.
Among the technical limitations will probably always be the difficulty
of simultaneously retaining both fine structure and mineral content in
the specimen presented for incineration. An inherent limitation will be
the technique's usual lack of specificity for individual minerals. Nevertheless, there should be many important applications for the microincineration technique in the future development of biological electron
microscopy.

REFERENCES

Albright, J. (1965). *J. appl. Phys.* **36**, 2615.
Alderton, G. and Snell, N. S. (1963). *Biochem. biophys. Res. Commun.* **10**, 139–143.
Aldrian, A., Jakopic, E., Reiter, O. and Ziegelbecker, R. (1967). *Radex Rdsch.*
     Issue No. **2**, 510–522.
Anderegg, J. W., Wright, M. and Kaesberg, P. (1963). *Biophys. J.* **3**, 175–182.
Anderson, T. F. (1951). *Trans. N.Y. Acad. Sci.* **13**, 130–135.
Arnold, M. and Sasse, D. (1963). *Acta histochem. Suppl.* **3**, 204–208.

Arstila, A. U., Jaakkola, S., Kalimo, H. and Helminen, H. (1966). *J. Microsc.* **5,** 777–780.

Ashworth, C. T., Leonard, J. S., Eigenbrodt, E. H. and Wrightsman, F. J. (1966). *J. Cell Biol.* **31,** 301–318.

Bahr, G. F., Peters, D. and Zeitler, E. (1965). *J. Histochem. Cytochem.* **13,** 3.

Bahr, G. F. and Zeitler, E. (1965). *Lab. Invest.* **14,** 955–977.

Bale, W. F., Bonner, J. F., Hodge, H. C., Wreath, A. and Bell, R. (1945). *Ind. Engng Chem. analyt. Edn* **17,** 491–495.

Bendet, I. and Trontyl, Z. M. (1963). *J. appl. Phys.* **34,** 2511.

Bergh, A. A. (1965). *Bell System Tech. J.* **44,** 261–271.

Berkeley, C., Churg, J., Selikoff, I. J. and Smith, W. E. (1965). *Ann. N.Y. Acad. Sci.* **132,** 48–63.

Bernhard, W. and Leduc, E. H. (1967). *J. Cell Biol.* **34,** 757–771.

Bernhard, W. and Nancy, M. T. (1964). *J. Microsc.* **3,** 579–588.

Bersin, R. L., Hollahan, J. R. and Holland, W. D. (1966). *In* "Proceedings Symposium on Trace Characterization—Chemical and Physical." pp. 514–518. National Bureau of Standards. Washington, D.C.

Bigelow, W. C. (1960). *In* "Physical Methods in Chemical Analysis" (W. G. Berl, ed.) 2nd edition, Vol. 1, pp. 620–660. Academic Press. New York.

Birks, L. S. (1963). "Electron Probe Microanalysis." pp. 1–253. John Wiley and Sons. New York.

Blackwood, J. D. and McTaggart, F. K. (1959). *Aust. J. Chem.* **12,** 114–121.

Boothroyd, B. (1964). *J. Cell Biol.* **20,** 165–173.

Borysko, E. (1963). *Microscope and Crystal Front* **14,** 7–13.

Bradley, D. E. (1961). *In* "Techniques for Electron Microscopy" (D. Kay, ed.) pp. 56–57. Charles C. Thomas, Springfield, Ill.

Brindley, G. W. (ed.) (1957). "Index to the X-Ray Powder Data File." p. 244 (minerals section). American Society for Testing Materials, Philadelphia.

Costantin, L. L., Franzini-Armstrong, C. and Podolsky, R. J. (1965). *Science N.Y.* **147,** 158–159.

Desler, H. and Pfefferkorn, G. (1962). *In* "Proc. Fifth Internat. Congr. for Electron Microscopy" (S. S. Breese, Jr., ed.) Vol. 1, p. EE-7. Academic Press, New York.

Doberenz, A. R. and Wyckoff, R. W. G. (1967). *J. Ultrastruct. Res.* **18,** 166–175.

Draper, M. H. and Hodge, A. J. (1949). *Nature, Lond.* **163,** 576–577.

Draper, M. H. and Hodge, A. J. (1950). *Aust. J. exp. Biol. med. Sci.* **28,** 549–557.

Drum, R. W. (1967). *J. Cell Biol.* **35,** 34A.

Eanes, E. D., Gillessin, I. H. and Posner, A. S. (1965). *Nature* **208,** 365–367.

Fernández-Morán, H. (1948). *Ark. Zool.* **40A,** 1–15.

Fernández-Morán, H. (1952). *Expl cell Res.* **3,** 282–359.

Finch, J. T. and Klug, A. (1967). *J. mol. Biol.* **24,** 289–302.

Fleischer, S., Fleischer, B. and Stoeckenius, W. (1967). *J. Cell Biol.* **32,** 193–208.

Galle, P. (1962). *Revue fr. Étud. clin. biol.* **7,** 1084–1086.

Garamvolgyi, N. and Kerner, J. (1962). *Acta physiol. hung.* **22,** 249–257.

Geymayer, W. (1966). "Beitrag zur Anwendung hochfrequenter Gasentladungen in Sauerstoff für elektronenmikroskopische Untersuchungen". Ph.D. Dissertation, Technische Hochschule. Graz. Austria.

Gilëv, V. P. (1958). *J. Ultrastruct. Res.* **1,** 349–358.

Giovanoli, R., Oswald, H. R. and Feitknecht, W. (1965). *J. Microsc.* **4,** 711–724.

Gleit, C. E. (1963). *Am. J. Med. Electronics* **2,** 112–118.

Gleit, C. E. (1966). *Microchem. J.* **10,** 7–26.

Gleit, C. E. (1967). *Am. Chem. Soc.*, Div. Fuel, Chem., Preprints, **11**, No. 2. pt 1, 211–219.

Gleit, C. E. and Holland, W. D. (1962). *Analyt. Chem.* **34**, 1454–1457.

Gleit, C. E., Holland, W. D. and Wrigley, R. C. (1963). *Nature* **200**, 69.

Gluskoter, H. J. (1965). *Fuel (Chicago)* **44**, 285–291.

Gonzales, F. (1962). *J. Cell Biol.* **15**, 146–150.

Grasenick, F. (1957). *Radex Rdsc.* Issue No. 5/6, 843–856.

Greaves, J. C. and Linnett, J. W. (1958). *Trans. Faraday Soc.* **54**, 1323–1330.

Greenawalt, J. W. and Carafoli, E. (1966). *J. Cell Biol.* **29**, 37–61.

Greenawalt, J. W., Rossi, C. S. and Lehninger, A. L. (1964). *J. Cell Biol.* **23**, 21–38.

Grove, E. L., Jones, R. A. and Mathews, W. (1961). *Analyt. Biochem.* **2**, 221–230.

Hennig, G. R., Dienes, G. J. and Kosiba, W. (1958). *In* "Proc. Second U.N. Internat. Conf. on Peaceful Uses of Atomic Energy," Vol. 7, pp. 301–306. United Nations. Geneva.

Hintzche, E. (1956). "Das Aschenbild Tierischer Gewebe und Organe. Methodik, Ergebnisse und Bibliographie." pp. 1–140. Springer, Berlin.

Hodge, H. C., LeFevre, M. L. and Bale, W. F. (1938). *Ind. Engng Chem. analyt. Edn.* **10**, 156–161.

Hohman, W. W. and Schraer, H. (1967). *J. Cell Biol.* **35**, 57A.

Hollahan, J. R. (1966). *J. chem. Education* **43**, A401–A416.

Horning, E. S. (1942). *In* "Cytology and Cell Physiology" (G. Bourne, ed.) pp. 160–188. Clarendon, Oxford, England.

Hyman, E. S. (1966). *Biophysics J.* **6**, 405–410.

Jacobs, M. H. and Pashley, D. W. (1962). *In* "Proc. Fifth Internat. Congr. for Electron Microscopy" (S. S. Breese, Jr., ed.). Vol. 1, p. DD4. Academic Press New York.

Jakopic, E. (1961). *In* "Proc. European Region. Conf. on Electron Microscopy" (A. L. Houwink and B. J. Spit, eds.), Vol. 1, pp. 559–563. Nederlandse. Vereniging voor Electronenmicroscopie. Delft.

Kaiser, A. D. (1966). *J. gen. Physiol.* **19**, 171–178.

Kassenbeck, P. (1958). *Melliand Textilber.* **39**, 55–61.

Klug, A., Franklin, R. E. and Humphreys-Owen, S. P. F. (1959). *Biochim. biophys. Acta* **32**, 203–219.

Koller, T. (1965). *J. Cell Biol.* **27**, 441–445.

Koller, T. and Bernhard, W. (1964). *J. Microsc.* **3**, 589–606.

Komnick, H. (1962). *Protoplasma* **55**, 414–418.

König, H. (1951). *Z. Phys.* **129**, 483–490.

Kruszynski, J. (1955). *Acta anat.* **24**, 164–171.

Kruszynski, J. (1963a). *Acta histochem.* **15**, 58–77.

Kruszynski, J. (1963b). *Acta histochem. Suppl.* **3**, 191–203.

Kruszynski, J. (1966). *In* "Handbuch der Histochemie" (W. Graumann and K. Neumann, eds.), Vol. 1, part 2, pp. 96–187. Gustav Fischer Verlag. Stuttgart.

McTaggart, F. K. (1964). *Nature* **201**, 1320–1321.

McTaggart, F. K. (1967). "Plasma Chemistry in Electrical Discharges." pp. 1–246. Elsevier, New York.

Mahl, H. (1945). *Ergebn. exakt. Naturw.* **21**, 207–217.

Moorthy, V. K., Prasad, E. G. and Kulkarni, A. K. (1965). *Trans. Indian Ceramic Soc.* **24**, 103–111.

Mulford, C. E. (1966). *Atomic Absorption Newsletter* **5**, 135–139.

Myers, H. M. and Engström, A. (1965). *Exptl cell Res.* **40**, 182–185.

Myerson, A. L. (1965). *J. chem. Phys.* **42**, 3270–3276.
Neuman, W. F. and Neuman, M. W. (1958). "The Chemical Dynamics of Bone Mineral." pp. 43–44. University of Chicago Press, Chicago, Ill.
Pashley, D. W. and Stowell, M. J. (1966). *J. vacuum Sci. Technol.* **3**, 156–166.
Pease, D. C. (1966a). *J. Ultrastruct. Res.* **14**, 356–378.
Pease, D. C. (1966b). *J. Ultrastruct. Res.* **14**, 379–390.
Pijek, J., Host, J. and Gillis, J. (1960). *In* "Proc. Internat. Symp. Microchem., Birmingham, 1958." pp. 48–58. Pergamon Press. Oxford.
Policard, A. (1923). *Bull. Soc. chim. France*, 4^{emme} serie **33**, 1551–1558.
Policard, A. (1929). *Protoplasma* **7**, 464–481.
Policard, A. (1942). *J. Royal Microscop. Soc.* **62**, 25–35.
Policard, A. and Bessis, M. (1952). *C. r. Séanc Soc. Biol.* **146**, 540–542.
Rasmussen, P. and Caulfield, J. B. (1960). *Lab. Invest.* **9**, 330–338.
Raspail, F. V. (1833). "Nouveau Système de Chimie Organique Fondé sur des Méthods Nouvelles d'observation." p. 528. Bailliere, Paris.
Rebhun, L. I. (1965). *Fedn Proc. Fedn Am. Socs. exp. Biol.* **24** (No. 2, part III). S217–S232.
Riemersma, J. C. (1963). *J. Histochem. Cytochem.* **2**, 436–442.
Rode, L. J., Lewis, Jr., C. W. and Foster, J. W. (1962). *J. Cell Biol.* **13**, 423–435.
Rode, L. J. and Williams, M. G. (1966). *J. Bact.* **92**, 1772–1778.
Sanui, H. and Pace, N. (1966). *Appl. Spectrosc.* **20**, 135–141.
Scott, D. B., Nylen, M. U., von Brand, T. and Pugh, M. H. (1962). *Exptl Parasitol.* **12**, 445–458.
Scott, G. H. (1933a). *Protoplasma*, **20**, 133–151.
Scott, G. H. (1933b). *Am. J. Anat.* **53**, 243–287.
Scott, G. H. (1937). *In* "Microscopical Technique" (C. E. McClung, ed.). 2nd edition. pp. 643–665. Hoeber. New York.
Scott, G. H. and Packer, D. M. (1939). *Anat Rec.* **74**, 17–45.
Sjöstrand, F. S. and Elfven, L. (1964). *J. Ultrastruct. Res.* **10**, 263–292.
Spit, B. J. (1961). *In* "Proc. Europ. Region Conf. Electron Microscopy". (A. L. Houwink and B. J. Spit, eds.), Vol. 1, pp. 569–657. Nederlandse vereniging voor Electronenmicroscopie, Dellt.
Streznewski, T. and Turkevich, J. (1959). *In* "Proceedings of Third Conference on Carbon" (S. Mrozowski, ed.), pp. 273–278. Pergamon, New York.
Stumpf, W. E. and Roth, L. J. (1965). *Cryobiol.* **11**, 227–232.
Tada, K. (1926). *Verh. jap. path. Ges.* **16**, 128.
Thomas, R. S. (1961). *Virology* **14**, 240–252.
Thomas, R. S. (1962). *In* "Proc. Fifth Internat. Congr. for Electron Microscopy" (S. S. Breese, Jr., ed.), Vol. 2, p. RR–11. Academic Press. New York, U.S.A.
Thomas, R. S. (1964). *J. Cell Biol.* **23**, 113–133.
Thomas, R. S. (1965). *J. Cell Biol.* **27**, 106A.
Thomas, R. S. (1967). *J. Ultrastruct. Res.* **21**, 159A.
Thomas, R. S. and Corlett, M. (1969). (In preparation.)
Thomas, R. S. and Greenawalt, J. W. (1964). *J. appl. Phys.* **35**, 3083.
Thomas, R. S. and Greenawalt, J. W. (1968). *J. Cell Biol.* **39**, 55–76.
Thomas, R. S. and Williams, R. C. (1961). *J. biophys. biochem. Cytol.* **11**, 15–29.
Tousimis, A. J. (1963). *In* "X-Ray Optics and X-Ray Microanalysis" (H. H. Pattee, V. E. Cosslett and A. Engström, eds.), pp. 539–557. Academic Press. New York.
Tranzer, J. P. (1965). *J. Microsc.* **4**, 319–336.

Trautz, O. R. (1955). *Ann. N.Y. Acad. Sci.* **60**, 696–712.
Trautz, O. R., Fessenden, E. and Newton, M. G. (1954). *J. dent. Res.* **33**, 687–688.
Turkevich, J. (1959). *Am. Scient.* **47**, 97–119.
Turkevich, J. and Streznewski, T. (1958). *Revue Inst. fr. Pétrole* **13**, 686–691.
Vose, G. P. (1963). *Trans. Am. microsc. Soc.* **82**, 48–54.
Wasserman, E. F. and Hines, R. L. (1967). *J. appl. Phys.* **38**, 196–201.
Watson, M. L. and Aldridge, W. G. (1961). *J. biophys. biochem. Cytol.* **11**, 257–272.
Weinbach, E. C. and von Brand, T. (1965). *Biochem. biophys. Res. Commun.* **19**, 133–137.
Weinbach, E. C. and von Brand, T. (1967). *Biochim. biophys. Acta* **148**, 256–266.
Williams, R. C. (1952). *Biochim. biophys. Acta* **8**, 227–244.
Williams, R. C. (1953). *Exptl cell Res.* **4**, 188–201.
Williams, R. C. and Smith, K. M. (1958). *Biochim. biophys. Acta* **28**, 464–469.
Williamson, G. K., Rickards, G. K. and Cornell, R. M. (1966). *J. Scient. Instrum.* **43**, 481–485.
Yasuzumi, G. and Sawada, H. (1950). *Cytologia* **15**, 295–298.

NOTE ADDED IN PROOF

Complete details of the low-temperature ultramicroincineration experiments briefly reported by Hohman and Schraer (1967) have now become available (Hohman, 1967). Also high-temperature ultra-microincineration experiments have been described in considerable detail by Boothroyd (1968). In both cases, the techniques were applied to thin-sectioned tissue, either avian shell gland (Hohman) or rat kidney cortex and rat epididymis (Boothroyd). Fairly conventional preparative procedures (buffered aldehyde fixation, epoxy embedding, sectioning onto water or dilute buffer) were used, and so, just as with our thin-section studies, results pertained only to "structure-bound" mineral. To avoid mineral in the fixative completely, Hohman used S-collidine-acetic acid as the buffer. Boothroyd used either cacodylate or sodium veronal.

Both workers mounted their sections on silicon monoxide membranes, and they have described modified but still not ideal procedures intended to make the membranes flatter. For Boothroyd's high-temperature experiments the electron microscope grids were of nickel-coated copper. Apparently nickel is sufficiently more resistant than copper to be acceptable. Hohman used molybdenum grids for low-temperature, excited oxygen incineration. For this technique these grids are apparently quite serviceable but they cannot be used at high temperature since molybdenum heated in air forms a volatile oxide and sublimes away.

Boothroyd has described a simple microfurnace which is mounted between electrodes in the vacuum evaporator, similar to the heating stage we have used. An advantage of the furnace is that it completely surrounds the electron microscope grid and an adjacent thermocouple junction, thus insuring that grid and junction are at the same temperature.

Viewing of the same specimen before and after incineration has been described by both workers, and their results confirm our own experience. With high-temperature ashing (550°C), previewing has no effect on the final ash pattern, but with low temperature ashing, a contamination film persists which is difficult to burn off. Also consistent with our own results, Hohman's low-temperature ashing experiments yield richer ash patterns, i.e. more ash and more organized detail, than are seen by Boothroyd after high temperature treatment. Nuclear structures, especially chromatin and nucleoli, show abundant residue in high-temperature ash patterns but the cytoplasm leaves little ash. In contrast, low temperature ash patterns show equally abundant residue in both nuclear and cytoplasmic areas and many details, such as endoplasmic reticulum, are recognizable. The mineral content of the starting preparations for both high- and low-temperature incineration was rather low, and so it was necessary to use relatively thick sections (Boothroyd, 100–120 mμ; Hohman, 100–500 mμ) to provide sufficient ash for visualization. As recognized by both authors, the resolution in both intact sections and ash patterns suffered from this thickness.

Osmium-fixed specimens also were microincinerated by both workers. In agreement with our preliminary findings on mitochondria (Thomas and Greenawalt, 1968), rather little difference is seen between the ash patterns of osmium-fixed and aldehyde-fixed preparations after low-temperature incineration. By contrast, much more ash remains in Boothroyd's high-temperature ash patterns from osmium-fixed than from aldehyde-fixed preparations. It is not clear, however, whether this difference is due entirely to retention of osmium, rather than due partly to better retention of mineral-binding structures which may be lost from aldehyde-fixed specimens during embedding. Electron probe microanalysis (see below) may answer this question.

Additional details of his briefly reported (Drum, 1967) ultramicroincineration experiments have been published by Drum (1968). The specimens were mounted on silicon-carbon membranes on nickel grids and incinerated at 650°C.

Bauer (1967) has also reported ultramicroincineration experiments of sorts. There is some question whether his preparation was completely ashed, however. The specimen was mounted on a carbon-filmed grid and incinerated at 500–600°C under vacuum. Boothroyd (1968) performed experiments under similar conditions and found that specimens were only carbonized, not fully ashed.

Extending previous studies (Berkley *et al.*, 1965), Berkley and co-workers (1967) have described micromanipulator isolation of micron-sized, pathological mineral particles from low-temperature microincinerated, thick (25μ) sections of lung tissue, and analysis of the individual, isolated particles by electron microscopy, electron diffraction and electron probe microanalysis.

The problem of preparing ultra-thin sections without loss of mineral constituents may have a solution if techniques recently developed by Appleton (1969) and Christensen (1969) prove practical. These workers describe thin sectioning of quick-frozen, unfixed tissue with mechanical mounting of the sections on filmed grids and subsequent freeze-drying. Dr. Christensen has kindly made available his manuscript ahead of publication. His sections show remarkably good preservation of ultra-structural detail, and the technique seems to be fairly simple. It is performed with a standard ultramicrotome (Sorvall MT-2) only slightly modified.

The problem of identifying minerals in ash patterns may perhaps best be solved by the use of electron probe microanalysis. In preliminary experiments, we have applied this technique to 1-micron thick sections of Tipula iridescent virus crystals before and after low-temperature ashing (Thomas and Corlett, 1969). Semi-quantitative analysis shows that little remains in the ash other than phosphorus, presumably present as polyphosphate. Thus the derivation of the ash from nucleic acid is confirmed. Higher resolution ash patterns from very thin sections of the virus confirm the dimpled or doughnut-like distribution of this polyphosphate within the sectioned viral core, and thus show with fair certainty the localization of the nucleic acid within the virus. Electron probe analysis should be generally useful in conjunction with high resolution microincineration, but especially so with the low-temperature ashing technique. Since analysis can be performed on sections which are only 10 to 20 times thicker than used for electron microscopy, the low temperature ashing can be performed under conditions of time and power input similar to those used for the ultrathin sections, and analytical results can be applied to the electron microscopic specimens with confidence. Modern electron probes can analyze for all of the biologically important light elements (see for example, Andersen, 1967) including carbon and nitrogen. Thus microprobe analysis applied to the same section before and after ashing can determine quantitatively not only what has been retained by the ashing, but also what has been removed.

Probe analysis will contribute to low-temperature ashing of thin sections a chemical basis of understanding which heretofore has been lacking.

Combined electron microscopy and electron probe analysis may also be usefully applied to sections which are only partially incinerated by the low-temperature technique. We have etched human hair cross-sections briefly in the oxygen plasma and obtained clean removal of the non-keratinous membrane and nuclear remnant material with little damage to the keratinous macrofibrils (unpublished, mentioned in Thomas, 1967). Similar etching experiments on biological specimens have been reported by Faberge (1965, 1966).

The temperature in a micro-region on the electron microscope grid during low-temperature incineration may be determined by use of microcrystals of various, low-melting organic substances. Geymayer (1966) has shown that the difference between boiling and sublimation of a crystal briefly treated in the plasma is clearly recognizable in the partially incinerated residue which remains. He used synthetic indigo; we have experimented with d-sorbitol, which melts in the range 87–95°C. These crystals are stable under vacuum conditions but sublime away when the oxygen discharge is turned on.

Interest in low-temperature incineration techniques continues to grow, and there are now at least four instruments for this purpose commercially available: Tracerlab LTA-600 (This instrument super- sedes the LTA-500. Tracerlab, 2030 Wright Ave., Richmond, Calif.); IPC Model 1001 Plasma Machine (International Plasma Corp., 25222 Cypress Avenue, Hayward, Calif.); Coleman, Model 40 RF Reactor (Coleman Instruments, 42 Madison St., Maywood, Ill.); Balzers Gasentladungsapparatur GEA 003 (Balzers AG, Balzers, F. Liechten- stein). In some cases, instruments have been assembled by researchers in their own laboratories, e.g. Doberenz and Wyckoff (1967 and personal communication); Frazier et al. (1967).

ADDITIONAL REFERENCES

Andersen, C. A. (1967). In "Methods of Biochemical Analysis" (D. Glick, ed.), Vol. 15, pp. 147–270. Interscience. New York.
Appleton, T. C. (1969). In "Autoradiography of Diffusible Substances" (L. J. Roth, ed.). (In press), Academic Press. New York.
Bauer, H. (1967). Vierteljahrsschrift Naturforsch. Gesell. Zürich 112, 173–197.
Berkley, C., Langer, A. M. and Baden, V. (1967). Trans. N.Y. Acad. Sci., Ser. II 30, 331–350.
Boothroyd, B. (1968). J. Roy. Microsc. Soc. 88, 529–544.
Christensen, A. K. (1969). In "Autoradiography of Diffusible Substances" (L. J. Roth, ed.). (In press), Academic Press. New York.

Drum, R. W. (1968). *J. Ultrastruct. Res.* **22,** 12–21.

Faberge, A. C. (1965). *J. appl. Phys.* **36,** 2615A.

Faberge, A. C. (1966). *J. appl. Phys.* **37,** 3920A.

Frazier, P. D., Brown, F. J., Rose, L. S. and Fowler, B. O. (1967). *J. Dent. Res.* **46,** 1098–1101.

Hohman, W. R. (1967). "A Study of Low Temperature Ultramicroincineration of Avian Shell Gland Mucosa by Electron Microscopy." Dissertation for Ph.D., The Pennsylvania State University. University Microfilms, Inc., Ann Arbor, Mich.

Small Angle Electron Diffraction in the Electron Microscope

R. P. FERRIER

Cavendish Laboratory, University of Cambridge, England

I. Introduction

THE study of diffraction effects from specimens which exhibit large periodicities (e.g. crystalline biological material in which the repeat distances are normally in the range 20–2000 Å) has been of considerable interest for many years and the technique normally employed in such studies is that of X-ray small angle diffraction. In 1960 Mahl and Weitsch published a paper in which they described the use of an electron microscope as a small angle diffraction camera and although there appears to have been little interest in the technique initially it has become of increasing importance in the last few years. This is principally due to the fact that small angle electron diffraction offers a number of advantages over the X-ray method not least of which is the ability to obtain both a high resolution image and a high resolution diffraction pattern from the same specimen area. The published work on the techniques and applications of small angle electron diffraction is spread over journals which cover the fields of physics, chemistry and biology and it is the purpose of this review article to summarize the more important features of the literature and to try to assess the role of small angle electron diffraction as a tool in structural studies.

In the second section of this article the various optical arrangements which have been devised to utilize a conventional electron microscope as a high resolution small angle diffraction camera will be discussed from the point of view of operational method, attainable resolution and suitability for particular types of investigation. The third section is concerned with the application of the techniques in the fields of physics, biology and polymer structure and the fourth section deals briefly with the complex problem of electron scattering cross-sections applicable in the small angle region (in this article the "small" angles correspond to specimen periodicities of 20 Å and above). The final section contains a critical discussion of the usefulness of small angle electron diffraction and comparisons are made with the alternative methods of X-ray and optical diffraction and electron microscopy.

II. Electron Optical Arrangements

If the electron microscope is to be operated as a small angle diffraction camera then the particular optical arrangement selected must satisfy two conditions. The first of these is obvious and is that the inherent angular resolution must be sufficient to resolve the detail in the diffraction pattern which is under study. This may be illustrated with reference to crystalline biological material which has periodicities up to 2000 Å or more. If we insert d = 1000 Å into the Bragg equation written in the small angle approximation

$$d\phi = \lambda \qquad (1)$$

where ϕ is the angle through which the incident electron beam is diffracted as it passes through the specimen i.e. $\phi = 2\theta$ Bragg and λ is the electron wavelength (in this section an electron accelerating voltage of 80 kV is assumed giving $\lambda = 4{\cdot}177 \times 10^{-2}$ Å) then we find that the angular separation of the diffracted spots will be $4{\cdot}1 \times 10^{-5}$ radian. This is a very small angle, but it will be shown in this section that angular resolutions of this order are easily attainable.

The second condition is that for focusing purposes the size of the diffraction pattern on the viewing screen must be large enough to allow observation of the resolved diffraction peaks. The size of the diffraction pattern on the viewing screen is governed by the camera length L which is given by

$$R = L\phi \qquad (2)$$

where R is the radial distance of a diffraction spot from the origin of the diffraction pattern. The camera length of the normal diffraction mode of an electron microscope is 40 cm. If we insert this value into equation (2) we find that for a periodicity of 1000 Å, R will be 25 μm which is barely resolvable even using a $10 \times$ binocular viewer. Hence for low angle electron diffraction the camera length should be of the order of metres or tens of metres depending on the required resolution.

The ability to focus the diffraction pattern on the viewing screen is highly desirable, but not absolutely essential, since a through-focal series can always be taken. Hence the absolute limit of useable resolution will depend on the grain size of the emulsion used to record the diffraction pattern and on the required angular resolution and available camera length; this will be discussed in more detail in Section II.D.

In comparing the various optical modes of small angle electron diffraction it is necessary to have some criterion for the limiting resolution in the diffraction pattern. In this article the criterion given by Ferrier and Murray (1966) will be adopted. This states that two diffraction spots will just be resolved when the separation of the spot centres is equal to the diameter of either spot. Neglecting any broadening effects it can be shown that the minimum resolvable angle a is given by the diameter of the spot formed on the final screen by the undiffracted electrons (Di) divided by the camera length, i.e.

$$a = \frac{Di}{L} \tag{3}$$

It will be shown in Section II.A that the value of a depends only on the illumination system used in the particular mode of operation and is equal to the angle subtended at the specimen by the diameter of the effective illumination source. If the value of a is substituted back into the Bragg equation (1) it is possible to find the value of the maximum lattice periodicity (d_{max}) which would give rise to a diffraction pattern at the resolution limit, i.e.

$$d_{max} = \lambda/a \tag{4}$$

A. *The Three Lens Methods and the Method of Bassett and Keller*

As mentioned previously the first technique for small angle electron diffraction was developed by Mahl and Weitsch (1960a) using an AEG-Zeiss EM 8 electron microscope which had a telefocus gun and no condenser lenses. A ray diagram of their method is shown in Fig. 1a. The specimen is mounted in the aperture control mechanism located between the diffraction and intermediate lenses. The objective lens acting as a condenser is set at maximum excitation to give the smallest possible image of the cathode cross-over; the diffraction lens is then adjusted to transfer this spot into the object plane of the projector lens. The diffraction pattern is focused in the same plane and is magnified by the projector lens on to the final screen. This technique has the major disadvantage that it is not possible to get a high resolution image of the specimen area contributing to the diffraction pattern without replacing the specimen in its normal position in the microscope column. In addition the resolution is not particularly high and is estimated to be of the order of 500–600 Å.

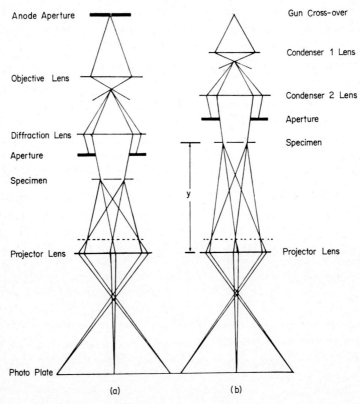

Anode Aperture

Objective Lens

Diffraction Lens

Aperture

Specimen

Projector Lens

Photo Plate

(a)

Gun Cross-over

Condenser 1 Lens

Condenser 2 Lens

Aperture

Specimen

y

Projector Lens

(b)

Fig. 1. (a) Ray diagram of the electron microscope for the three lens small angle diffraction method of Mahl and Weitsch. Reproduced with permission from the authors. (b) Ray diagram of the three lens method of Ferrier.

Bassett and Keller (1964) and Ferrier (1964) have developed modified versions of the Mahl and Weitsch technique which to a large extent overcome the difficulties discussed previously. The three lens method devised by Ferrier using an A.E.I. EM 6 microscope is suitable for most modern electron microscopes which have a double condenser lens system and a ray diagram of this mode is shown in Fig. 1b. In this method the specimen is in its normal position in the microscope column and the objective and intermediate lenses are not excited. The first condenser lens is set to have its minimum focal length and the image of the cathode cross-over which it forms is focused by the second condenser lens into the object plane of the projector lens, the diffraction pattern from the specimen being formed in the same plane. By varying the excitation of the projector lens the camera length at the recording plane can be varied in the range 12–70 m.

The area of the specimen contributing to the diffraction pattern is defined by the condenser aperture. Since this cannot be much smaller than 10 μm without running into difficulties and is more normally 50 μm or 100 μm, the method is most suitable for studying relatively large specimen areas and is particularly useful for Debye-Scherrer ring patterns. Area selection may also be made using the objective aperture but this method has the slight disadvantage that some of the scattered electrons from the peripheral region of the specimen area will be excluded from the diffraction pattern. It should be noted that in order to avoid electrostatic charging effects the specimen should be mounted on a conducting substrate (see Section III.A 4).

The theoretical angular resolution of the three lens method can be calculated using equation (3). The value of Di is given by,

$$Di = d_c M_{C_1} M_{C_2} M_P \quad | \tag{5}$$

where d_c is the diameter of the cathode cross-over and M_i is the magnification of the "i"th lens.) Since (see Fig. 1b)

$$L = y M_P \tag{6}$$

$$a = \frac{Di}{L} = \frac{d_c M_{C_1} M_{C_2} M_P}{y M_p} = \frac{d_c M_{C_1} M_{C_2}}{y} \tag{7}$$

Inserting the numerical values for the parameters describing the EM 6 microscope

$$d_c = 40 \ \mu, \ M_{C_1} = 0\cdot05, \ M_{C_2} = 5\cdot0, \ y = 34 \text{ cm}$$

the values of a and d_{max} are calculated to be

$$a = 3\cdot10^{-5} \text{ radian}$$

$$d_{max} = 1200 \text{ Å}$$

It should be noted that the angular resolution as defined by equation (7) depends only on the illumination system of the microscope and is given by the angle subtended at the specimen by the diameter of the effective illumination source. In future discussions this will be the criterion used to calculate the limiting angular resolution.

A ray diagram of the small angle diffraction mode developed by Bassett and Keller is shown in Fig. 2a. The particular microscope

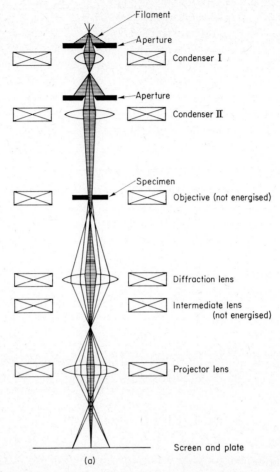

Filament

Aperture

Condenser I

Aperture

Condenser II

Specimen

Objective (not energised)

Diffraction lens

Intermediate lens
(not energised)

Projector lens

Screen and plate

(a)

FIG. 2. (a) Ray diagram of the electron microscope for the small angle diffraction method of Bassett and Keller. Reproduced with permission from the authors.

used in their investigations was a Philips EM 200 which has three independent lenses below the objective lens. The essential difference between this method and the previous one is that the diffraction pattern is magnified in two stages rather than one. The objective and intermediate lenses are not excited and the first condenser lens is set at maximum excitation. The image of the cathode cross-over formed by this lens is focused into the object plane of the diffraction lens by the second condenser lens. The diffraction pattern then formed is magnified on to the final screen. No analysis was made of the theoretical resolution of the method, but the diffraction patterns which they obtained indicate that the limiting resolution is ∼4000 Å. Compared to the Ferrier method, the use of two stages of magnification certainly gives a greater degree of flexibility in the choice of camera lengths, although no figures are available for the range of this parameter.

It is highly desirable in small angle diffraction studies to have a high resolution image of the area contributing to the diffraction pattern. Since the objective lens is not excited in the Ferrier and the Bassett and Keller methods this necessitates marking the particular area of interest in some way prior to the excitation of the objective lens. For small areas Bassett and Keller achieved this by replacing the diffraction lens by the intermediate lens at a suitable excitation. This arrangement gives an out-of-focus image of the diffracting area, the image magnification being dependent on the focal length chosen for the intermediate lens. The image is photographed and then the small condenser aperture is replaced by a much larger one which allows a few grid squares to be viewed; the area is then marked by a double exposure and can be identified when the objective lens is excited for high resolution imaging. A similar, but not so precise, method can be used for the Ferrier mode. In this case an out-of-focus image of a region surrounding the area of interest (the actual diameter of the region is approximately twice that of the area used in forming the diffraction pattern) is obtained by switching off the second condenser lens and, in the same manner as discussed above, the area is marked by a double exposure. These methods of area relocation cannot be made exact and if a precise knowledge of the specimen area is required then one of the other small angle diffraction modes must be used.

B. *Selected Area and Very Long Camera Length Methods*

Ferrier and Murray (1966) have shown that the microdiffraction procedure (Boersch, 1936, 1937; Le Poole, 1947), which is the mode normally available in the electron microscope, is capable of very high angular resolution. However, because the available camera length is short (∼40 cm), the upper limit to the lattice periodicities which can be studied is set by the graininess of emulsion used to record the diffraction pattern.

The ray diagram of the electron microscope operated in the selected area microdiffraction mode is shown in Fig. 2b. The image of the cathode cross-over, formed above the specimen by the first and second condenser lenses, acts as the effective illumination source of the diffraction pattern. The diffraction pattern of the specimen is formed close to the back focal plane of the objective lens and is transferred by the intermediate and projector lenses on to the final screen. A real image of the specimen is formed in a plane close to the intermediate lens and an aperture (the diffraction aperture) placed in this plane will define the area of the specimen contributing to the diffraction pattern. The magnification of the objective lens is $\sim$40$\times$ and hence a 25 μ diffraction aperture will define an area of 0·6 μm at the specimen. Hence the technique is best suited to the study of small specimen areas or small single crystals. It should be noted that if the area selection is to be precise then precautions must be taken and these have been discussed by Agar (1960).

The angular resolution of the selected area mode is given by the angle a subtended by the diameter d_c of the effective illumination

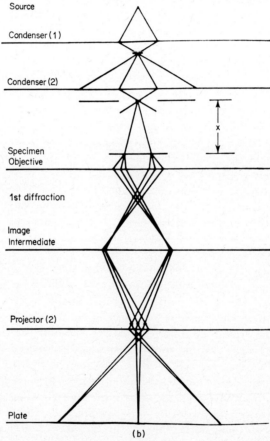

FIG. 2. (b) Ray diagram of the electron microscope for the selected area mode of operation.

source at the specimen. Hence (see Fig. 2b)

$$a = \frac{d_c M_{C_1} M_{C_2}}{x} \tag{8}$$

and if both condenser lenses are set at maximum excitation to give the smallest possible effective illumination source, the values of the parameters in equation (8) for the A.E.I. EM 6 microscope are

$$d_c = 40 \ \mu\text{m}; \quad M_{C_1} = 0\cdot05; \quad M_{C_2} = 0\cdot3; \quad x = 15 \ \text{cm}.$$

which gives

$$a = 4 \times 10^{-6} \ \text{radian}$$

$$d_{\text{max}} = 10{,}000 \ \text{Å}.$$

At a camera length of 40 cm the diffraction spot separation for $d = 10{,}000$ Å would be only $1\cdot6 \ \mu\text{m}$ which is far below the limit of even the best photographic emulsions and hence the useful resolution depends on the available camera length. Since the value of L is given by

$$L = f_o M_I M_P \tag{9}$$

where f_o is the focal length of the objective lens and M_I is the magnification of the intermediate lens, then L can be increased either by increasing the value of the product $M_I M_P$ or by increasing f_o. The value of $M_I M_P$ cannot be increased by more than a factor of 2 above the present value of the microscope and any additional increase in L must be achieved by increasing f_o. However to retain the selected area facility (i.e. the specimen image in the plane of the diffraction aperture) when f_o is increased, the specimen must be moved further from the objective lens. In the A.E.I. EM 6 microscope the specimen can be raised $\sim$5 cm above its normal position at which point the maximum value of L is $\sim$5 m.

If the objective lens is operated weakly then the spherical aberration is high and the image quality for the high specimen position will be poor. To overcome this difficulty Ferrier and Murray have used a special holder to enable the specimen to be raised for high resolution diffraction and lowered for high resolution imaging. Since the specimen remains continuously in view during these operations area relocation is relatively simple. A very similar technique in which the specimen was raised above the normal plane has been described by Yeh and Geil (1967).

In some diffraction studies it is possible to relax the conditions necessary for the selected area mode of operation and this has led to the development of the very long camera length mode (Ferrier and Murray, 1966). In this mode the area selection is performed by the objective aperture and the specimen is retained in its normal position

164 R. P. FERRIER

in the microscope column. The camera length can be increased by increasing f_o and a limit is not reached until the diffraction pattern is imaged in the diffraction aperture plane. The diffraction pattern is then magnified by both the intermediate and projector lenses and camera lengths in the range 10–500 m may be obtained. The method is particularly suited for high resolution work where an extended area of the specimen is to be examined and an image of the area at a magnification of $\sim$100$\times$ may be produced by changing the excitation of the intermediate lens. Since the angular resolution of the selected area mode is independent of the focal length of the objective lens the same theoretical resolution limit applies to the very long camera length method.

C. *The Four Lens Methods*

Two optical arrangements which use four of the microscope lenses have been described in the literature and since in each case the illumination system is identical to that of the selected area diffraction mode the theoretical angular resolution is given by equation (8). The first of the four lens methods was developed independently by Drahos and Delong (1966) and by Wade and Silcox (1967); a ray diagram is shown in Fig. 3a. The specimen is situated in its normal position in the microscope column, the objective lens is inoperative and area selection is achieved by means of the objective aperture. A virtual diffraction pattern may be considered to be formed in the plane of the effective illumination source situated below the second condenser lens and this is imaged on to the viewing screen by the intermediate and projector lenses. The camera length is given by

$$L = xM_IM_P \tag{10}$$

and can be varied by changing the excitation of the projector lens. For the A.E.I. EM 6 microscope this variation is in the range 4–15 m.

This method suffers from the same disadvantage as the methods described in Section II.A in that the objective lens must be excited if a high resolution image of the area contributing to the diffraction pattern is required. A method of area relocation is therefore necessary and this could be achieved using an area marking technique similar to that described by Bassett and Keller, the out-of-focus image being formed by switching off the intermediate lens.

The second four lens method is that due to Wade (1966) and a ray diagram is shown in Fig. 3b. The method is identical to the previous one except that the intermediate lens has been replaced by the objective lens at a suitably weak excitation. The camera length is given by

$$L = xM_oM_P \tag{11}$$

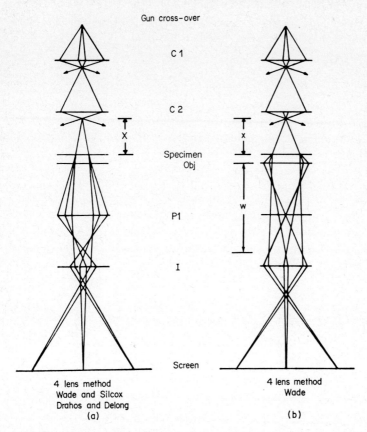

FIG. 3. (a) Ray diagram of the electron microscope for the four lens method due to Drahos and Delong (1966) and Wade and Silcox (1967). Reproduced with permission from the authors. (b) Ray diagram of the Wade four lens method. Reproduced with permission from the author.

and for the A.E.I. EM 6 microscope can be varied in the range 20–80 m. Wade has shown that the above equation can be rewritten as $L \simeq WM_P$, that is the method has a similar advantage to that of the selected area mode in that the camera length is virtually independent of the position of the effective illumination source. In fact a 20% variation in W gives only a 2% variation in L.

A second advantage of this method over the other four lens method is that the image of the area contributing to the diffraction pattern may be obtained directly by altering the strength of the objective lens, the image magnification being a maximum of 20,000× for the EM 6 microscope.

The four lens methods described in this section are best suited to high resolution studies of diffraction effects from relatively large specimen areas.

D. *Ultrahigh Resolution Method*

Since the angular resolution in small angle electron diffraction depends only on the quality of the illumination system and on the angle subtended at the specimen by the effective illumination source, a further improvement in resolution over the selected area micro-diffraction mode is possible if the objective lens is used as a third condenser lens to give an even smaller effective illumination source. This ultrahigh resolution mode has been discussed by Curtis *et al.* (1967) and a ray diagram of their method is shown in Fig. 4. The two condenser lenses and the objective lens are set at maximum excitation to give the smallest possible image of the cathode cross-over above the specimen. The specimen is located in the mechanism normally

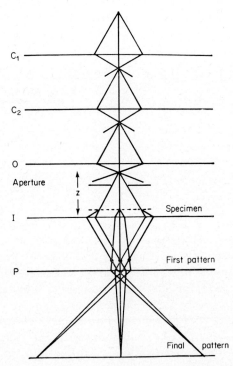

FIG. 4. Ray diagram of the electron microscope for the ultrahigh resolution mode of operation.

used for the diffraction aperture and hence can be accurately aligned on the optic axis. The specimen area is defined by an aperture placed in contact with the specimen and hence the area under observation has to be pre-selected. A more versatile arrangement would be obtained if a separate aperture mechanism could be inserted above the specimen.

The theoretical angular resolution of this method is given by

$$a = d_c M_{C_1} M_{C_2} M_O / y \qquad (12)$$

and if the optimum parameters for the EM 6 microscope are inserted the following values are obtained

$$a = 1 \times 10^{-7} \text{ radian}$$

$$d_{max} = 40 \ \mu m.$$

Since the effective illumination source is only 130 Å in diameter, it might be expected that lens aberrations would have a serious effect on the spot size. The two lens aberrations which are important are astigmatism in the illumination system, which can be corrected by the means of the built-in stigmators, and spherical aberration in the objective lens. The effect of spherical aberration is to produce an increase in the diameter of the effective source of $C_s \beta^3$ where C_s is the spherical aberration constant and β is the angle subtended at the effective source by the specimen area. In the EM 6 microscope a 400 μm aperture at the specimen gives a value of $\beta = 1 \cdot 5 \times 10^{-3}$ radian and using a realistic value of $C_s = 1$ cm the increase in effective source size is ~ 1 Å and hence negligible. It must be emphasized that a screen placed in the plane of the effective illumination source would see a spot considerably larger than 130 Å, but by limiting the specimen area only rays from part of the effective source contribute to the diffraction pattern.

One of the problems which arises in using the ultrahigh resolution technique is that the angular aperture of the objective lens is large and hence electrons can pass round the diffraction aperture control mechanism, in which the specimen is located, and be focused by the outer portions of the intermediate lens to give a distorted caustic in the diffraction pattern. Electrons may also reach the screen after reflection from lens guard tubes. The normal objective aperture is too close to the objective cross-over to be effective in limiting the lens aperture but this difficulty has been overcome by replacing it with another aperture held 2 cm below the normal position in a holder which fits into the normal specimen block. The correct position of the aperture on the optic axis can therefore be adjusted using the specimen position control mechanism.

In the ultrahigh resolution technique only two lenses are available to focus and magnify the diffraction pattern. This implies that the maximum available camera length is limited, which can lead to difficulties. The camera length is given by

$$L = f_I M_P \tag{13}$$

where f_I is the focal length of the intermediate lens. For the EM 6 microscope the maximum value of L is 35 m and if the highest angular resolution is required the spot separation at the recording plane is only 3·5 μm. The photographic plates normally used in the electron microscope are not capable of such spatial resolution. A frequency response of at least 5000 lines/cm is required and this is close to the limit of the best Kodak "MR" emulsions. Because of the small separation of the diffraction spots it is also impossible to focus the diffraction pattern on the fluorescent screen and a through-focal series of exposures is necessary. However because of the small size of the diffraction pattern such a series can be accommodated on a single photographic plate. A through-focal series is also essential for the highest angular resolutions since the depth of focus at the screen is only ∼1 cm compared with the 10 cm separation of the screen and photographic plate.

There are not many systems of fundamental interest which exhibit periodicities in the range 1–40 μm and hence in practice the use of the ultrahigh resolution mode is likely to be limited. However, the technique does illustrate the very high sensitivity of the electron microscope when operated as a small angle diffraction camera.

E. *Resolution Checks and Camera Length Calibration*

In the previous paragraph the theoretical angular resolutions applicable to the various modes of small angle diffraction have been calculated. It is important to have some means of testing the angular resolution not only to confirm the theoretical predictions, but also to act as an occasional check on the performance of the microscope. Test specimens for angular resolution should cover the range of Bragg spacings from 1000 Å up to 40 μm and a number of different systems are available.

A very useful test specimen may be prepared from polystyrene latex spheres. These spheres can be obtained with diameters in the range 1000 Å–1 μm and within a given batch the standard deviation of the sphere diameters is of the order of 1%. If the spheres could easily be crystallized to form rafts with a few hundred particles along a side, sharp spot diffraction patterns would be obtained and would serve as ideal angular resolution tests for all but the ultrahigh resolution mode.

However Smart and Burge (1965) found in their investigation of the diffraction patterns from 880 Å spheres that the latex sphere rafts were not sufficiently ordered to give more than the first few diffraction orders. For this reason diffraction patterns from random arrays of spheres are normally used as resolution tests.

The Fourier transform of a single sphere is given by (Guinier and Fournet, 1955)

$$F(s) = 4\pi R^3 \left(\frac{\sin U - U \cos U}{U^3} \right) \tag{14}$$

where R is the sphere radius, $U = 2\pi RS$ and $S = \phi/\lambda$. The diffracted intensity is proportional to $F(s)^2$ and consists of a series of ring maxima separated by zeros of intensity. For large values of S the maxima satisfy the condition

$$2\pi R \Delta S = \pi \tag{15}$$

which is identical with the Bragg equation in the form $2R\phi = \lambda$ and hence the high order ring separation corresponds to the particle diameter.

The Fourier transform of a random array of N spheres is $N^{\frac{1}{2}} F(s)$ except at the centre peak (Guinier, 1964). Hence the diffraction pattern of such an array is essentially the same as that of a single sphere except that the ring intensities are increased and the half-width of a single ring is approximately half the inter-ring spacing, which makes resolution difficult. Latex spheres have been studied by X-ray diffraction and it has been shown by Danielson et al. (1952) that so long as the array remains disordered, the density of packing has little effect on the positions of the diffraction maxima. Hence random arrays of spheres similar to that shown in Fig. 5a form a useful test specimen for checking angular resolution. The theoretical resolution of the Ferrier three lens method has been confirmed by the diffraction pattern of an array of 1260 Å diameter spheres (Fig. 5b) in which the rings are easily visible. For the very long camera length method diffraction patterns from spheres up to 8000 Å diameter have been obtained with adequate resolution and a pattern from 3650 Å particles using this mode is shown in Fig. 5c. Drahos and Delong (1966) have also used latex spheres to check the resolution of their four lens method.

For the low angle diffraction modes which have theoretical angular resolutions of 10^{-5} radian or better, a more suitable resolution test specimen is the replica of an optical diffraction grating frequently used in image magnification calibration in the electron microscope. The replica consists of a nitrocellulose film (subsequently dissolved away), shadowed with gold or platinum and backed by a carbon film, and it

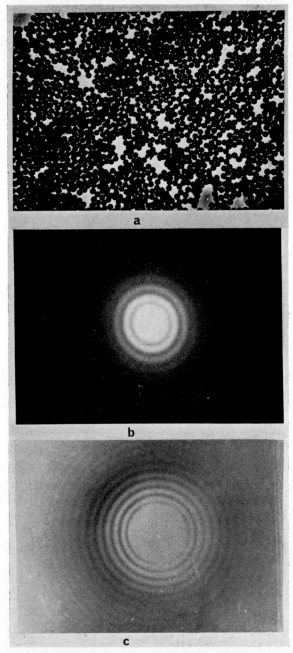

Fig. 5. (a) Electron image of an array of 7960 Å diameter latex spheres. (b) Small angle diffraction pattern from an array of 1260 Å latex spheres using the Ferrier three lens method. (c) Small angle diffraction pattern from an array of 3650 Å spheres using the very long camera length method.

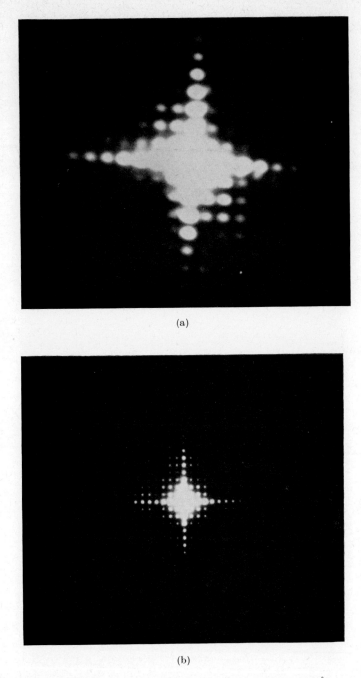

(a)

(b)

FIG. 6. (a), (b) Small angle electron diffraction patterns from 4630 Å cross grating replicas taken using the very long camera length method and the ultrahigh resolution method respectively.

may be obtained in a range of spacings from 4630 Å to 2 μm. The Fourier transform of a grating is a lattice of sharp maxima reciprocal to the grating and the spot separations are governed by the Bragg equation. A 4630 Å cross-grating specimen has been used by Ferrier and Murray to check the resolution of the very long camera length method and an example of such a pattern is shown in Fig. 6a. This may be compared to the diffraction pattern in Fig. 6b which is from a similar specimen but taken in the ultrahigh resolution diffraction

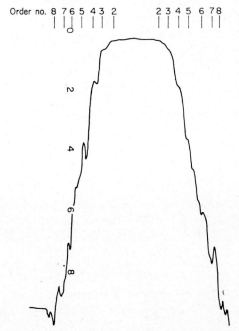

Fig. 7. Microphotometer trace from the diffraction pattern of a copper grid (d = 12·5 μm); ultrahigh resolution method.

mode. For the selected area diffraction mode the 4630 Å grating diffraction pattern is only just resolvable on the photographic plate when the specimen is raised 5 cm above its normal position ($L = 5$ m).

For the ultrahigh resolution technique it is not easy to find suitable resolution test specimens. Curtis et al. (1967) have used 1500 line/inch copper mesh (d = 12·5 μm) as a test specimen and a microphotometer trace from the pattern is shown in Fig. 7. This shows the diffraction peaks to be clearly resolved and confirms that the resolution is close to the predicted value of 40 μm.

It has been shown (Murray, 1967) that the diffraction effects produced by small crystals also provide a useful test of angular resolution. The diffraction pattern from a crystal consists of a series of maxima with the intensity about each lattice point given by the shape transform of the crystal. For a specimen in the form of a parallelepiped the angular separations of the maxima are then given by

$$\theta = \lambda/x_i \qquad (16)$$

where x_i are the crystal dimensions. For a cubic crystal such as MgO oriented with one of the crystal faces perpendicular to the incident electron beam, the intensity distribution around each lattice point is a square array of maxima. The maxima are broad, but there are several advantages in using such patterns as resolution checks. Firstly the shape transform occurs convoluted with each reciprocal lattice point, including the zero order, and hence resolution tests can be made out to large angles. In addition there is a wide range of crystallite sizes in a specimen of MgO smoke and a suitable crystal can be found for each resolution range.

Murray has shown that in the selected area microdiffraction mode the angular resolution when the specimen is in the normal position ($L \approx 80$ cm)—in which case the resolution is limited by the photographic plate and not the optics—is such that shape transform maxima from an MgO crystal of side 1700 Å can just be resolved. If the crystallites are oriented such that the electron beam enters and leaves the crystal through non-parallel faces, each reflection is split due to refractive index effects and this will be discussed in detail in Section III.A3. This type of splitting has been used by Bassett and Keller (1964) to check the resolution of their small angle diffraction technique.

If small angle electron diffraction is to be used in the accurate determination of periodicities then it is essential to know the value of the camera length used in any particular investigation. From a knowledge of the geometry of the microscope and the manner in which the focal lengths of the lenses vary with lens excitation it is possible to calculate the camera length directly using the equations which define L. However this method can lead to relatively large errors of several percent due to lens hysteresis effects. A far more reliable method of determining L is to use a standard specimen. Ideally the standard should be mounted on the same grid as the specimen under observation, in which case the unknown periodicity can be found directly in terms of the known periodicity of the standard. This method has been used by Bassett and Keller (1964) in their studies of polymer structure, the standard specimen being poly-4-methyl pentene-1, for which the inner diffraction ring corresponds to a periodicity of 9·3 Å. A double exposure was used to get the diffraction patterns of the standard and the normal specimen on the same plate.

Murray and Ferrier (1969) have used a slightly different method in

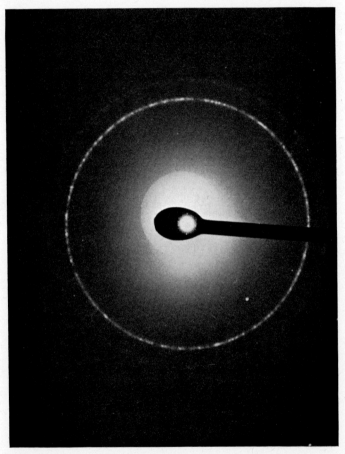

FIG. 8. Illustration of a calibration diffraction pattern for a catalase single crystal the aluminium support film acting as the standard specimen.

determining the lattice periodicities of catalase. Catalase crystals are small ($\sim$1 μm side) and their diffraction patterns were obtained using the selected area microdiffraction mode. In this case instead of using a separate standard specimen mounted on the grid, the negatively stained catalase crystals were mounted on to aluminium (or gold) films, which not only act as the specimen substrate but also as the standard specimen and therefore the diffraction patterns of the sample and standard can be obtained simultaneously. In practice the catalase pattern is relatively more intense than the aluminium and hence two exposures were used. The photographic plate was first exposed for the catalase pattern and then the diffraction beam-stop was inserted to cut out the catalase pattern and the plate was re-exposed to show up the aluminium pattern as illustrated in Fig. 8. Since there is a large difference between the periodicities of the aluminium and catalase the inner ring of the aluminium pattern is several centimetres from the diffraction pattern origin and therefore a small correction ($\sim$0·5%) must be applied to the measured value of the diameter of the ring to take account of the radial distortion of the projector lens. The lattice periodicities of catalase were determined to an accuracy of 1%, as will be discussed in more detail in Section III.B.

It is frequently inconvenient to mount the standard specimen on the same grid as the sample and in this case a separate standard must be used. In practice the standard specimen is inserted into the microscope immediately after the diffraction pattern of the sample has been recorded, care being taken to ensure that the position of the standard in the microscope column is as close as possible to that occupied by the sample. Any lens trimming necessary to get a focused diffraction pattern of the standard specimen should be done using a lens whose excitation has least effect on the camera length.

The particular standard objects chosen for calibration purposes will depend on the nature of the specimens under investigation and where possible the periodicity of the standard should be of the same order as that of the specimen.

F. *Discussion*

In the previous sections we have discussed the techniques which have been developed for the observation of small angle electron diffraction, the theoretical angular resolutions have been derived and the means of checking these experimentally have been discussed. A parameter which has not so far been mentioned is the lateral coherence (Δx_{coh}) of the electron beam in the specimen plane (see Heidenreich, 1964). This is a quantity of some importance since it determines the maximum periodicity which can be studied while still retaining the simple relationship between the diffraction pattern and the Fourier transform of the object. The problem of coherence has been considered by a number of authors (Ferrier and Murray, 1966; Smart, 1968; Curtis, 1968) and their conclusion is that for any small angle diffraction mode

R. P. FERRIER

TABLE I

Method	Lenses excited	Specimen position	Area defining aperture	Specimen area defined by aperture of diameter	Range of camera lengths (in metres)	Angular resolution (in radians at 80 kV)
Mahl and Weitsch method†	OD_1P	In diffraction aperture holder	Objective	0·8 d	15–50	8×10^{-5}
Ferrier 3-lens method†	C_1, C_2, P	Normal	Condenser (Objective)	0·6 d	12–70	3×10^{-5}
Method of Bassett and Keller‡	C_1, C_2, D, P	Normal	Condenser	0·1 d–0·5 d	No figures available	8×10^{-6}
Selected-area micro-diffraction method	C_1, C_2, O, I, P	Normal or raised above objective	Diffraction	0·025 d (normal specimen position)	0·4–0·8	4×10^{-6}
				0·3 d (specimen 5 cm above normal position)	2·5–5·0	
Very long camera length method	C_1, C_2, O, I, P	Normal	Objective	d	10–500	4×10^{-6}
4-lens Method of Drahos and Delong	C_1, C_2, I, P	Normal	Objective	d	4–15	4×10^{-6}
4-lens Method of Wade	C_1, C_2, O, P	Normal	Objective	d	20–80	4×10^{-6}
Ultra high resolution method	C_1, C_2, O, I, P	In diffraction aperture holder	Aperture placed in contact with specimen	d	10–35	1×10^{-7}

† For a Zeiss EM 8 Microscope.   ‡ For a Philips EM 200 Microscope.

the lateral beam coherence is greater than or equal to the limiting value of specimen periodicity set by the angular resolution criterion, i.e. $\Delta x_{coh} \geqslant d_{max}$. For this reason coherence is not a serious problem in small angle electron diffraction.

In discussing the angular resolution in small angle electron diffraction account must be taken of any electrical or mechanical instabilities which may exist in the electron microscope. Murray (1967) has discussed the various factors which could degrade the angular resolution and his analysis shows that in the electron microscope the built-in mechanical and electrical stability necessary for high resolution imaging is also sufficient for there to be no serious deterioration of the angular resolution in small angle electron diffraction. It is, however, important to align the microscope correctly if optimum resolution is to be achieved. Procedures for the various modes should be worked out for individual microscopes and carefully followed before starting an investigation.

The modern electron microscope provides us with a highly versatile diffraction camera and the characteristics of the various modes are summarized in Table I. With two exceptions the data given in the table are those applicable to an A.E.I. EM 6 microscope. However, the values of limiting resolution and camera length applicable to other commercial microscopes can be calculated from the relevant equations if the microscope characteristics are known. The mode of operation selected for any particular application will depend on a number of factors including the type of specimen to be examined and the required angular resolution and camera length; this will be illustrated in the next section when the applications of small angle electron diffraction are discussed. In this context it is worth noting that provided the area of the specimen illuminated remains constant, the intensity in a diffraction spot is proportional to the square of the angular resolution and hence since lack of intensity can be a serious problem it is necessary to select carefully the value of angular resolution to be used in a particular investigation.

III. APPLICATIONS OF SMALL ANGLE ELECTRON DIFFRACTION

Although the Abbe theory of image formation states that the information contained in a diffraction pattern is identical to that in the image of the specimen, there is no direct method of recording the relative phases of the diffraction spots. Since this information is essential in carrying out a Fourier analysis to reconstruct the object, it might well be thought that diffraction is a very poor substitute for imaging. However, this is not in fact the case for several reasons. The information contained in a diffraction pattern is displayed in a different manner to that in the image and provides a statistical analysis of the periodicities within the specimen area examined. This information can be of value in helping to interpret the electron microscope image. Also in imaging conditions in the electron microscope there are difficulties associated with lens aberrations, contrast and focusing which are not so severe in the case of electron diffraction. Finally there are cases where small angle diffraction provides information which could either not be obtained in any other way or at best only with considerable difficulty.

To date, small angle electron diffraction has been applied to investigations in the fields of physics, biology and polymer structure and it is under these headings that the applications will be discussed in the following paragraphs.

A. *Applications in Physics*

a. *The Structure of Evaporated Films.* The study of the properties of thin vacuum condensed metallic films has become of increasing interest in recent years not only from a fundamental viewpoint but also because of their device applications. For polycrystalline films many of the properties, e.g. magnetic, electrical and optical, depend critically on the film thickness and microstructure and hence structural studies of films from initial growth to continuous film are of considerable importance. The major tool in such studies has been transmission electron microscopy and by this means it has been shown (Sennett and Scott, 1950; Pashley, 1965) that after nucleation at random sites on the substrate surface, film growth proceeds first by the nuclei coalescing to form an island type structure and then the islands grow and coalesce to form the continuous film.

The first application of small angle electron diffraction in this field was reported by Mahl and Weitsch (1960a) who showed that a thin film with an island type structure will give a small angle diffraction ring at an angle corresponding quite closely to the mean island separation. A somewhat more detailed discussion of small angle diffraction effects from thin films has been given by Wade and Silcox (1967). They show that in agreement with theory, a small angle diffraction ring arising purely from structural effects will only be observed when there are discontinuities in the film (see Fig. 9). These discontinuities may be in the form of physical gaps between the separate islands or grains in the film, or they may arise from the presence of foreign matter such as oxide between the grains. When the extent of the discontinuities is small they may not be visible in an in-focus micrograph, although they will give rise to Fresnel fringes in out-of-focus

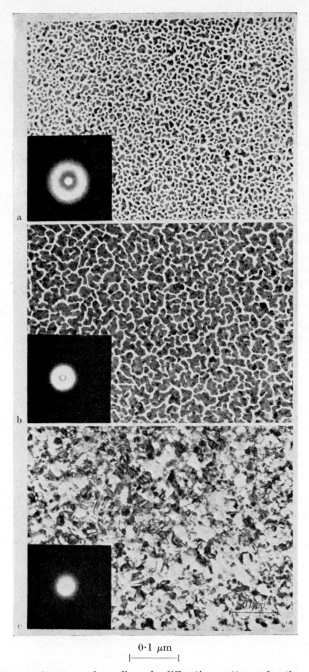

0·1 μm
|————————|

FIG. 9. Electron images and small angle diffraction patterns for three gold films prepared by evaporation on to carbon substrates held at room temperature. Note that in (a) and (b) the discontinuous nature of the film produces a small angle diffraction ring whereas in (c) the film is continuous and no diffraction ring is observed. The ring in (a) corresponds on the Bragg law to a periodicity of ∼100 Å. Reproduced with permission from Wade and Silcox (1967).

conditions. In this case small angle diffraction is a more convenient method of detecting the discontinuous nature of the film. Wade and Silcox have also shown that under certain evaporation conditions columnar growth of the crystallites can occur (Fig. 10a). The diffraction pattern from such a structure shows a small angle ring when the incident electron beam is normal to the film plane (Fig. 10b), but on tilting the film relative to the beam the ring breaks up into two spots due to the influence of the shape transform of the columns (Fig. 10c).

The observation of thin film growth has been carried out by in-situ transmission electron microscopy, but difficulties are encountered in the initial growth stages due to lack of contrast in the image and Grigson and Dove (1966) estimate that the limit of observable island size is $\sim$20 Å. Extensive studies of thin film growth characteristics have also been made using the normal high angle electron diffraction pattern as the basis of the analysis (for a review of this work see Grigson, 1968). Many of these studies were not made in an electron microscope, but in scanning electron diffraction equipment with direct intensity recording and with velocity filtering to enable the inelastically scattered electrons to be excluded from the diffraction pattern. For an island type film structure it can be shown that the intensity in a high angle diffraction ring is proportional to $N_i N_a$ where N_i is the number of islands irradiated and N_a the average number of atoms in an island. An island type structure will also give rise to a small angle diffraction ring and since the ring intensity is now proportional to $N_i N_a^2$ small angle diffraction provides a more sensitive means of detecting the initial growth stages (Denbigh and Dove, 1967; Tompsett et al., 1967). The elastic small angle diffraction patterns from a growth sequence of silver on carbon, taken from the paper of Tompsett et al. is shown in Fig. 11 and illustrates the marked changes in the intensity profiles which occur for relatively small changes in the average film thickness. To interpret the patterns, a quantitative theory of small angle diffraction was developed for the particular case of an island type structure. Values for the mean island size and mean island separation were obtained by computer fitting of the theoretical diffraction profile to the observed intensities. Although assumptions had to be made in deriving the theoretical intensity profile the computed parameters were found to agree well with values obtained from analysis of electron micrographs at later growth stages and hence the technique is one of considerable promise for this type of structure determination.

In the small angle region the differential cross-section for inelastic electron scattering is normally considerably greater than that for elastic scattering (see Section IV). The inelastically scattered electrons

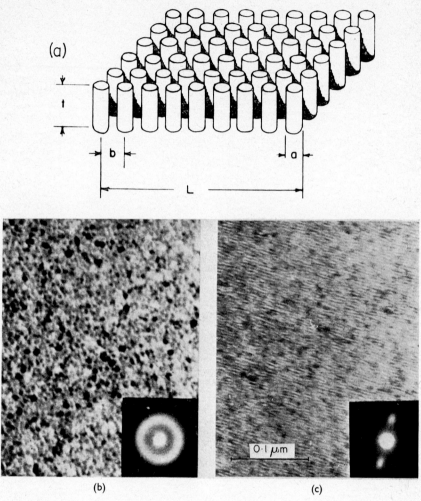

FIG. 10. (a) Schematic illustration of columnar structure in evaporated metal films. (b) Out-of-focus micrograph and small angle diffraction pattern from a permalloy film 300 Å thickness prepared by vacuum deposition on to a carbon substrate at a rate of 3 Å/sec. The electron beam was incident normal to the film and there is no evidence for a columnar structure. (c) The same area of the film as in (b) but with the film plane tilted through an angle of 60° to the incident beam direction. The influence of the shape transform of the columnar structure causes the small angle diffraction ring to split into two spots. Reproduced with permission from Wade and Silcox (1967).

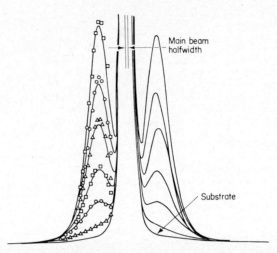

FIG. 11. Small angle diffraction patterns from a growth sequence of silver on carbon at successive increments of 0·75 Å average film thickness. The electrons contributing to the pattern were "filtered" i.e. they had lost less than 2 eV in energy. The plotted points were obtained by curve fitting the theoretical intensity profile to the observed intensity curves. Reproduced with permission from Tompsett *et al.* (1967).

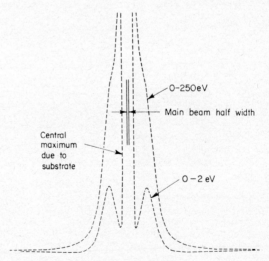

FIG. 12. Filtered and unfiltered diffraction profiles of a 5 Å silver film on a carbon substrate. Filtered profile consists largely of elastically scattered electrons, unfiltered profile contains up to 250 eV loss electrons.

contribute an intense background to the diffraction pattern and if quantitative intensity measurements are required the inelastic electrons must be excluded from the pattern. This problem may be illustrated with reference to Fig. 12 which shows a diffraction pattern from the growth sequence described in the previous paragraph. In the figure the elastic diffraction profile may be compared to that obtained when electrons with energy losses up to 250 eV (i.e. effectively all the scattered electrons) are allowed to contribute to the pattern; the improvement in the contrast of the small angle ring is striking. In this case the exclusion of the inelastic electrons was achieved using a retarding-field electron velocity filter (Boersch, 1953); other types of velocity filters and analysers which have been constructed would be suitable for this purpose and the reader is referred to a review article by Klemperer (1965) which deals with these electron optical devices. As yet no technique has been described in the literature which would allow a complete elastic diffraction pattern to be displayed in a form suitable for photographic recording. For this reason the technique normally employed is to scan the diffraction pattern across an aperture below which is the filter device, and to record the elastic intensity directly using a scintillator-photomultiplier assembly. In this way the intensity versus scattering angle curves may be recorded on an x-y plotter (Denbigh and Grigson, 1965). To utilize this technique modifications must be made to the standard electron microscope and a schematic diagram of such a modification made in the author's laboratory (Ferrier and Curtis, 1969) is shown in Fig. 13. For high resolution work the intensities in the small angle diffraction pattern are very weak and noise is a severe problem. Amplification of the weak signals is necessary prior to recording and to avoid the problem of drift associated with d.c. amplification, phase sensitive detection techniques are employed which allow a.c. amplification of the signal. The necessary beam chopping is achieved by feeding an a.c. voltage on to the pair of deflection plates located between the defining aperture and the velocity filter.

b. *Magnetic Structure.* The study of the domain structure of thin ferromagnetic specimens by electron microscopy has proved of considerable importance since the initial development of Lorentz microscopy by Boersch and Raith (1959) and by Hale *et al.* (1959). There are now a number of different ways in which the microscope can be operated to show "magnetic" contrast and these have been reviewed recently by Grundy and Tebble (1968). An electron beam traversing a ferromagnetic film will be deviated by the Lorentz force through an

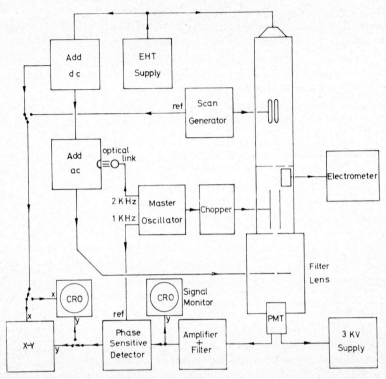

Fig. 13. Schematic illustration of the technique of scanning electron diffraction with velocity filtering as applied in an electron microscope.

angle ϕ and for small deviations ϕ is given by

$$\phi = 4\pi M_s d\left(U^2 + \frac{2m_o c^2}{e}\, U\right)^{-\frac{1}{2}} \tag{17}$$

where U is the electron accelerating voltage, M_s is the saturation magnetization of the material and d is the film thickness. The above equation is based on the assumption that the magnetization is constrained to lie in the film plane, which is true only for thin films, and that the bulk values of M_s and film density are applicable. For a particular case the value of M_s can in principle be inferred from out-of-focus micrographs, but a better method is to observe the beam deviation directly in the small angle diffraction pattern (Schaffernicht, 1963; Boersch et al., 1961; Ferrier and Wade, 1964). Two examples of such patterns taken using the three lens method of Ferrier are shown in Fig. 14. The whole of the incident beam will be deviated by the internal field and there will be no "central spot" unless there is a hole

(a)

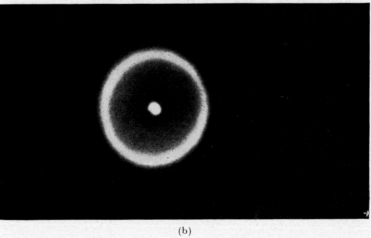

(b)

FIG. 14. Rings formed in the diffraction image by electron beam deviation in ferro-magnetic thin films. The presence of the centre spot in (b) is due to a crack in the film.

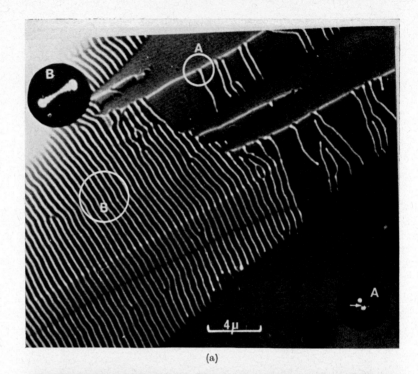

(a)

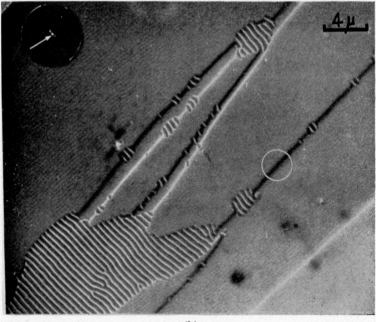

(b)

Fig. 15.

or crack in the film. From the ring diameters of these patterns and knowing the camera length and film thickness it is possible to calculate the value of M_s exhibited by the specimen. Ferrier and Wade found discrepancies between the observed and bulk values of M_s for thin (200–1000 Å) evaporated films of iron, nickel and permalloy, the ratio $(M_s$ observed$)/(M_s$ bulk$)$ being dependent on the substrate temperature during deposition. The temperature dependence of the saturation magnetization can also be determined from small angle diffraction studies if a heating stage is available.

In specimens which are of suitable thickness for examination by electron microscopy the magnetization is not necessarily constrained to lie in the specimen plane. The particular spin configuration exhibited by a specimen will be determined by the specimen thickness and magnetic properties, and small angle electron diffraction studies can prove invaluable in investigating the magnetic structure of such specimens. Ferrier and Puchalska (1968) have shown that permalloy films evaporated at oblique incidence and of thickness 1700–3500 Å exhibit a "weak" stripe domain structure for angles of incidence $\theta \leqslant 45°$ and a "strong" stripe domain structure for angles of incidence $\theta \geqslant 45°$. For films evaporated at $\theta = 45°$ the two types of stripe domains can co-exist in the same film. The transformation from weak to strong stripe domain structure was observed to occur in two different ways and the mechanisms were determined by analysis of the corresponding small angle diffraction patterns as illustrated in Fig. 15(a),(b). In one case (Fig. 15a) the initial stage of growth of the strong stripe domains was the formation of 360° walls in alternate domains; the 360° walls subsequently grow together to form the strong stripe domain structure. The small angle diffraction pattern from a region containing a Bloch wall and a 360° wall is shown in the inset of Fig. 15a and the position of the origin of the diffraction pattern is indicated. Analysis of this pattern shows that the direction of the average magnetization relative to the film plane in the regions of weak stripe domains differs in alternate domains. In the domains in which the 360° walls grow

---

Fig. 15. (a) Lorentz micrograph of a permalloy film of thickness $t = 2500$ Å prepared by vacuum evaporation on to a glass substrate at an angle of incidence $\theta = 45°$. The micrograph shows the weak and strong stripe domain structures and the 360° walls growing from the Bloch walls. The insets A and B show the small angle diffraction patterns from the corresponding areas marked by the circles. The position of the "central spot" in inset A was determined in a separate experiment and is shown marked by the dot at the tip of the arrow. (b) Lorentz micrograph of a permalloy film $t = 2500$ Å, $\theta = 45°$. The strong stripe domains are nucleated directly in the Bloch walls. The inset shows the diffraction pattern from the region marked by the circle, the position of the "central spot" being marked by the dot at the tip of the arrow.

the average magnetization direction lies at an angle of 80° to the film plane and in the other domains the angle is 50°. In each case there will be a relatively high density of free surface poles and the 360° walls are created to reduce the magnetostatic energy. The second mechanism is illustrated in Fig. 15b and in this case the small angle diffraction pattern shows that the average magnetization direction in the weak stripe domains is at an angle of 60° to the film plane and is anti-parallel in alternate domains. Hence there is no reason why one domain should be more favourable than another for the growth of the strong stripe domains. The strong stripe domains are therefore nucleated directly in the Bloch walls and grow out equally into neighbouring domains.

The diffraction pattern from the strong stripe domain structure is illustrated in the second inset of Fig. 15a and an analysis of this pattern should lead to the spin configuration which gives rise to the stripe domain contrast. Analyses of this type have been made of the spin configuration in a type of stripe domain structure observed in cobalt foils thinned from the bulk (Goringe and Jakubovics, 1967;

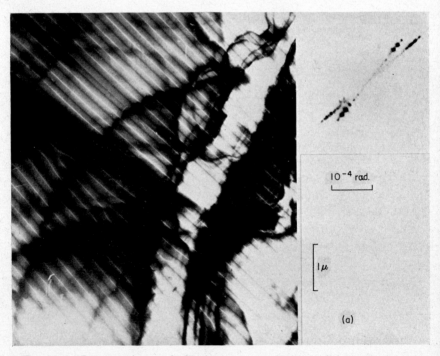

FIG. 16. (a) Lorentz micrograph showing an array of anti-parallel domains in a thin cobalt foil and the corresponding small angle diffraction pattern arising from the magnetic structure.

Wade, 1967). A Lorentz micrograph of the cobalt domain structure and the corresponding diffraction pattern are shown in Fig. 16a. The set of anti-parallel domains act as a phase grating and the intensity $I(s)$ in the diffraction pattern is given by a product of two components

$$I(s) = I_1(s) \times I_2(s) \tag{18}$$

$I_1(s)$ corresponds to the interference pattern produced by a diffraction grating with the periodicity of the stripe domains and composed of infinitely narrow slits. $I_2(s)$ corresponds to the diffraction pattern from a single slit of width equal to the domain periodicity and with the appropriate phase variation across it. The intensity distribution was calculated on the basis of a model in which it was assumed that the domain wall width was infinitely narrow and the magnetization direction in alternate domains was anti-parallel and at an angle to the specimen normal. The resulting intensity distribution is shown in Fig. 16b and the agreement with the observed diffraction pattern is very good. In principle the spin configuration could be calculated directly (without recourse to a model) by a Fourier analysis using the

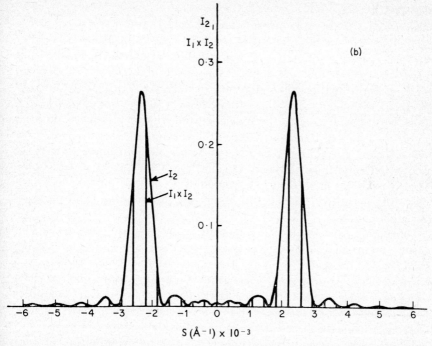

FIG. 16. (b) The theoretical values of $I_2(s)$ and $I_1(s)\,I_2(s)$ as a function of angle computed on the basis of the model proposed for the domain structure in (a). Reproduced with permission of Goringe and Jakubovics (1967).

observed diffraction pattern intensities. However, an analysis of this type is difficult because there is no way of recording the relative phases of the diffraction spots.

Small angle electron diffraction provides a powerful tool for the study of magnetic structure, and it is probable that this is one of the fields in which the techniques will prove of most value.

c. *Fine Structure in Diffraction Patterns.* The distribution of electrons scattered by a crystal is to a first approximation proportional to the square of the Fourier transform of the lattice potential. Thus, as discussed previously, the intensity in the region of a reciprocal lattice point is proportional to the square of the crystal shape transform and for a parallelepiped is given by equation (15). In addition for polyhedral crystals, electrons entering and leaving the crystal through pairs of non-parallel faces will be deviated by an effective refractive index μ which on the two beam approximation is given by (Sturkey, 1948)

$$\mu = 1 - \frac{V_o \pm V_{hkl}}{2U} \tag{19}$$

where V_o is the crystal inner potential and V_{hkl} the real part of the coefficient of Fourier potential of the (hkl) reflection. Hence a beam of electrons passing through two non-parallel crystal faces will be split into two components, the angular separation of which is proportional to V_{hkl}. The splitting will be present in both the Bragg reflection and the zero order beam and from a knowledge of the crystal geometry and its orientation relative to the incident beam the coefficients of Fourier potential can be determined directly without recourse to intensity measurements, the interpretation of which is difficult under dynamical diffraction conditions (Moliere and Niehrs, 1955; Cowley *et al.*, 1957). The determination of accurate values of V_{hkl} is of importance since they are necessary for crystal structure determination by Fourier analysis.

Diffraction spots exhibiting fine structure resulting from the two effects mentioned above have been observed in conventional high resolution diffraction cameras (Rees and Spink, 1950; Moliere and Niehrs, 1955). However, in these cameras it was impossible to select small specimen areas and hence the fine structure of the zero order beam could not be detected due to the large amount of inelastic scattering from the substrate used to support the small crystals.

The selected area diffraction mode allows the examination of very small specimen areas and hence the effect of inelastic scattering from the substrate can be considerably reduced. Ferrier and Murray (1968) have shown that this technique can be used to examine the fine structure of the zero order beam in diffraction patterns from small MgO crystals as illustrated in Fig. 17. Their analysis of this method shows that it has distinct advantages for the determination of the V_{hkl} of weak reflections and hence could prove of considerable importance in crystal structure determination.

FIG. 17. Double refraction maxima convoluted with the shape transform function on the zero order beam produced by several MgO crystals.

The high angular resolution of the small angle diffraction techniques is applicable in the high angle as well as the small angle region of diffraction patterns. Hence the methods can be used to study fine structure in the high angle diffraction pattern if the region of interest is brought into view on the fluorescent screen by means of the beam tilt controls. One example of such an application is illustrated in Fig. 18 which shows the diffraction pattern from a zinc sulphide crystal containing an array of stacking faults. The fine structure between the Bragg reflections arises from the stacking faults which act in a manner similar to a slit in optical Fraunhöfer diffraction (Fitzgerald and Mannami, 1966).

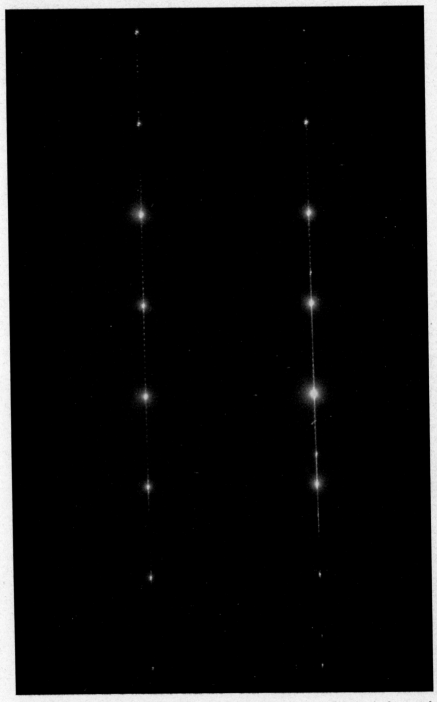

FIG. 18. Part of the high angle diffraction pattern from a zinc sulphide single crystal containing an array of stacking faults.

d. *Electrostatic Charging Effects.* In an electron microscope the high energy incident beam causes the emission of secondary electrons from the specimen. If the specimen is an insulator a charge will build up until a dynamic equilibrium is reached when the rate of charge generation is balanced by some neutralization mechanism. The first quantitative study of specimen charging was reported by Mahl and Weitsch (1959, 1960b) who observed that shadow images of thin insulating foils gave the appearance of fluctuating bright and dark spots—the "bee-swarm" effect as it was subsequently called (Dove, 1964). On the assumption that the electric fields were confined to the specimen volume, they calculated the strength of the microfields as 10^8 V/m and proposed that the mottled appearance was due to charge neutralization of local regions of high positive charge by field emission from neighbouring regions. Specimen charging effects have also been studied by other workers (Dove, 1964; Drahos and Delong, 1965; Komoda and Hosoki, 1966) all of whom used the off-focus technique in the observations.

An alternative method of studying specimen charging is to use the techniques of small angle scattering to observe directly the deflections of the incident electron beam produced by the electric fields built up on the specimen. Murray (1967) and Curtis (1968) have used the very long camera length method to investigate the electrostatic charging of collodion and formvar films supported over different types of grids. The objective aperture was used to select the area of interest and Fig. 19 illustrates the type of deflection patterns obtained for different settings of the specimen relative to the aperture. When the selected area does not contain the centre of a grid square there are no electrons scattered in the zero angle direction which indicates that the centre of the grid square is a point of zero field. A careful study of diffraction patterns of this type also shows that the electrons passing closest to the grid bars are deflected through the largest angles. The deflection patterns from collodion films mounted on rectangular aperture grids of differing widths can be used to give information on the distribution of electrostatic potential on the charged films. An analysis of the results shows that the magnitude of the potential is in the range 1–20 V depending on the assumptions made in the calculations (Curtis, 1968).

In the discussion of the three lens methods of small angle diffraction given in Section II.A it was stated that insulating support films should be avoided in small angle diffraction studies. The reason for this is that if the specimen area irradiated contains a portion of a grid bar, a deflection pattern from the charged foil will always be present and this will tend to obscure diffraction effects in the very small angle

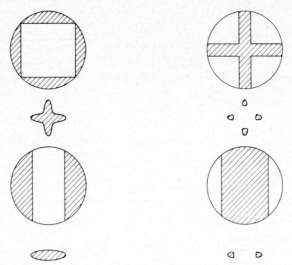

FIG. 19. Small angle deflection patterns obtained from charged collodion films when the area defining aperture is varied in position relative to the grid bar structure.

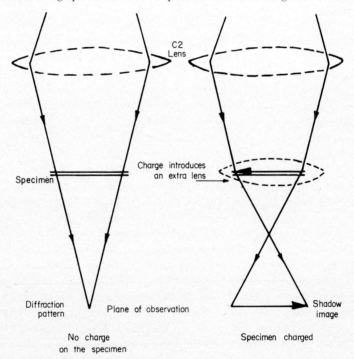

FIG. 20. The mechanism of the "lens effect". When a grid bar is not included in the irradiated area of the specimen the part which is exposed to the beam charges up to such an extent that it forms a converging electrostatic lens. This lens produces a point-projection image of the film in the plane in which the small angle diffraction pattern is normally found. Reproduced with permission from Curtis (1968).

region. Even worse effects occur if the irradiated area does not contain a grid bar, for in this case it is not possible to obtain a diffraction pattern. This effect can be explained with the aid of Fig. 20. Varying the excitation of the second condenser lens alters the specimen area illuminated and when this area is small enough so that a grid bar is not intersected, the shadow image (i.e. the out-of-focus diffraction pattern) "blows-up" into one of much higher magnification as shown

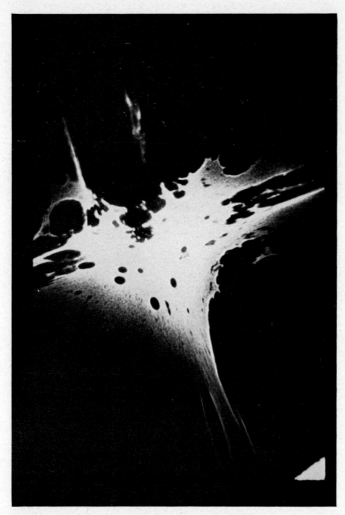

FIG. 21. Shadow image of latex spheres on a collodion film produced by the "lens effect". The optical arrangement of the microscope was such that in normal conditions a small angle diffraction pattern would be obtained on the viewing screen.

in Fig. 21. This indicates that in the absence of grid bar illumination the potential on the insulating film is considerably increased and the charged film acts as a convergent electrostatic lens. For this reason the phenomenon has been termed the "lens effect." From observations of this type Curtis has been able to show that the field emission mechanism proposed for the charge neutralization is incorrect and that the stabilizing effect of the grid bars is almost certainly due to the capture by the film of secondary electrons emitted by the grid bars. This model has also been used to explain quantitatively the "bee-swarm" effect.

B. *Applications in Biology*

Crystalline biological specimens frequently exhibit large periodicities and investigation of their structure has mainly been either by conventional electron microscopy or by X-ray small angle diffraction. The first reports of the application of small angle electron diffraction in

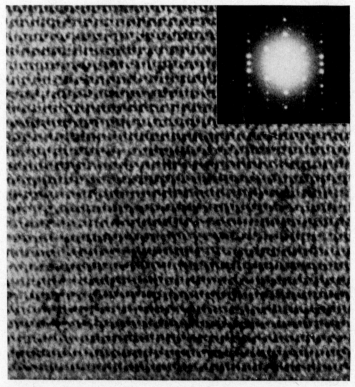

Fig. 22. Electron micrograph and small angle diffraction pattern of a crystal of catalase negatively stained with 2% ammonium molybdate. ×450,000.

the biological field were by Mahl and Weitsch (1960a) who obtained a diffraction pattern from an array of collagen fibrils and by Smart and Burge (1965) who obtained diffraction patterns from assemblies of virus particles. A more extensive study of the application of electron diffraction in biology has been made by Murray and Ferrier (1967) and this work will be discussed in the following paragraphs.

The selected area diffraction mode was applied in the study of the structure of the beef liver enzyme catalase. Clear diffraction patterns and images from this material were obtained when the specimen was negatively stained with a 2% solution of ammonium molybdate at a pH of 5·5. Examples are shown in Figs 22–24. It was never found possible to obtain diffraction patterns from unstained crystals nor from crystals dried under vacuum and then treated with negative stain. These observations are in agreement with the work of Hall (1950) and indicate that the crystals disintegrate under the effect of vacuum and before electron irradiation. This problem of specimen instability is one of the major sources of difficulty in structural studies by electron microscopy or diffraction and will be discussed in detail later.

In studies of periodic biological material a combination of imaging and diffraction studies can prove useful and is easily achieved in the microdiffraction mode merely by changing the excitation of the inter-mediate lens. An example which illustrates this point is shown in Fig. 23 which is the image of a catalase crystal supported over a hole in a carbon film and the corresponding diffraction pattern. A unit cell as determined by electron diffraction includes part of two adjacent parallel molecular chains which in the micrograph appear identical. However, the presence of the odd order reflections in the second and third layer lines indicates that there must be some characteristic difference between the neighbouring chains and this was confirmed by micrographs from other specimens (see Fig. 22).

Electron micrographs of catalase frequently show detail below the 20 Å level. However, a careful examination shows that this detail does not repeat periodically and hence there must be some doubt that it represents true structure in the specimen. These observations are reflected in the small angle diffraction patterns which show a rapid fall off in scattered intensity with angle and the lack of any maxima corresponding to periodicities less than 20 Å. Since the diffraction pattern provides a statistical analysis of periodicities in the specimen it is a much more sensitive and convenient test of periodicity than the visual examination of electron micrographs.

One of the major advantages of small angle diffraction relative to electron imaging is in the determination of accurate lattice parameters.

FIG. 23. Electron micrograph and small angle diffraction pattern of negatively stained crystal of catalase supported over a hole in the carbon substrate. ×350,000.

Magnification calibration in imaging conditions is difficult and accuracies are seldom better than 5%. In small angle electron diffraction, however, the camera length can be accurately calibrated using a standard specimen. In the study of catalase a gold (or aluminium) film was used as both the substrate and the standard specimen (see Section II.E for details). The dimensions of the catalase lattice projection were determined from 40 independent diffraction patterns as

$$a = 64 \cdot 2 \pm 0 \cdot 7 \text{ Å}$$
$$c = 168 \cdot 8 \pm 0 \cdot 7 \text{ Å}$$

In an attempt to determine the third dimension of the catalase unit cell a series of tilting experiments were carried out. The specimen was clamped between two tubular wedges in the normal specimen holder and by varying the angle of the wedges and utilizing the $\pm 5°$ stereo tilt mechanism a large range of tilt angles could be achieved. The micrographs and diffraction patterns were essentially similar to those obtained from crystals in the normal orientation (c.f. Figs 22

Fig. 24. Electron micrograph and small angle diffraction pattern from a negatively stained catalase crystal tilted through an angle of 45° about an axis which is indicated by the arrow in the figure. × 140,000.

and 24) and no additional reflections from the third dimension of the crystal were observed. An analysis of these results indicates that it is probable that the negative stain replicates detail near the surface on one side of the crystal only and hence one is essentially examining a two dimensional rather than a three dimensional specimen.

Two other proteins, ferritin and collagen, have been studied by the selected area microdiffraction mode. Compared with catalase both these specimens are much less sensitive to the effects of vacuum and clear diffraction patterns have been obtained from them without recourse to negative staining. Figure 25 shows an electron micrograph from a ferritin crystal and the corresponding small angle diffraction pattern. A rough calibration of the diffraction pattern gave $a = b = 110 \pm 10$ Å for the unit cell dimensions of the lattice projection. The fact that very few reflections are visible in the diffraction pattern is attributed to the disordered nature of the crystal, which is evident on close examination of the micrograph. In the ferritin specimens, the area of carbon substrate surrounding the crystals is always covered by a dense random dispersion of ferritin molecules. Diffraction patterns from such areas are composed of a series of rings and a radial distribution analysis of such a pattern will lead to a value for the radius of gyration of the molecule.

There are a number of difficulties associated with the application of small angle electron diffraction methods to structural studies of biological material. Perhaps the most important problem is that of specimen preservation particularly in the case of protein crystals. To some extent the use of negative staining techniques offsets this difficulty; however, it appears that only the surface structure of crystals may be replicated and it would be highly desirable to be able to observe the crystal as a whole. Perhaps a more promising solution lies in the use of the atmospheric microcell (Stoyanova and Mikhailovski, 1959; Dupouy *et al.*, 1960) in which the specimen may be immersed in a controlled atmosphere. In this way the specimen damage due to dehydration should be drastically reduced, although this may be balanced by specimen damage resulting from chemical reaction with free radicals such as H_2O_2 created by electron bombardment of the water vapour (Heide, 1962). The advent of high voltage electron microscopy (for a review article on the subject see Dupouy, 1968) should help in overcoming the problem of specimen preservation. The increased penetration available at high accelerating voltages will make the construction of wet-cells somewhat easier and, in addition, for a particular specimen radiation damage due to the electron beam will be reduced.

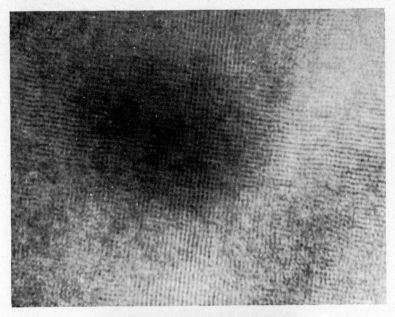

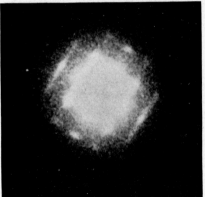

FIG. 25. Electron micrograph and small angle diffraction pattern from a disordered ferritin crystal. × 100,000.

Another problem which arises in small angle diffraction is the intense background scattering due mainly to inelastic scattering in the specimen and its support film. In general the best way to tackle this problem is to use scanning electron diffraction techniques with velocity filtering (see Section III.A 1) to reject all the inelastically scattered electrons from the diffraction pattern. An example of this is illustrated in Fig. 26 which shows the total and elastic profiles from a catalase diffraction

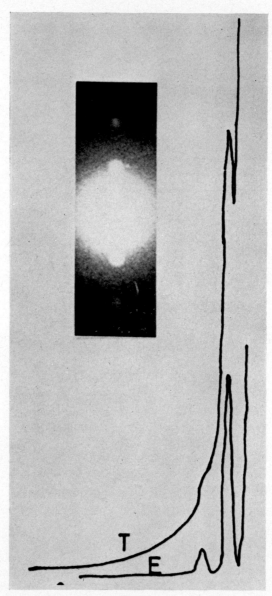

FIG. 26. The total (T) and elastic (E) diffraction profiles from a negatively stained crystal of catalase. A photograph of the unfiltered small angle diffraction pattern is inserted for comparison.

pattern, a photograph of which is inserted for comparison. The large gain in contrast in the diffraction pattern is clearly visible and this type of recording would almost certainly be essential if a full structural analysis was to be made.

In the case of single crystal or single particle diffraction studies a further improvement of the contrast in the diffraction pattern may be achieved if the shape of the aperture defining the area of the specimen contributing to the diffraction pattern is optimized for the particular specimen under investigation. This may be illustrated with reference to tobacco mosaic virus (T.M.V.) particles which have a projected area of 3000 Å × 100 Å. In the selected-area diffraction mode a circular diffraction aperture will of course define a circular area at the specimen and hence for a T.M.V. particle the ratio of specimen area/substrate area contributing to the pattern will be low. The requirement then is for a very small diffraction aperture which in projection in the specimen plane can be adjusted to a size of about the same length as the particle and 2–3 times its width. (Unfortunately any aperture narrower than this will make the virus particle diffraction pattern uninterpretable because of its superimposed shape transform.) For the T.M.V. case an aperture of size 10 × 0·5 μm would be suitable but such apertures are not commercially available. A novel method of overcoming this difficulty is to use an ordinary circular aperture and tilt it so that it is "seen" by the specimen as a very eccentric ellipse (Murray and Ferrier, 1969). A special holder can be constructed to allow the aperture to be tilted and aligned on the optic axis of the microscope.

C. *The Structure of Polymers*

X-ray small angle diffraction studies have shown that most crystal-line polymers exhibit discrete reflections at angles corresponding to periodicities in the range 100–400 Å; this work has been reviewed by Statton (1964) and by Geil (1966). On the basis of the X-ray results alone it is extremely difficult to interpret the observed periodicities in terms of the morphology of the specimen and hence the possibility of combining imaging and small angle diffraction studies in an electron microscope is a very attractive one. Bassett and Keller (1964) were the first authors to report such studies, their work being carried out on highly drawn polyethylene films from which surface layers were detached for examination in the electron microscope. In these studies a variety of diffraction effects were found, as illustrated in Figs. 27 and 28. Although the types of pattern were qualitatively similar to those observed in X-ray studies, the periodicities were considerably greater being in the range 1000–2000 Å. In this type of investigation small

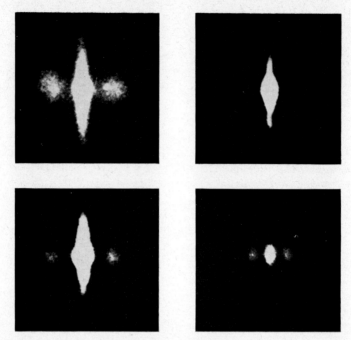

FIG. 27. Some typical small angle electron diffraction patterns of drawn polyethylene. The spacings are in the range 1000–2000 Å and the draw direction is vertical. Reproduced with permission from Bassett and Keller (1964).

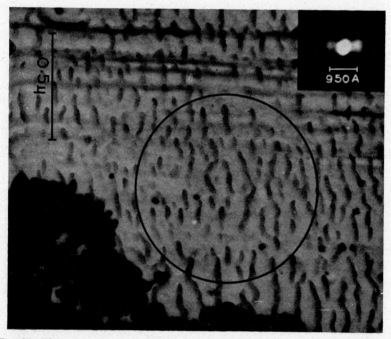

FIG. 28. Electron micrograph of a drawn polyethylene specimen and the small angle diffraction pattern of the area indicated by the circle. Reproduced with permission from Bassett and Keller (1964).

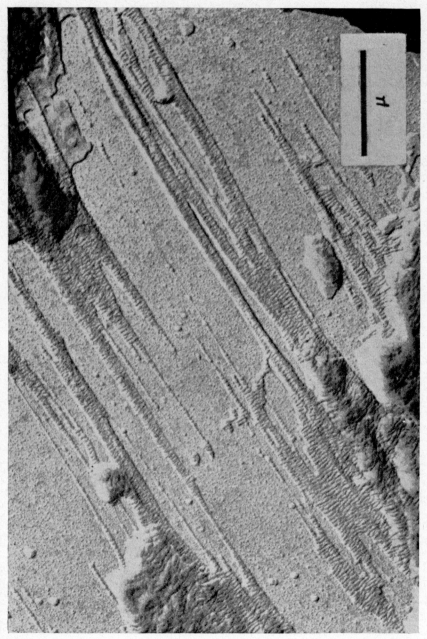

FIG. 29. Electron micrograph showing the striated structure formed in polyethylene after annealing at 118°C for 21 hours.

angle diffraction provides a sensitive and convenient test of regularly repeating structure.

Small angle electron diffraction has also been applied by Yeh and Geil (1967) to studies of polyethylene terepthalate (PETP) and polyethylene. These authors used the selected area diffraction mode and one of the interesting results on PETP was a negative one in that an annealed specimen (Fig. 29) did not exhibit a diffraction pattern, whereas bulk specimens treated in a similar manner would be expected to give an X-ray pattern. They suggest in explanation that electrons may be more sensitive than X-rays to defects in a structure. Perhaps a more plausible explanation is that the absence of a diffraction pattern is caused by a combination of two effects. Firstly, if the structure is not perfectly periodic, the intensity in the diffraction spots will be smeared out making detection more difficult. Secondly, the regions which exhibit structure in the micrograph are not extensive in comparison with the disordered regions and hence any diffraction effects may be swamped by the inelastic scattering from the specimen area irradiated.

IV. ELECTRON SCATTERING AT SMALL ANGLES

It is beyond the scope of this review article to present a detailed discussion of the complex theory of the scattering of medium fast electrons by matter and the reader is referred to a general review article by Scott (1963), to a discussion by Calbick (1964) of the theory applicable to the thin films of interest in electron microscopy and to a review article by Raether (1965) on the theoretical and practical aspects of plasmon excitation and interband transitions. Nevertheless to appreciate fully the scope and the problems of small angle diffraction it is necessary to have a knowledge of the theoretical predictions for the elastic and inelastic scattering cross-sections, and of course precise cross-section data will be required if a full structural analysis is to be attempted. Of the recent theories of small angle electron scattering only those of Lenz (1954) and of Burge and his co-workers (Burge and Smart, 1969; Smart, 1968; Misell, 1968) have been specifically extended to cover the angular range of interest; these theories will be outlined in the following paragraphs and the results will be discussed.

By applying the Born approximation in a wave mechanical treatment and assuming spherically symmetric atoms, Mott (1930) derived an expression for the effective elastic differential cross-section of an atom in the form

$$\frac{d\sigma_e}{d\Omega} = [f_e(\phi)]^2 = \frac{4}{a_H^{*2}q^4}(Z - f_x)^2 \qquad (20)$$

where a_H^* is the relativistic Bohr radius, f_x and f_e are the atomic scattering factors for X-rays and elastic electrons respectively and $q = (4\pi/\lambda) \sin \phi/2$, ϕ being the angle through which the electrons are scattered. The Mott equation is difficult to manipulate and in his calculations Lenz used instead a scattering formula due to Wentzel (1932)

$$\frac{d\sigma_e}{d\Omega} = \frac{4}{a_H^{*2}q^4} \frac{Z^2}{\left(1 + \dfrac{1}{q^2 R^2}\right)^2} \qquad (21)$$

which follows from the Born approximation for the potential at r in the screened Coulomb field

$$V(r) = \frac{Ze}{r} \exp\left(-r/R\right) \qquad (22)$$

By finding the limit of equation (20) as $q \to 0$, the atomic radius R can be expressed in terms of $f_e(0)$, the elastic scattering factor at zero angle, and on this basis Lenz derived an equation for R in the form

$$R^2 = \frac{\Theta}{6Z} \qquad (23)$$

where

$$\Theta = \int_0^\infty \rho(r) 4\pi r^4 \, dr \qquad (24)$$

$\rho(r)$ being the radial electron density distribution in the atom. For carbon and chromium Lenz used Hartree wave functions to evaluate equation (24).

In 1932 Morse showed that the effect of inelastic scattering could be incorporated into the Mott expression (equation (20)) by the addition of a term S identically equal to the incoherent scattering factor for X-rays. Hence the equation defining the atomic differential inelastic cross-section is

$$\frac{d\sigma_i}{d\Omega} = \frac{4}{a_H^{*2}q^4} S \qquad (25)$$

Koppe (1947) showed that for inelastic scattering q must be replaced by q_i where

$$q_i = \frac{2\pi}{\lambda} \left[\phi^2 + \left(\frac{E}{2E}\right)^2\right]^{\frac{1}{2}} \qquad (26)$$

E being the incident electron energy and ΔE the energy lost during a particular inelastic collision. The value of ΔE was taken by Koppe to be $J/2$ where J is the primary ionization energy; in this way a rough mean of ionization and excitation was included. For S Lenz used the classical expression of Raman (1928) and Compton (1930)

$$S = Z - \frac{f_x^2}{Z} \tag{27}$$

and, on the basis of a Wentzel type field, substituted for f_x

$$f_x = \frac{Z}{1 + q_i^2 R^2} \tag{28}$$

giving

$$\frac{d\sigma_i}{d\Omega} = \frac{4Z}{a_H^{*2} q_i^4} \left(1 - \frac{1}{(1 + q_i^2 R^2)^2} \right) \tag{29}$$

The differential elastic and inelastic cross-sections for carbon calculated from equations (21) and (29) are shown plotted in Fig. 30.

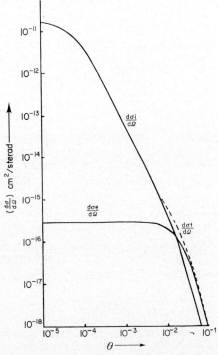

FIG. 30. The theoretical elastic and inelastic differential scattering cross-sections for carbon at 50 kV; from calculations by Lenz (1954).

Within the Born approximation the most accurate expression for S is probably that due to Waller and Hartree (1929)

$$S = Z - \sum_i |f_i|^2 - \sum_{i \neq j} \sum |f_{ij}|^2 \tag{30}$$

where f_i is the atomic scattering factors for the ith electron of the atom and the exchange terms f_{ij} between orbitals of the same spin are included to take account of the Pauli exclusion principle which forbids transitions between occupied states of the atom. Equation (30) was the basis of a comprehensive set of calculations of S and $d\sigma_i/d\Omega$ by Smart using Hartree-Fock wave functions where available or Hartree-Fock-Slater wave functions. In calculating $d\sigma_i/d\Omega$ the value of ΔE in the expression for q_i was derived using the Bohm-Pines (1953) theory of plasmon excitation in metals. For elastic scattering Smart used the Mott expression in the form

$$\frac{d\sigma_e}{d\Omega} = \frac{4}{a_H^* q^4} [Z - \sum_i |f_i|^2]^2 \tag{31}$$

The results of these calculations for the ground state of carbon are shown in Fig. 31.

Inelastic scattering in metals may also be described in terms of the plasma oscillation and interband transition theories. Ferrell (1956, 1957) has shown that on the basis of the Bohm-Pines theory the differential cross-section for the excitation of a plasmon is given per

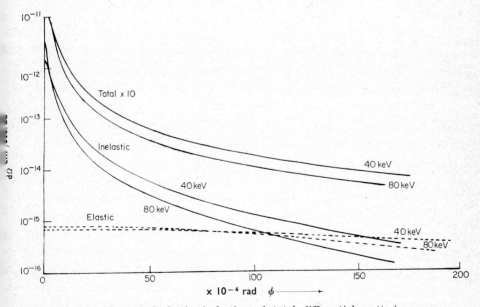

FIG. 31. The theoretical elastic, inelastic and total differential scattering cross-sections for the ground state of carbon. Waller-Hartree free atom calculation. Reproduced with permission from Smart (1968).

atom by

$$\frac{d\sigma_p}{d\Omega} = \frac{1}{2\pi a_H^* n} \frac{\theta_E}{(\theta_E^2 + \phi^2)} G^{-1} \qquad (32)$$

where $\theta_E = \Delta E_p/2U$, ΔE_p is the characteristic plasmon loss, n is the number of atoms per unit volume and G^{-1} is a factor which is unity for small angles but falls off to zero at the plasmon cut-off angle ϕ_c due to exchange effects. Misell has used equation (32) to calculate the differential plasmon cross-section in the small angle range. His results for aluminium are shown in Fig. 32 and may be compared with the values of $d\sigma_i/d\Omega$ from the Waller-Hartree atom calculations of Smart which are also displayed in the figure.

One possible method of improving the inelastic cross-sections would be to include the measured energy loss spectrum rather than a single value of ΔE or ΔE_p. That is, we can write

$$\frac{d\sigma_i}{d\Omega} = \int_0^U \frac{d\sigma_i}{d\Omega} (\phi, E) f_1(E) dE \qquad (33)$$

where U is the accelerating voltage and the energy loss distribution is

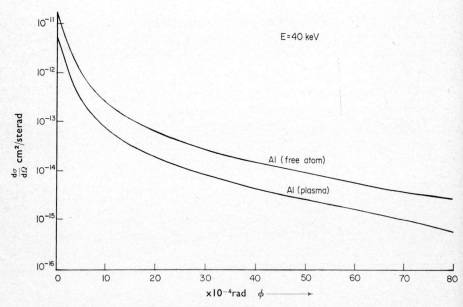

FIG. 32. Inelastic differential scattering cross-sections for aluminium on the free atom (Waller-Hartree) and plasmon excitation theories (60 kV). Reproduced with permission from Smart (1968) and Misell (1968).

normalized to unity

$$\int_0^U f_1(E)\,dE = 1 \tag{34}$$

Misell has investigated the effects of such a procedure and the results for aluminium at accelerating voltages of 20 and 100 kV are shown in Fig. 33. These results show that the inclusion of $f_1(E)$ in the Waller-Hartree free atom calculation of $d\sigma_i/d\Omega$ is only significant at angles less than 10^{-4} radian. Qualitatively the results for the plasmon loss calculations are similar but the effect of $f_1(E)$ is very small as would be expected.

The scattering equations which have been discussed in the preceding paragraphs are for single atoms and hence the results are only applicable to very thin films. Account must be taken of plural and possibly

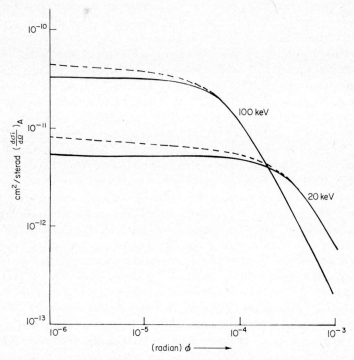

FIG. 33. Comparison of the theoretical inelastic differential scattering cross-section of aluminium (Waller-Hartree free atom) including the energy loss function $f_1(E)$ with that calculated on the basis of a single energy loss value.

$$-\left(\frac{d\sigma i}{d\Omega}\right)_A \qquad ---\left(\frac{d\sigma i}{d\Omega}\right)_A \text{ with } f_1(E)$$

multiple scattering if the theories are to be compared with experimental results. Plural scattering theories have been developed by Lenz (1954), Smith and Burge (1963) and Misell (1968). Misell's theory has been applied to the Waller-Hartree calculations and Smart has compared her experimental results with the predictions of this theory. For carbon and aluminium she finds much better agreement with the Waller-Hartree formulation than with the plasmon calculations in the small angle region where inelastic scattering predominates.

At this point in the discussion some words of caution must be interposed. The theoretical calculations of Lenz and Smart are based on the assumption of isolated spherically symmetric atoms and hence are only strictly applicable to the description of the scattering in monatomic gases at low pressures. The effect of bringing the atoms together to form a solid will be to alter the wave functions in the outer parts of the atom, and this must influence the electron scattering in the small angle region; therefore, even for the case of an amorphous solid there must be considerable doubt that the cross-sections give even a reasonable approximation to the scattering in the range 10^{-4}–10^{-5} radian.

There are also difficulties associated with the experimental verification of the theoretical predictions of small angle scattering since the intensity scattered by the specimen in this region depends in a complex way on the particular structure of the specimen under investigation. One example of this is the enhanced elastic intensity in the small angle diffraction pattern from an island type structure as discussed in Section III.A 1. Another example of a different type is found in the work of Ferrier et al. (1969) on the diffraction patterns from replica optical gratings. The most interesting result of this investigation was that a replica formed by shadowing the grating with an amorphous film of carbon gave rise to a very strong diffraction pattern similar to that displayed in Fig. 34. The energy loss characteristics of the diffracted intensities were investigated, using the scanning technique with velocity filtering as described in Section III.A 1, and it was found that the pattern did not contain a significant quantity of electrons which had lost more than 2 eV in energy. This is somewhat surprising since in the angular range of the diffraction pattern the theoretical value of $d\sigma_i/d\Omega$ is some four or five orders of magnitude greater than $d\sigma_e/d\Omega$. The tremendous enhancement ($\sim 10^6$ times) of the elastically diffracted intensity relative to the inelastic scattering is due almost entirely to the periodic 20% thickness variation created by the shadowing process. Calculations based on this thickness variation, and using the film inner potential (a quantity directly related to $f_e(0)$) as a parameter, give intensities which are in excellent agreement with the observed values.

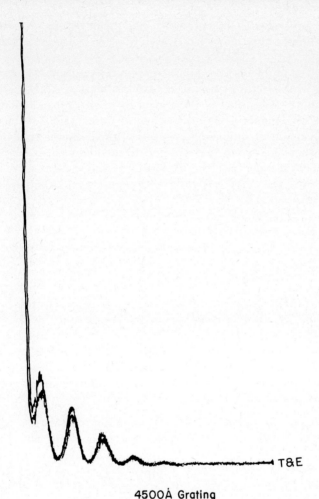

4500Å Grating

FIG. 34. The total and elastic diffraction profiles from a carbon replica of an optical
diffraction grating (d = 4650 Å).

From the above discussion it is clear that any agreement between
experimental and theoretical differential scattering cross-sections must
be viewed with scepticism unless structural effects have been taken
into account and this will be difficult. In particular there seems little
hope of using small angle scattering measurements to obtain accurate
elastic cross-sections in the small angle region. However, for small
angles the slow variation of $d\sigma_e/d\Omega$ predicted by theory is almost
certainly correct. Hence the main difficulty lies in determining accurate

values of $f_e(0)$ and this is probably best achieved by measuring the specimen inner potential by electron diffraction or electron interference techniques.

Despite the problems raised in the previous paragraphs the theoretical scattering cross-sections discussed earlier almost certainly provide at least a qualitative picture of the scattering of electrons at small angles. From the viewpoint of the experimental observation of small angle diffraction the most important theoretical prediction is that in general inelastic scattering would be expected to predominate at small angles. It is for this reason that the exclusion of the inelastically scattered electrons from the small angle diffraction pattern is of importance (see Section III.A 1).

V. Conclusions

The techniques of high resolution electron diffraction, as applied in an electron microscope, have been developed to a stage where they may usefully be applied to problems in a variety of fields. However, in many applications electron diffraction is in competition with the well established methods of electron microscopy and X-ray diffraction, and in the biological field with the more recently applied technique of optical diffractometry. Hence to assess the usefulness of electron diffraction it is necessary to draw a critical comparison between it and the other three methods.

1. Probably the most important advantage of electron diffraction relative to the X-ray technique is the possibility of obtaining a high resolution image of the specimen area under investigation. In addition in small angle diffraction it is experimentally much easier to achieve the necessary high angular resolution with electrons than is the case with X-rays.

2. Relative to X-rays the interaction of electrons with matter is considerably stronger and this allows a much smaller volume of material to be studied thus avoiding the often difficult problem of growing the relatively large single crystals necessary for X-ray diffraction studies. Even with these smaller volumes, photographic exposure times are of the order of seconds in electron diffraction compared to the hours necessary in the X-ray case. Disadvantages of the strong electron interaction are that the specimen thickness which can be examined with electrons is strictly limited. For crystals of finite thickness dynamical diffraction theory (see Hirsch et al., 1965) must be used in the

interpretation of the diffracted intensities, as compared to the X-ray case where the simpler kinematic theory is normally applicable.

3. The fact that the electron possesses a charge allows electron diffraction to be applied to certain problems which could not be studied using X-ray diffraction, e.g. the investigation of the spin configuration in magnetic films.

4. One of the major problems of applying small angle electron diffraction in the biological field is that of specimen preservation in the vacuum of the microscope, although this difficulty might be overcome in the future by the use of the wet cell techniques mentioned in Section III.B. Specimen preservation is not a serious problem in X-ray diffraction.

5. Although it is the inadequacies in respect of contrast, focusing and resolution of the present electron microscope technique which make the diffraction capability desirable, there is still the very considerable problem of deriving the phases of the diffracted beams if a Fourier analysis is to be attempted. In addition it is doubtful if a complete structure determination is feasible until there is more complete understanding of the complex nature of electron scattering at small angles. Hence it is probably the ability of electron diffraction to give a statistical analysis of the periodicities in a specimen, which for the time being, will be the most useful advantage over electron microscopy.

6. Unit cell dimensions can be determined more accurately by electron diffraction than by electron imaging and this will be particularly useful for crystals which cannot be grown of sufficient size for X-ray work.

7. The technique of optical diffraction, as applied by Klug and Berger (1964) in studies of stained virus specimens, essentially performs the same role as electron diffraction. However, whereas the electron technique is performed directly on the specimen, the optical technique requires a photographic image of the specimen as a starting point and is therefore more time consuming. In addition it should be noted that the optical diffraction pattern is the Fourier transform of the optical transmission function of the photographic plate rather than of the specimen, and consequently is dependent on conditions of observation in the microscope. On the other hand, if one wishes to operate on the diffraction pattern to remove unwanted reflections prior to imaging, this is much easier to do in the optical diffraction technique than in the electron method.

It should be clear from the discussion above that electron diffraction is not destined to supersede the other techniques. Nevertheless in a complementary role it should prove a powerful tool in a wide range of structural investigations.

ACKNOWLEDGEMENTS

The author wishes to acknowledge discussions with R. E. Burge, G. H. Curtis and R. T. Murray and is indebted to G. H. Curtis for critical comments on the manuscript.

REFERENCES

Agar, A. W. (1960). *Br. J. appl. Phys.* **11,** 185.
Bassett, G. A. and Keller, A. (1964). *Phil. Mag.* **9,** 817.
Boersch, H. (1936). *Ann. Physik,* **26,** 63.
Boersch, H. (1937). *Ann. Physik,* **27,** 75.
Boersch, H. (1953). *Z. Phys.* **134,** 156.
Boersch, H. and Raith, H. (1959). *Naturwiss.* **46,** 574.
Boersch, H., Raith, W. and Weber, H. (1961). *Z. Phys.* **161,** 1.
Bohm, D. and Pines, D. (1953). *Phys. Rev.* **92,** 609.
Burge, R. E. and Smart, J. (1969). *Phil. Mag.* (In Press).
Calbick, C. J. (1964). "Physics of Thin Films," Vol. 2, p. 63, (Ed. Hass). Academic Press, New York, U.S.A.
Compton, A. H. (1930). *Phys. Rev.* **35,** 928.
Cowley, J. M., Goodman, P. and Rees, A. L. G. (1957). *Acta Crystallogr.* **10,** 19.
Curtis, G. H., Ferrier, R. P. and Murray, R. T. (1967). *J. Scient. Instrum.* **44,** 867.
Curtis, G. H. (1968). Ph.D. Thesis, University of Cambridge, England.
Danielson, W. E., Shenfil, L. and Du Mond, J. W. M. (1952). *J. appl. Phys.* **23,** 860.
Denbigh, P. N. and Dove, D. B. (1967). *J. appl. Phys.* **38,** 99.
Denbigh, P. N. and Grigson, C. W. B. (1965). *Br. J. appl. Phys.* **42,** 305.
Dove, D. B. (1964). *J. appl. Phys.* **35,** 1652.
Drahos, V. and Delong, A. (1965). *Czech. J. Phys.* **15,** 760.
Drahos, V. and Delong, A. (1966). *Nature, Lond.* **209,** 801.
Dupouy, G. (1968). "Advances in Optical and Electron Microscopy," Vol. 2, p. 167, (Eds. Barer and Cosslett). Academic Press, London.
Dupouy, G., Perrier, F. and Durrieu, L. (1960). *C.R. Acad. Sci. Paris,* **251,** 2836.
Ferrell, R. A. (1956). *Phys. Rev.* **101,** 554.
Ferrell, R. A. (1957). *Phys. Rev.* **107,** 450.
Ferrier, R. P. (1964). "Proc. Third European Conf. Electron Microscopy, Prague," Vol. A, p. 115. Royal Microscopical Society, London.
Ferrier, R. P. and Curtis, G. H. (1969). (To be published.)
Ferrier, R. P., Curtis, G. H. and Murray, R. T. (1969). (To be published.)
Ferrier, R. P. and Murray, R. T. (1966). *J. R. Microsc. Soc.* **85,** 323.
Ferrier, R. P. and Murray, R. T. (1968). *Br. J. appl. Phys. Ser. 2,* **1,** 207.
Ferrier, R. P. and Puchalska, I. B. (1968). *Physica Stat. Solidi,* **28,** 335.

Ferrier, R. P. and Wade, R. H. (1964). "Proc. Int. Conf. on Magnetism, Nottingham," p. 873. Institute of Physics.
Fitzgerald, A. G. and Mannami, M. (1966). *Proc. R. Soc.* **A293**, 169.
Geil, P. H. (1966). *J. Polymer Sci.* **C13**, 149.
Goringe, M. J. and Jakubovics, J. P. (1967). *Phil. Mag.* **15**, 393.
Grigson, C. W. B. (1968). "Adv. in Electronics and Electron Physics," Suppl. 4, p. 187. Academic Press, New York, U.S.A.
Grigson, C. W. B. and Dove, D. B. (1966). *J. Vac. Sci. Tech.* **3**, 120.
Grundy, P. J. and Tebble, R. S. (1968). *Adv. Phys.* **17**, 153.
Guinier, A. (1964). "X-ray Diffraction," p. 43. W. H. Freeman, London.
Guinier, A. and Fournet, G. (1955). "Small Angle Scattering of X-rays," p. 57. Wiley, New York, U.S.A.
Hale, M. E., Fuller, H. W. and Rubinstein, H. (1959). *J. appl. Phys.* **30**, 789.
Hall, C. E. (1950). *J. biol. Chem.* **185**, 749.
Heide, H. G. (1962). *J. Cell Biol.* **13**, 147.
Heidenreich, R. D. (1964). "Fundamentals of Transmission Electron Microscopy," p. 104. Interscience, London, England.
Hirsch, P. B., Howie, A., Nicholson, R. B., Pashley, D. W. and Whelan, M. J. (1965). "Electron Microscopy of Thin Films," p. 384. Butterworth, London, England.
Klemperer, O. (1965). *Rep. Prog. Phys.* **28**, 77.
Klug, A. and Berger, J. E. (1964). *J. mol. Biol.* **10**, 565.
Komoda, T. and Hosoki, S. (1966). "Proc. 6th Int. Conf. on Elec. Microscopy," p. 35. Maruzen, Tokyo, Japan.
Koppe, H. (1947). *Z. Phys.* **124**, 658.
Lenz, F. (1954). *Z. Naturforsch.* **9a**, 185.
Le Poole, J. B. (1947). *Philips Tech. Rev.* **9**, 33.
Mahl, H. and Weitsch, W. (1959). *Naturwiss.* **46**, 487.
Mahl, H. and Weitsch, W. (1960a). *Z. Naturforsch.* **15a**, 1051.
Mahl, H. and Weitsch, W. (1960b). *Optik*, **17**, 487.
Misell, D. L. (1968). Ph.D. Thesis. University of London, England.
Moliere, K. and Niehrs, H. (1955). *Z. Phys.* **140**, 581.
Morse, P. M. (1932). *Physikal. Z.* **33**, 443.
Mott, N. F. (1930). *Proc. R. Soc.* **A127**, 657.
Murray, R. T. (1967). Ph.D. Thesis. University of Cambridge, England.
Murray, R. T. and Ferrier, R. P. (1967). *J. Ultrastruct. Res.* **21**, 361.
Murray, R. T. and Ferrier, R. P. (1969). (To be published.)
Pashley, D. W. (1965). *Adv. Phys.* **14**, 327.
Raman, C. K. (1928). *Indian J. Phys.* **3**, 357.
Raether, H. (1965). "Springer Tracts in Modern Physics," Vol. 38, p. 84. Springer-Verlag, Berlin.
Rees, A. L. G. and Spink, J. A. (1950). *Acta Crystallogr.* **3**, 316.
Schaffernicht, K. (1963). *Z. Angew. Phys.* **15**, 275.
Scott, W. T. (1963). *Rev. mod. Phys.* **35**, 231.
Sennett, R. S. and Scott, G. D. (1950). *J. opt. Soc. Am.* **40**, 203.
Smart, J. (1968). Ph.D. Thesis. University of London, England.
Smart, J. and Burge, R. E. (1965). *Nature, Lond.* **205**, 1297.
Smith, G. H. and Burge, R. E. (1963). *Proc. phys. Soc.* **81**, 612.
Statton, W. O. (1964). "New Methods of Polymer Characterisation," Vol. 6, p. 231 (Ed. Ke). Interscience, New York, U.S.A.

Stoyanova, I. G. and Mikhailovski, G. A. (1959). *Biophysika*, **4**, 483.

Sturkey, L. (1948). *Phys. Rev.* **73**, 183.

Tompsett, M. F., Heritage, M. B. and Grigson, C. W. B. (1967). *Nature, Lond.* **215**, 29.

Wade, R. H. (1966). C.E.N.G. Technical Note EL/319. Grenoble, France.

Wade, R. H. (1967). *Physica Stat. Solidi*, **19**, 847.

Wade, R. H. and Silcox, J. (1967). *Physica Stat. Solidi*, **19**, 57.

Waller, I. and Hartree, D. R. (1929). *Proc. R. Soc.* **A124**, 119.

Wentzel, G. (1932). *Z. Phys.* **40**, 590.

Yeh, G. S. Y. and Geil, P. H. (1967). *J. Mat. Sci.* **2**, 457.

The Assessment of Electron Microscopic Autoradiographs

M. A. WILLIAMS

*Department of Human Biology and Anatomy,
The University of Sheffield, Sheffield, England*

I. Introduction

THE production of autoradiographs at the electron microscope level is a technique of growing importance, since it offers us the use of a wealth of metabolic, pharmacological and endocrinological data to combine with cell morphology. We can thus obtain information on where small molecules bind to the cell, where they are made into macromolecules and where these products go.

In studies of this kind we are concerned with *localizing* and *quantifying* radioisotopes within ultrastructural features, two objectives which are not wholly distinct. This chapter reviews the problems inherent in the technique, the means of abrogating or minimizing their effects and the consequent potential of the method.

II. Preparing the Specimen

A. *Fixation and Embedding of Cells and Tissues*

In order to understand tissue autoradiographs it is necessary to have information on the survival of the labelled products during the preparation of the tissue for microscopy. Most labelled compounds when administered to tissues give rise to a variety of products. In many cases (especially when studying the synthesis and migration of macro-molecules) it is expected that low molecular weight compounds will be removed by the processing, while the macromolecules will be totally preserved. Almost complete extraction of the low molecular weight label is usually achieved, (Caro and Palade, 1964; Droz and War-shawsky, 1963; Stein and Stein, 1967; Cope and Williams, 1969a & b). The observations of Peters and Ashley (1967) indicate that chemically bifunctional fixative reagents such as glutaraldehyde that can cause cross-linking, may cause low molecular weight label to be bound irreversibly to the tissue. However, this only appears to be of conse-quence when tissue is fixed in the presence of an excess of a high activity radiochemical. This might occur very shortly after injecting a radiochemical *in vivo*, or more especially when labelling has been achieved *in vitro* without added cold carrier. Fixatives such as formaldehyde can be used more safely under these conditions.

The survival of macromolecules after fixation and embedding by the usual EM preparation techniques has been subjected to surprisingly little truly quantitative examination. Osmium tetroxide does not appear to be an especially good fixative for proteins (Dallam, 1957; Bennett and Luft, 1959; Wood and Luft, 1965) especially when buffered with S-collidine. Luft and Wood (1963) found that 8–15% of in-corporated H^3-methionine was lost from osmium tetroxide fixed tissues. However, the use of glutaraldehyde might be expected to result in much more efficient fixation since it is a better crosslinking reagent (Millonig and Marinozzi, 1968; Amsterdam and Schramm, 1966; Bowes and Cater, 1965; Quiocho and Richards, 1966). Maunsbach (1966) found virtually no loss of I^{125}-labelled albumin after perfusion fixation of kidney cells with glutaraldehyde followed by osmium tetroxide. Potassium permanganate seems to be an especially inefficient fixative for proteins (Hake, 1965; Bradbury and Meek, 1960). Form-aldehyde is known to extract up to 12% of the protein from some tissues prepared for light microscopy (Merriam, 1958) and is inferior to glutaraldehyde in model systems (Flitney, 1966).

The evidence for the quantitative retention of DNA is almost entirely histochemical (Ryter and Kellenberger, 1958; Huxley and Zubay, 1961; Moses, 1956) and lacks truly quantitative measurements. How-ever the success of Feulgen staining, tritiated thymidine autoradio-graphy and enzyme digestion studies testifies to near complete retention. RNA fixation likewise has not been studied systematically. Information is particularly lacking on the EM preparation methods. However, Sirlin and Loening (1968) have shown that histological methods using Carnoy's fixative and formaldehyde are highly effective in fixing 4S RNA. However, Schneider and Maurer (1963) and Schneider and Schneider (1964) report extraction of RNA by formalin fixatives. Morphological and histochemical evidence suggests that ribosomal RNA survives well at least after osmium tetroxide and glutaraldehyde fixation.

Many autoradiographic studies have been made on carbohydrate biosynthesis (Peterson and Leblond, 1964; Neutra and Leblond, 1966a,b; Coimbra and Leblond, 1966; Northcote and Pickett-Heaps, 1966; Fewer et al., 1964). Most papers record no quantitative studies on survival during fixing and embedding. A great deal of glycogen is preserved by permanganate fixation (Luft, 1956) and osmium tetroxide fixation (Swift and Rasch, 1958; Watson, 1958), and is especially obvious after the use of alkaline lead stains (see Revel, 1964). Truly quantitative study of the degree of preservation is, however, lacking. Glutaraldehyde fixation followed by embedding in "water-miscible" methacrylates (Leduc and Holt, 1965; Cope, 1968) results in extraction of glycogen. Formaldehyde has been shown to be ineffective as a fixative for mucopolysaccharides (Józsa and Szederkenyi, 1967; Engfeldt and Hjertquist, 1967). However, glutaraldehyde-osmium tetroxide fixation appears to be effective in fixing hyaluronic acid (Barland et al., 1968).

It is quite evident that much quantitative work remains to be done on the retention of all types of labelled macromolecules during fixing and embedding. Studies involving particular products or classes of product would considerably enhance the value of the autoradiographic observations.

In contrast to the scarcity of data on macromolecules, lipids have been subjected to numerous studies in the last two or three years. It has become clear that neutral lipids are preserved to markedly different degrees by different fixing and embedding procedures, but in no case are they preserved in their entirety, (Idelman, 1965; Korn and Weisman, 1966; Casley-Smith and Day, 1966; Ashworth et al., 1966; Stein and Stein, 1968; Cope and Williams, 1968; Saunders et al., 1968; Buschmann and Taylor, 1968; Dermer, 1968). A summary of much of the recently published data on neutral fat survival in EM preparations is given in Table I. It seems clear that fixation involving osmium tetroxide is usually superior to other forms of fixation, provided the lipid has olefinic groups. Saturated lipids, e.g. palmitic acid, are preserved to a much smaller degree. Low temperature processing can also preserve neutral fat to some extent in the absence of osmium tetroxide fixation (Cope, 1968; Cope and Williams, 1968). It seems

TABLE I

Collected Data on the Survival of Neutral Lipids after Fixing and Embedding Tissue for Electron Microscopy

Lipid studied and tissue	Preparation procedure	Percentage retained	Assay method	Reference
H³-Palmitic acid and its neutral glycerides in Acanthamoeba sp.	Glutaraldehyde Ethanols Epoxypropane Maraglas	0	Chemical	Korn and Weisman (1966)
H³-Palmitic acid and its neutral glycerides in Acanthamoeba sp.	Osmium tetroxide Ethanols Epoxypropane Maraglas	0	Chemical	Korn and Weisman (1966)
H³-Palmitic acid and its neutral glycerides in Acanthamoeba sp.	Permanganate Ethanols Epoxypropane Maraglas	0	Chemical	Korn and Weisman (1966)
H³ Glyceryl trioleate Liver	Formaldehyde Ethanols*	0	Liquid scintillation counting	Ashworth et al. (1966)
H³ Glyceryl trioleate Liver	Osmium tetroxide Ethanols*	73	Liquid scintillation counting	Ashworth et al. (1966)
Oleic acid H³ and its neutral glycerides Liver	Glutaraldehyde Osmium tetroxide Ethanols Epon	74	Liquid scintillation counting	Stein and Stein (1967)
Oleic acid H³ in chylomicrons (mainly as triglycerides)	Glutaraldehyde Osmium tetroxide Ethanols Epon	59	Liquid scintillation counting	Carlier et al. (1967)
Oleic acid H³ in chylomicrons (mainly as triglycerides)	Glutaraldehyde Osmium tetroxide 70% Ethanol Epon	71	Liquid scintillation counting	Carlier et al. (1967)
Glyceryl trioleate H³ and some diolein and monolein Peritoneal macrophages	Glutaraldehyde Osmium tetroxide Ethanols	43	Liquid scintillation counting	Cope and Williams (1968)

Substance / Tissue	Treatment / Embedding		Method	Reference
...oyl oleates H³ Peritoneal macrophages	Freeze drying GMA embedding	52	Liquid scintillation counting	Cope and Williams (1968)
Glyceryl oleates H³ Peritoneal macrophages	"Inert Dehydration" (Pease, 1966) GMA embedding	26	Liquid scintillation counting	Cope and Williams (1968)
Glyceryl oleates H³ Peritoneal macrophages	Glutaraldehyde GMA embedding (Leduc et al., 1963)	0	Liquid scintillation counting	Cope and Williams (1968)
Glyceryl oleates H³ Peritoneal macrophages	"Low Temperature" (−20°C) fixation dehydration embedding in GMA-Styrene (Cope, 1968)	42	Liquid scintillation counting	Cope and Williams (1968)
Glyceryl oleates H³ Peritoneal macrophages	"Low Temperature" (−20°C) fixation dehydration embedding in GMA-Butyl methacrylate (Cope, 1968)	30	Liquid scintillation counting	Cope and Williams (1968)
Palmitic acid H³ and glyceride derivatives Jejunum	Osmium tetroxide Ethanols*	32–48	Liquid scintillation counting	Saunders et al. (1968)
Oleic acid H³ and glyceride derivatives Jejunum	Osmium tetroxide Ethanols*	95	Liquid scintillation counting	Saunders et al. (1968)
Linoleic acid H³ and glyceride derivatives Jejunum	Osmium tetroxide Ethanols*	86	Liquid scintillation counting	Saunders et al. (1968)
Cholesterol H³ and esters Jejunum	Osmium tetroxide Ethanols*	40	Liquid scintillation counting	Saunders et al. (1968)
Linoleic H³ acid Intestine	Osmium tetroxide Epoxypropane Araldite	74	Liquid scintillation counting	Buschmann and Taylor (1968)
Glycerides of oleic acid H³ Intestine	Osmium tetroxide Acetones*	79	Liquid scintillation counting	Dermer (1968)

* Tissue not embedded and hence no data obtained beyond the dehydration stage.

TABLE II

Collected Data on the Survival of Phospholipids after Fixing and Embedding Tissue for Electron Microscopy

Material examined	Fixing and embedding method	% Retained	Assay method	Reference
Muscle and liver fragments, subcellular fractions	Osmium tetroxide Alcohols Butyl Methacrylate	71	Chemical	Dallam (1957)
Phospholipids containing palmitic acid H³ Acanthamoeba	Osmium tetroxide Ethanols Epoxypropane Maraglas	87	Liquid scintillation counting	Korn and Weisman (1966)
Phospholipids containing palmitic acid H³ Acanthamoeba	Permanganate Ethanols Epoxypropane Maraglas	75	Liquid scintillation counting	Korn and Weisman (1966)
Phospholipids containing palmitic acid H³ Acanthamoeba	Glutaraldehyde Ethanols Epoxypropane Maraglas	16	Liquid scintillation counting	Korn and Weisman (1966)
Phosphatidyl choline H³ Liver	Glutaraldehyde Osmium tetroxide Ethanols Epon	85	Liquid scintillation counting	Stein and Stein (1967)

Phosphatidyl choline H^3 Lung	Osmium tetroxide Ethanols Epoxypropane Epon	62	Liquid scintillation counting	Morgan and Huber (1967)
Phosphatidyl choline H^3 Lung	Formaldehyde Osmium tetroxide Ethanols Epoxypropane Epon	83	Liquid scintillation counting	Morgan and Huber (1967)
Phosphatidyl choline H^3 Lung	Glutaraldehyde Osmium tetroxide Ethanols Epon	90	Liquid scintillation counting	Morgan and Huber (1967)
Phosphatidyl choline H^3 Lung	Tricomplex (Elbers et al., 1965) Epon	78	Liquid scintillation counting	Morgan and Huber (1967)
Phospholipids containing oleic acid H^3 Intestine	Osmium tetroxide Acetones*	82	Liquid scintillation counting	Dermer (1968)

* Tissue not embedded and hence no data obtained beyond the dehydration stage.

likely that both the physical state of the lipid (droplets, micelles, molecular dispersion) and the nature of the cellular material (single cells or tissue blocks) affect the extent of extraction. Despite the fact that no truly satisfactory tissue preparation method exists, EM autoradiographs can be prepared from material containing labelled neutral fat (Jersild, 1966; Stein and Stein, 1967a, b; Williams and Carr, 1968). However, it is still not certain how much differential extraction or translocation of label has occurred. The comparison of several different fixing and embedding methods is a useful approach (Williams and Carr, 1968), but until an entirely satisfactory method is found, none of the results may be regarded as definitive. Extensive analysis and detailed interpretation of such experiments is probably not justified.

Insofar as they have been studied, phospholipids appear to be more easily fixed than neutral fats. The data obtained by various authors are shown in Tables II and III.

Most workers have used labelled fatty acids or choline, thus either labelling lipids generally (including several classes of phospholipid) or solely phosphatidyl choline. Most authors have observed that when osmium tetroxide is included in the technique more than 70% (and usually 80–90%) of the phospholipid is preserved. Cope and Williams (1969a,b) labelled phosphatidyl choline and phosphatidyl ethanolamine (the two major phospholipid classes) separately using H^3-choline and C^{14}-ethanolamine (see Table III). Quantitative examination of ten different preparation methods revealed (a) that phosphatidyl ethanolamine is generally more easily fixed than phosphatidyl choline; (b) osmium tetroxide fixation retains 90–100% of both phospholipids; (c) Baker's post-chromation technique was also highly efficient; and (d) other techniques (including permanganate fixation) were less efficient. More than 60% of the phospholipid can be preserved using glutaraldehyde fixation if low temperatures ($-20°C$) are employed throughout the process (see Cope, 1968).

It seems reasonable, therefore, to accept that EM autoradiography of phospholipids is feasible provided a suitable fixative is chosen. The conventional processes using osmium tetroxide appear to be quite satisfactory for the purpose.

Attempts have recently been made to apply electron microscopic autoradiography to the study of drug and hormone action (Wolfe et al., 1962; Taxi and Droz, 1966; Stirling, 1967; Williams and Baba, 1967; Simard, 1967). Such autoradiographs clearly only reveal that fraction of the drug within the cell that will withstand the solvent action of fixative and dehydrating fluids. This residual radioactivity must either be incorporated into or bound strongly on to a macro-

Table III

Survival of Phosphatidyl Choline and Phosphatidyl Ethanolamine
in Rat Liver Fixed and Embedded in Various Ways

Fixing and embedding technique	Percentage retained	
	Phosphatidyl Choline	Phosphatidyl Ethanolamine
Glutaraldehyde Buffer wash Ethanols Epoxypropane Araldite	0	53
Glutaraldehyde Buffer wash Osmium tetroxide Ethanols Epoxypropane Araldite	89	99
Osmium tetroxide Ethanols Epoxypropane Araldite	97	97
Permanganate Buffer wash Ethanols Epoxypropane Araldite	50	78
Formaldehyde Dichromate Ethanols Epoxypropane Araldite (Baker 1946 fixative)	88	99
Glutaraldehyde Buffer wash GMA	3	70
Low temperature fixing and embedding (Cope, 1968) (Glutaraldehyde–GMA butyl methacrylate −20°C)	64	68
"Inert Dehydration" (Pease, 1966)	24	36
Freeze drying GMA	0	22
Freeze substitution Ethanol–Glutaraldehyde −20°C	15	79

Data obtained by scintillation counting. (Summarized from Cope and Williams, 1969a,b.)

molecule or supramolecular element. In the case of most hormones, no evidence of actual incorporation is known. Strong binding seems to be the most likely explanation of positive autoradiographs, although the type of chemical bond involved is not clear. In the case of some drugs, actual incorporation may occur, or the drug may form covalent bonds with the tissue macromolecules. The relationship between the bound fraction and the "pharmacologically active" fraction is a problem that in most cases still remains. At the EM level (unlike the optical microscope level) no "soluble compound" techniques (Stumpf and Roth, 1964, 1966; Appleton, 1965) are available. The evolution of such techniques will help to answer some of these problems. The preparation of ultrathin sections (frozen or dry) without embedding may be considered a step in this direction (Bernhard and Nancy, 1964; Bernhard, 1965; Koller, 1964; Koller and Bernhard, 1964; Tranzer, 1965).

B. *Ultramicrotomy*

The great majority of electron microscopic autoradiographs are prepared from ultrathin sections. Isotopically these sections are "infinitely thin". The silver grain yield of an EM autoradiograph reflects the absolute amount of isotope present rather than the isotopic concentration. Thus, if sections from a uniformly labelled source are considered, a 1000 Å thick section will yield twice as many grains per unit area as a 500 Å one, when the two specimens are processed identically. Furthermore, if a section of uneven thickness is prepared from the same uniformly labelled source, then the grain density over its various parts will reflect the thickness of the section in those regions. It is clear, therefore, that electron microscopic autoradiographs can only be accurately assessed with the aid of information on the topography of the sections and the range of mean section thicknesses that is involved.

1. *Mean section thickness*

It is commonly the practice in electron microscope laboratories to assess the thickness of ultrathin sections roughly by the interference colours they exhibit as they float on the water bath (Peachey, 1958; Bachmann and Sitte, 1960). However, it has been pointed out elsewhere (Williams and Meek, 1966) that if all sections that appear to be of similar interference colour are assumed to be of equal mean thickness, then some considerable errors are incurred. The measurement of numbers of sections of each interference colour by a scintillation counting method, by interference microscopy or by combined auto-

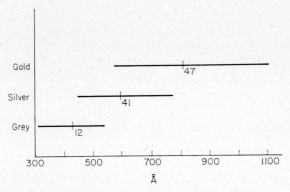

Fig. 1. Range of thickness of grey, silver and gold interference colour sections, measured by scintillation counting on methacrylate sections. (From Williams and Meek, 1966.)

radiography and microdensitometry revealed that each colour contained a considerable range of thicknesses (see Figs 1 and 2, Table IV). Furthermore, it was clear that each colour showed an overlap of thicknesses with the adjacent colours. This overlap indicates that there is considerable error in the "colour coding" of sections of any given thickness. The colour that a given section appears varies with the illumination system, the room conditions and the appearance of adjacent sections. The judgement of the ultramicrotomist is not constant from day to day, nor is it identical with the judgement of a

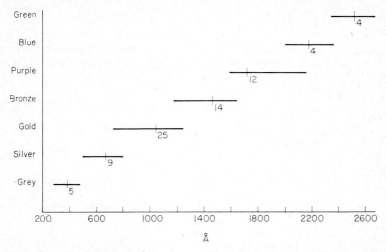

Fig. 2. Ranges of thickness of Araldite sections of various interference colour, measured by interference microscopy. (From Williams and Meek, 1966.)

TABLE IV

Thicknesses of Single Ultrathin Sections of
Various Interference Colours

Colour	Number examined	Average thickness (Å) + S.D.
Grey	12	429 ($\pm$72)
Silver	41	594 ($\pm$81)
Gold	47	811 ($\pm$138)

Measurements by scintillation counting. (Data taken from Williams and Meek, 1966.)

second operator. It is clear, therefore, that if all the sections used in an autoradiographic experiment are randomly taken ones of a single apparent interference colour, considerable variation in section thickness and hence silver grain yield will be built into the experiment. Differences of $\pm30\%$ would be commonplace with occasional larger differences.

In fact, ultrathin sections are usually collected as ribbons. Such samples are certainly not random. Ribbons of sections sometimes show a smaller variation than sections taken from the knife singly. However, ribbons of sections frequently show quite as much variation as singly taken ones. (See Table V—data taken from Williams and Meek, 1966.) Similar variation is also clearly seen in Araldite sections when they are examined by the same autoradiographic-densitometric technique

TABLE V

Thickness of Ribbons of Methacrylate Sections (silver interference colour). Measurement by Combined Autoradiography and Microdensitometry. Calibrated by Scintillation Counting of Single Sections

Ribbon No.	No. of sections	Mean thickness Å (nearest 5Å)	Range as % of mean	
			Lowest	Highest
1	7	550	-8%	$+13\%$
2	8	480	-43%	$+56\%$
3	6	460	-17%	$+12\%$
4	6	490	-15%	$+25\%$
5	15	515	-19%	$+45\%$
6	7	540	-30%	$+28\%$
7	6	500	-24%	$+32\%$
8	7	605	-18%	$+22\%$

(unpublished observations). Typical sets of thicknesses for ribbons are:

1. 575 Å, 615 Å, 540 Å, 610 Å, 510 Å, 415 Å, 485 Å, 745 Å
   (Methacrylate—from Williams and Meek, 1966).
2. 640 Å, 620 Å, 630 Å, 670 Å, 580 Å
3. 420 Å, 440 Å, 440 Å, 510 Å, 560 Å
4. 500 Å, 455 Å, 495 Å, 365 Å, 610 Å, 500 Å, 640 Å ⎬ Araldite
5. 460 Å, 445 Å, 410 Å, 470 Å, 405 Å, 550 Å
6. 490 Å, 580 Å, 715 Å, 675 Å, 650 Å, 680 Å

The tendency for the last section of a ribbon to be either the thinnest or thickest of the set, is explained by the ultra-microtomist ceasing to cut when a very obvious change in thickness occurs. If this was not done the variation would extend over a wider thickness range and more than one interference colour.

It follows from these data that attempts to compare the yield of silver grains on different ultrathin sections or ribbons of sections are likely to result in considerable errors. Differing grain counts over two sections can only be said with confidence to represent different isotope concentrations when the grain density difference is a factor of two or more.

If the experiments dictate that the overall level of isotope in two or more samples be compared, then the problem is best solved by making optical microscopic autoradiographs from $1\,\mu$ sections from the same blocks. Since these sections are not truly "infinitely thick" it is best to measure their thickness by interference microscopy. Most ultramicrotomes when set to cut semi-thin (area $1\,\mu$) sections produce material within the range of the nominal value $\pm 10\%$. Alternatively, if optical microscope preparations are not used, some means must be found for checking the thickness of the ultrathin sections actually autoradiographed. Sections of about 1000 Å thickness can be measured with about 5% error using a double-beam interference microscope fitted with a half shade device and using mercury green light (Cosslett, 1960; Williams and Meek, 1966). In observations on the binding of di-isopropyl-fluorophosphate-H[3] to motor endplates Salpeter (1967) checked microtome performance when cutting approximately 1000 Å sections by means of multiple beam interferometry (Tolansky, 1948). The measurement of the thickness of each section in all ribbons cut is very difficult and time consuming, and application to silver sections in the 400–600 Å range gives about 15–20% error. Thus at present no convenient method is available for thin sections. However, it seems likely that suitable instrumentation will become available in the reasonably near future.

2. *Intrasection thickness variation*

Ultrathin sections often exhibit considerable thickness variation over their various regions. These variations may be divided into two broad categories—those which are associated with specific elements in the tissue and those which are not. The second category are found when sectioning pure embedding media. Since this second category is not associated with specific ultrastructural features it will be termed "non-systematic". Topographical changes associated with particular features will be referred to as "systematic".

a. *Non-systematic variations.* These variations (which exclude overt "chatter" and knife marks) have a similar range of forms with methacrylates and epoxy resins, and in the presence or absence of embedded tissue. The production of such non-systematic variations by a particular microtome can be admirably monitored by studying uniformly radioactive embedding media. Autoradiography followed by repeated line scans with a specular densitometer gives much information. The commonest form of variation has a wedge-shaped elevation. In these cases the section is thicker at one edge than at the opposite edge. These forms vary from those with the two edges perhaps only 10% different in thickness, to others where the section tapers linearly to zero thickness. In some cases the slope may be convex or concave. Some sections occur in which the thickest edge is that first touched by the knife. In other cases the reverse is true. Occasionally sections taper appreciably in a direction parallel to the knife-edge. These sections may taper simultaneously in two directions almost at right angles. Many of these forms are illustrated in Figs. 3 and 4, which are microdensitometer traces from stripping film autoradiographs of ultrathin Araldite sections uniformly labelled with Sulphur 35. The incidence of wedge-shaped sections is 15–20% although a proportion of these only taper mildly. In the author's laboratory three different makes of ultramicrotome, (gravity operated mechanical feed-Cambridge-Huxley, rotary hand-operated mechanical feed-Sorvall Porter-Blum MT. 1 and automatic thermal advance-LKB Ultratome I types) all gave rather similar results.

Wedge-shaped sections can give rise to great differences in grain yield in the various parts of an autoradiograph. This problem is difficult to control. However, the answer lies in evaluating the microtome performance. In many cases this can be done by drying down ultrathin sections onto glass strips and viewing them with a phase contrast microscope. A highly absorbing phase plate is to be preferred. Under these conditions severely wedge-shaped forms can be seen since the thinnest edge will be invisible or nearly so, while the others exhibit a

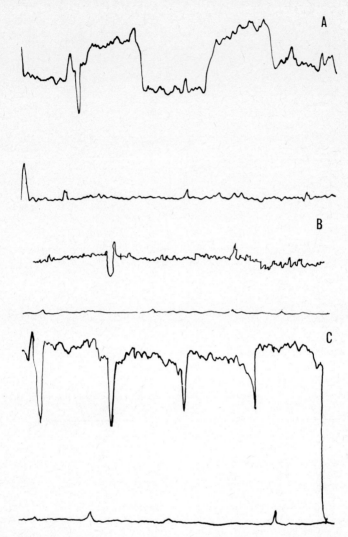

FIG. 3. Microdensitometer traces from autoradiographs of ribbons of ultrathin sections uniformly labelled with Sulphur-35. All ribbons were of silver interference colour. Note the variation in mean thickness in ribbon (A) compared to ribbon (B) (4 sections). Note occasional wedge-shaped sections. Lower line on each trace indicates background density.

bright line (viewing in air, negative phase contrast). In this way it is possible to discern when the microtome is performing absolutely optimally. When this is achieved quite long ribbons can be cut with scarcely a faulty section (see Fig. 3).

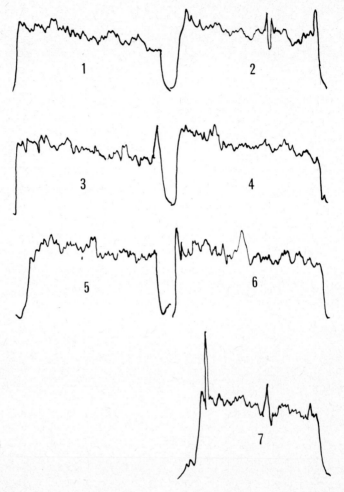

Fig. 4. Microdensitometer traces from an autoradiograph of an ultrathin section
(grey interference colour) uniformly labelled with Sulphur-35. Seven line scans perpendicular to the knife edge are shown.

Further non-systematic intrasection thickness variations commonly
occur. These have no apparent pattern (Fig. 4). The amplitude and
frequency of the variation changes considerably from ribbon to ribbon.
The frequency can be as high as 20–50 μ, i.e. it approaches the single
cell level. The best ribbons can be almost free of it. There is no easy
means of detecting all the small details and hence it is a difficult form
of variation to control completely. Viewing by interference microscopy
is helpful. It seems likely that this form of unevenness is partly

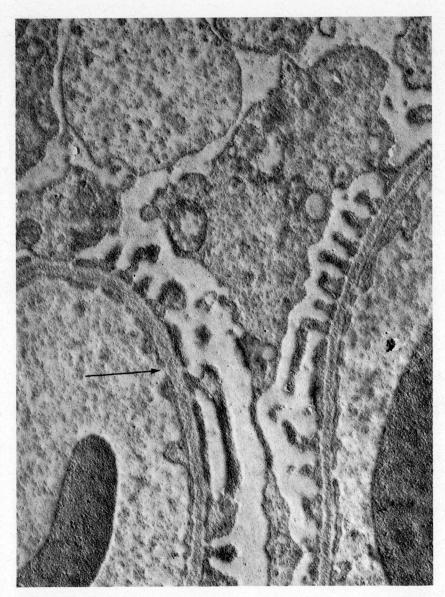

Fig. 5. Ultrathin section of kidney glomerulus, grey interference colour shadowed with gold-palladium at 25°. Raised areas show white shadow effects. Arrow indicates direction of shadowing. ×21,000

responsible for the subjective error inherent in attempts to judge interference colours (and hence thickness) by the eye. In the case of uneven sections the colour noted by the operator is resulting from an integration of many small regions, each region having a slightly different colour (see Cosslett, 1967; Rösch, 1960).

b. *Systematic variations.* Ultrathin sections of cells show variations of thickness associated with particular cytological features. These variations can be conveniently examined by shadowing of the section surface with metal. Gold-palladium or platinum works well at angles of 20–40°. Williams and Kallman (1955) and Watson (1956) used the technique to study irradiated methacrylate sections, thus obtaining useful information of a three-dimensional nature. Application of the technique to unirradiated sections of epoxy-resin embedded cells reveals a variety of cytological features which are depressed below or raised above the general section surface. Features which are very often found markedly raised above the general level are red blood cells (see Fig. 5) and bacterial cells, and collagen bundles (see Fig. 6). Most unit membranes are raised up, but to a much lesser degree. Red cells and unit membranes are raised on both the bottom and top faces of sections.

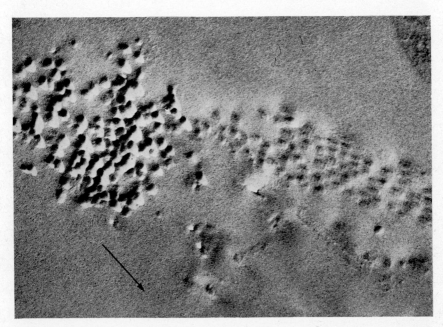

Fig. 6. Ultrathin section of rat kidney (grey interference colour) shadowed with gold-palladium at 25°. Note the raised collagen bundles in transverse section giving sharp shadows. ×31,000. Arrow indicates direction of shadowing.

Collagen is usually raised on both sides, but some raised bundles correspond to depressed features or holes on the adjacent section (Maser *et al.*, 1967). Many basement membranes are significantly below the general surface level (see Fig. 7) on both sides of the section. Measurement of shadow lengths indicate that features may be raised 40–400 Å above the general level on a grey or silver section of perhaps 500 Å thickness.

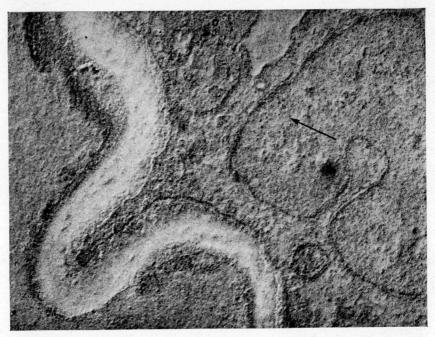

FIG. 7. Ultrathin sections of rat kidney shadowed with gold-palladium at 25°. Note the basement membrane of Bowman's Capsule depressed below the section surface. × 24,000. Arrow indicates direction of shadowing.

The origin of these various formations is of importance to the auto-radiographer. Those cases where raised areas on one section match up with depressed areas on the adjacent one must indicate pulling and tearing of the feature (usually collagen or other fibre). In this way sections may not contain an amount of the feature that is proportional to the section thickness. This could give rise to autoradiographic errors. Features which behave in this way are commonly fibrous and dense, thus admitting relatively little penetration of the embedding medium (see Andrews, 1965; Maser *et al.*, 1967). The cases where the feature is raised or depressed on both surfaces are probably not important problems. The raised and lowered features appear to represent swelling and shrinkage after cutting respectively. These events appear to be related to the properties peculiar to those particular features (Andrews, 1965; Sadoh and Christensen, 1967). The mechanism is, however, not entirely clear, since the phenomenon is more marked in thinner sections (grey and silver interference colours) than in thicker ones (gold and purple interference colours). It seems likely that redistribution of embedding medium relative to biological specimen during cutting and subsequent stretching with solvent vapour, plays some part. If these topographical features truly represent changes in the section *after* cutting, then they are not of a serious nature as far as autoradiography is concerned.

C. *Emulsion Application, Exposure and Development*

In order to achieve maximum resolution with a given nuclear emulsion, it must be applied to the specimen as a closely packed mono-granular layer. Initially, such layers proved difficult to produce, but now several reliable methods are available (Caro and van Tubergen, 1962; Granboulan, 1965; Salpeter and Bachmann, 1964). While each of these methods has its own drawbacks, with practice, each can be made to give reliable results, and it is probably true to say that this step is no longer a technical problem.

Exposure and development offer no technically difficult steps. The exposure conditions depend on the emulsion. In some cases an atmosphere free of oxygen is recommended (see Salpeter and Bachmann, 1964; Ray and Stevens, 1953; Herz, 1959). Development presents a choice between chemical and physical methods (Caro and van Tubergen, 1962; Meek and Moses, 1963; Salpeter and Bachmann, 1964; Kopriwa, 1967). The method used has some influence on resolution (Bachmann and Salpeter, 1965; see also Section III.C) and also on efficiency (see Section III.E).

D. *Selection and Sampling of Biological Material*

In all EM work there is a sampling problem, since observations can only be made from a small amount of tissue taken from a limited number of organisms. The approach is therefore more than ordinarily susceptible to errors caused by taking an atypical plant or animal. This limitation has to be accepted but the errors can be minimized by using where possible inbred strains, a particular sex, age, etc. In EM autoradiography precautions of this kind are especially necessary, since fewer sections are studied as autoradiographs than might be the case in a purely morphological study. Several further orders of selection occur in autoradiography. If, for instance, liver is being studied, it is necessary to decide whether the sections being analysed are a representative sample of this particular liver. In addition, having prepared the EM autoradiographs we need to know if the micrographs prepared from them adequately represent the sections originally coated with emulsion. The study of a representative sample from any particular liver is best approached by studying light microscope autoradiographic preparations from many parts of the liver and then taking for EM study a few blocks which appear typical. Having produced sections from the selected blocks, some means has to be found for sampling within the autoradiographs produced. This may be done either by taking micrographs of all the material, thus eliminating sampling altogether, or some sort of systematic treatment of each grid square may be used. Both of these approaches are independent of the presence or absence of grains. If silver grains are very few it may be necessary to take micrographs of all visible grains. In this case all the tissue has to be recorded. A less satisfactory expedient consists of taking micrographs of all grains and some sort of reference areas as a comparison. It is difficult to avoid introducing bias into such a technique, especially if the tissue is highly heterogeneous.

In the methods described below it is assumed that animal and tissue sampling are appropriately controlled. It is suggested that the set of micrographs of EM autoradiographs obtained are treated as a single sample, which is not necessarily entirely morphologically representative of the whole tissue. However, it is assumed that the micrographs are either a complete record of the EM autoradiographs or are at least a representative unbiased sample of them.

III. STUDY OF THE RESULTANT PREPARATIONS
A. *Background and Chemography*

Before the autoradiographs are analysed it is necessary to eliminate the possibility that the grain patterns are due to "background" or to positive chemography (production of a latent image by direct chemical action). Background due to fogging during handling of the emulsion is uncommon but can be detected by the frequent presence of grains over most of the specimen, including on the support film where the section is absent. If such preparations are common the fault may lie in contaminated glassware and materials or in poor darkroom facilities.

The presence of silver grains on empty embedding medium adjacent to tissue frequently indicates that the label is extracted by the embedding monomers. Neutral fat is sometimes very soluble in embedding monomers (Cope and Williams, 1968; Williams and Carr, 1968). Extraction of this type can be seen by the decreasing frequency of grains on the empty embedding medium with increasing distance from the specimen. This problem can sometimes be greatly reduced or eliminated by changing to another fixing and/or embedding system.

The possibility of positive chemography can be examined by making autoradiographs of similarly prepared but unlabelled material. The presence of positive chemography especially at particular sites in a labelled specimen cannot be conclusively ruled out. However, the use of unlabelled controls can confirm that the possibility is remote. The use of a thin inert layer between the tissue and emulsion (e.g. evaporated carbon) further helps to reduce the possibility.

Negative chemography (densitization of the emulsion or eradication of the latent image by direct chemical action (Rogers, 1967)(has been observed in autoradiography at the optical microscope level. The possibility can be examined by observing the behaviour of "fogged" emulsion layers overlying ultrathin tissue sections. The phenomenon is uncommon in electron microscopic preparations, at least in the author's material.

B. *Requirements for an Analytical Technique*

When devising a method for collecting data from EM autoradiographs several requirements must be met:

1. The method must take into account the "resolution" of the EM autoradiographic method and the organization of the cells. Resolution is a term which may have a variety of definitions according to the situation. In light microscopic autoradiography Doniach and Pelc (1950) defined the resolution of a system thus: "the resolving power for a source of zero diameter is defined by the distance between the point of maximum exposure and the point at which the number of developed grains is halved". Lamerton and Harriss (1954) however, pointed out the necessity of considering a *pair of sources* preferably of defined diameter. Their definition for two uniformly active cylindrical sources was: "Two autoradiographic images can just be resolved when the blackening from one cylinder at the midpoint is half that at the edge of the cylinder". They did not discuss horizontal line sources.

In these definitions we are considering *blackening* caused by a multiplicity of silver grains. In EM autoradiography grains are relatively few. In this case resolution has to be defined in terms of the *probability* of a grain being formed. Caro (1962) defined resolution as the distance from a point source to where the probability of a grain being formed falls to 50%. He was thus able to calculate a "resolution" of the order of 1000 A for Ilford L4 emulsion. Caro and Schnös (1965) subsequently demonstrated resolutions of this order using ultrathin sections. Bachmann and Salpeter (1965) have taken a slightly different approach. They have calculated the sizes of circles that have various probabilities of enclosing the silver grain derived from a point source and conversely of enclosing the source, if drawn around the grain. This type of definition is a more practical one, although it does not go beyond a consideration of point sources. In EM autoradiography it is necessary to consider the recognizable ultrastructural features as isotope sources, e.g. mito-chondria, lysosomes, nuclei or perhaps nucleoli or various parts of the nucleus. Thus it is necessary to consider resolution in EM autoradio-graphy in terms of the shape and spatial organization of the potential isotope sources. The point resolution data of Bachmann and Salpeter must be applied in a way that permits due consideration of these factors.

2. The method must be of a form that allows statistical analysis of the results. Examples of analyses that may be necessary would be com-parison of the grain distribution with a random one, comparison of one distribution with another, comparison of one source with another or calculation of confidence limits for grain densities.

3. The method must eliminate problems posed by silver grains over-lying the outlines of more than one ultrastructural feature. Silver grains positioned in this way often comprise 30–50% of the total grains on autoradiographs of cellular material. This is so, even when the "sources" correspond to well-defined organelles such as mitochondria, ergastoplasm, etc. If material like ergastoplasm is subdivided into say "cisternae" and "lamellae", then the proportion may be even higher. None of the available nuclear emulsions have a small enough grain size markedly to affect this problem. In many authors' work, silver grains thus positioned are allocated equally to either side of the boundary or according to some other arbitrary rule (Fedorko and Hirsch, 1966; Stein and Stein, 1968). In other cases the grains are apparently allocated subjectively. In many cases no mention is made of the problem at all. Clearly, any method devised must take this difficulty into account or the result may be subject to bias.

4. The method must allow for the necessity of relating the numbers of silver grains over an item, to the fractional volume of that item in the cell. This necessitates measuring the areas of various cell components on micrographs. Point or line analysis (Chalkley, Cornfield and Park, 1949; Loud, 1962) can be conveniently used for this purpose as suggested by Ross and Benditt (1965). Planimetry has also been used

(Hirsch, Zelickson and Hartmann, 1965). Any method devised must incorporate means of area measurement, the line or point analysis approach being the most convenient.

No method so far available meets all these requirements. Many authors apparently rely on purely subjective methods for assessment. Others have attempted relatively simple procedures. Coimbra and Leblond (1966) and Maunsbach (1966) have attempted to plot histograms of the frequency of silver grains at different distances from given types of organelle comparing the result with the theoretical curve derived by Caro (1962) for the distribution of silver grains around a point source. This method is unworkable when applied to most cells. It takes no account of the shapes, sizes and distributions of the various organelles. It is quite possible to obtain similar curves for two types of organelle when only one is labelled, since when an organelle is widespread in the cell, it may be impossible for grains to be formed very far from it, even though the structure is in fact completely unlabelled. It is difficult to compare the curve derived from an object which takes a highly attenuated form, with that from a source of compact form. Neither object approximates to a point source. Similarly the curve for a point source cannot be used for comparing the grain frequencies around two discs of widely different size. However, in some cases the cell is organized in a highly regular fashion, as in striated muscle. In these cases valuable information can be obtained with this simple method. An application of this type will be described below.

The distribution of silver grains over some areas can be tested for randomness by superimposing a squared screen. The frequency of squares with 0, 1, 2, etc. grains can then be compared to that expected for a random distribution (given by the Poisson distribution). This method, although conveniently simple, is of limited value, since it takes note neither of tissue organization nor of autoradiograph resolution.

None of these methods provide a means of allocating silver grains which are situated on the edges of two items.

The method to be described below takes account of the "resolution" of EM autoradiography and the organization of the cells and allows the application of statistical methods. Specific activities of various organelles can be obtained. A particularly important feature is the means it gives for analysing silver grains lying on the edges of two features, and over a mixture of small features. Thus this source of bias is eliminated and additional information is gained concerning the labelling of organelle boundaries and small organelles which are ordinarily beyond the "resolution" of the EM autoradiograph method.

C. *The Analysis*

The method consists in essence of four operations:

1. Collection of data from silver grains. Each silver grain is reduced in complexity by taking the midpoint of its longest axis and drawing a circle around this point. The circle is chosen to have a diameter equivalent to the "resolution" of the particular auto-radiographic system (according to Bachmann and Salpeter, 1965). The potential isotope sources within this circle are noted.
2. Analysis of the areas and organization of the potential isotope sources by the superimposition of circles equivalent to silver grains—hereafter referred to as "effective area" measurement.
3. Measurement of actual areas presented by the various cytological features (potential isotope sources).
4. Collation of the data obtained in the last three operations.

1. *Obtaining data from silver grains*

Chemical developers normally produce a filamentous silver grain. The only reasonably reproducible means of taking the centre of such objects is to use the centre of the longest axis. Since each chemical developer produces its own characteristic range of grain structures, the circle for one developer may not precisely correspond with that used for another. Hence it is recommended that only one developer is used throughout the work and that the development conditions are rigorously standardized.

The size of the circle is chosen to equal the "resolution" of the particular system in use, defined according to the suggestion of Bachmann and Salpeter (1965), i.e. the circle has 50% confidence of enclosing the site of the disintegration. Using Ilford L4 emulsion and assuming a section thickness of 500 Å, the circle has a radius of approximately 1250 Å. If desired, a higher probability circle can be used. This will be of correspondingly greater size. However, 60–70% is the practical limit, and in many circumstances this may prove inconveniently large.

It is necessary to decide before the analysis is commenced, which ultrastructural features are to be considered as single entities. For example, mitochondria are usually classified as a single entity. Rough e.r. also might be termed a single entity, although if the cisternae are wide enough it may be possible to split the feature up into cisternae and lamellae. Whichever features are chosen to be single ones, a significant proportion of the silver grains is likely to be found lying astride the junction of two features. Thus arises a second group of entities hereafter termed "junctional" items (see Fig. 8).

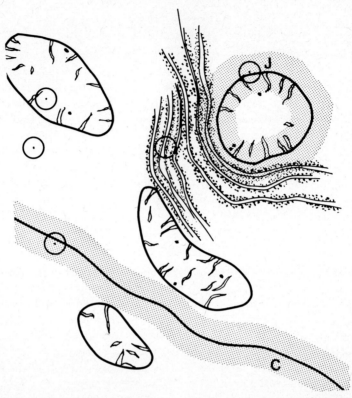

FIG. 8. Diagrammatic representation of a liver cell to show the nature of single "junctional" and "compound" items. Circles lying wholly on a mitochondrion, on rough endoplasmic reticulum (e.r.) or on smooth e.r. (white regions) are on single items. The stippled area "C" is a compound item. The stippled area "J" represents junctional items. Two types of "junctional" items are present, (a) mitochondrion/smooth e.r. and (b) mitochondrion/rough e.r.

In addition to single and "junctional" items, a third group of items is found, termed "compound items". "Compound items" are composed of features smaller than the circle diameter together with whatever surrounding material is included within the circle. (The surrounding material must itself also occur as a single item, otherwise the compound one would have to be considered single.) An example of the compound item would be "plasma membrane/smooth endoplasmic reticulum". (Smooth endoplasmic reticulum also occurs singly, whereas plasma membrane cannot, since its diameter is so small (see Fig. 8)). The use of these three types of item, when applied to most animal cells gives rise to about 10–30 possible grain categories. However, silver grains are usually confined to only a proportion of these.

The number of silver grains required in any particular analysis depends on several factors. If the grains are confined to one or a few items, less grains may be necessary than if the distribution is more dispersed. Thus, consider a cell where all the label is nuclear; 50–100 grains would suffice to give a strong indication that the label was almost entirely nuclear. However, the possibility of 5–10% of cytoplasmic label could not be excluded. One thousand silver grains all overlying the nucleus, would suggest that cytoplasmic label was very likely to be less than 1% of the total. If the grain distribution is broad, then the total number necessary will depend upon the proportion of grains on a particular item, and on the precision with which its grain count is required to be estimated. Consider the binomial distribution; when $npq \geqslant 100$ then the distribution approximates to the normal distribution. Thus, for a given item A which has 10% of the total grain count, if more than 100 grains are counted the estimate of A will be $10 \pm$ one standard deviation (S.D.) on 67·3% of occasions, and within $10 \pm 1·96$ S.D. on 95% of occasions. However, at least 30 grains would be needed on any item to calculate 95% confidence limits. Thus 95% confidence limits on a count of 30 grains are 19·3–40·7. Hence if the area had only 10% of the total grains then 300 grains would be required in the total analysis. If the item had only 2% of the total then a total of 1500 grains would have been necessary. However, 30 grains would be the *minimum* required for any item. The $1·96 \times$ S.D. of 30 is too large for most purposes. Hence 50 or 100 grains on the item would be more reasonable. If 100 grains are used then $1·96 \times$ the S.D. $= 19·6$. If the item has only 10% of the total grains, 1000 grains are needed, but if it has only 2% then the total required is 5000.

If it is desired simply to compare the overall grain distribution with some other distribution such as a random one, then relatively few grains may be needed, (perhaps 100–200). If χ^2 is used, the limiting factor will be the necessity for keeping the "expected" values reasonably large, e.g. >5 (Bailey, 1959). This may necessitate pooling some of the items. If pooling is not feasible or appears to conceal differences then it will be necessary to collect further data.

2. *Analysis of effective areas by the application of circles*

Circles were either scored on cleared X-ray film or drawn on PVC sheet using "Letraset" instant lettering. The size of the circles used in most experiments was 7·5 mm diameter—equivalent to 2500 Å (50% confidence) on a 30,000 diameters electron micrograph. In most of the experiments, observations were made using circles arranged on the screen in a random fashion. These screens were prepared by treating two adjacent edges of a square sheet as axes and then placing circles by drawing random coordinates taken from a table of random numbers. It was convenient to draw a circle upon the screen and consider only those 2500 Å circles which fell within it. The circumference of the circle could then be subdivided, providing numbered reference marks. Radii were also drawn to decrease the chance of counting circles twice (see Figs 9 and 10). The screens were made in a variety of diameters, but the most convenient were large enough to circumscribe a print on 16″ × 20″ paper. A screen of this size can conveniently bear 200 circles. The reference marks around the circumference allow the screen to be

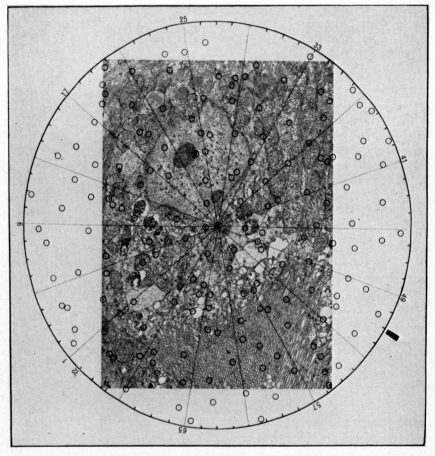

FIG. 9. Shows the circular screen in position on a micrograph. Note the randomly arranged circles. Radii are used for reference during repeated application by rotation, and for facilitating data collection.

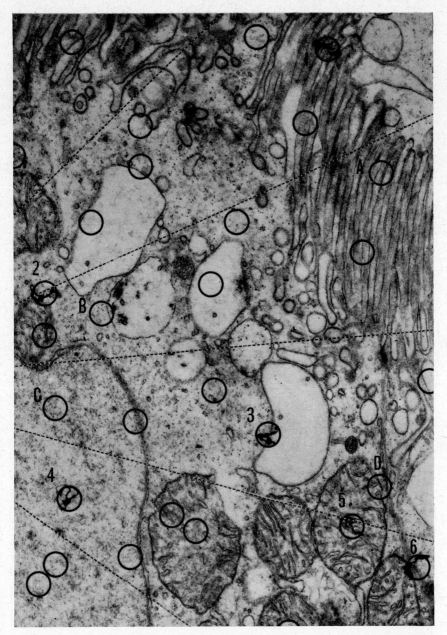

Fig. 10. Representation of an electron microscopic autoradiograph of a kidney tubule cell. The micrograph is shown with circles drawn around the silver grains. Note that some are on single items (e.g. 1, 4), some on junctional items (e.g. 2, 3) and some on compound items (e.g. 6). A screen is represented in position, superimposing numerous "random" circles and showing several radii. The circles show examples of single (A, C), junctional (B) and compound (D) items. The magnification is $\times 0.83$ of that used in practice.

applied systematically (by rotation) giving data on as many circles as is desired. Using a 200 circle screen one application per print may be sufficient. However with a smaller screen repeated application may be necessary. The print size used may vary provided its longest axis is shorter than the screen diameter, since the number of circles applied will be proportional to the print area. If the micrograph is wider than the screen diameter the area has to be subdivided, and this increases the volume of work.

The random screens described above have been used to avoid problems posed by periodicity in the cell structures. However, if the experimenter is satisfied that no such problem exists, then a regular screen can be used with the circles at the intersects of a grid (see Fig. 11). This type

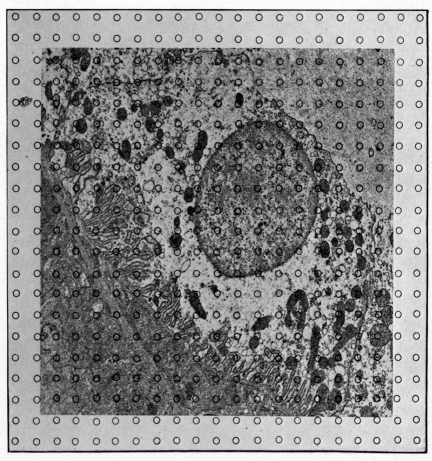

Fig. 11. Regular screen in position on a micrograph.

of sampling slightly reduces sampling errors (see Eränkö, 1955; Hennig, 1967). When working to a standard print magnification of 30,000 diameters, the largest convenient print size is on 16″ × 20″ paper. This means that a print corresponds to about 250 μ^2—approximately equal to the profile of a parenchymal cell. On such a print, about 400 circles are sufficient for most purposes. This is especially true if a set of prints is studied, each of which has a rather similar composition. If the prints differ markedly, then more circles may be required for each print, since the possibility is increased of a minority of prints including some unique feature. In instances such as this, or when an item comprising a small part of the total is of particular interest, the circle number must be increased.

The number of circles necessary to obtain a measure of the effective area of a particular ultrastructural feature with a given per cent standard deviation, can be conveniently calculated using the normal approximation to the binomial distribution. Table VI shows the

TABLE VI

Standard Error as a Percentage of the Mean for Different Values of P* using Various Sample Sizes (n)†

| n† | \multicolumn{5}{c}{P*} |
	0·02	0·05	0·1	0·2	0·5
100	70·7	44·7	31·6	22·4	14·2
400	35·3	22·4	15·8	11·2	7·1
900	23·6	14·9	10·5	7·5	4·7
1600	17·7	11·0	7·9	5·6	3·5
3600	11·8	7·4	5·3	3·7	2·4

* Fraction of the total area occupied by the item.
† Number of circles applied.

standard deviations (expressed as per cent) of area estimates of various regions comprising different proportions of the total area (expressed as P values). For example, a region A where P = 0·1 would require 1000 circles to be applied, before the standard deviation of the area estimate obtained falls to 10% of the mean. On the other hand if 4000 circles are applied a similar level of accuracy could be attained for an area comprising only 2% of the total.

"Effective area" estimates on a kidney cell profile are shown in Table VII. Data is given for approximately 400 circles applied with each of two screens and for increasing numbers of circles applied with

TABLE VII

Estimates of the Percentage Effective Area of
Various Items in a Kidney Cell Profile

Item	Screen used and number of circles applied					
	A 415	B 428	A+B 843	A 1008	A 1851	A 4068
Nucleus	18·79	14·95	16·84	15·18	15·94	16·42
Ribosomes/ plasma membrane	2·90	2·80	2·85	1·79	2·27	2·53
Dense bodies/ ribosomes	7·23	8·64	7·95	8·04	8·00	6·98
Phagosomes	3·86	3·27	3·56	3·37	3·46	3·42
Phagosomes/ ribosomes	2·65	3·98	3·32	4·46	3·94	3·76
Nucleus/ ribosomes	1·93	1·87	1·90	2·18	2·05	2·26
Mitochondria	14·70	14·02	14·35	15·08	14·75	14·58
Ribosomes	22·65	20·33	21·47	22·71	22·15	20·85
Mitochondria/ ribosomes	15·90	20·33	18·15	16·17	17·07	17·11
Mitochondria/ ribosomes/ plasma membrane	1·20	1·16	1·19	1·88	1·57	2·38
Smooth vesicles/ ribosomes	1·69	2·57	2·14	2·28	2·22	2·41
Mitochondria/ ribosomes/ nucleus	0·24	0·47	0·36	0·30	0·33	0·40
Dense bodies	5·78	5·14	5·45	5·86	5·67	6·26
Dense bodies/ mitochondria/ ribosomes	0·48	0·47	0·47	0·50	0·49	0·44
Mitochondria/ phagosomes	0	0	0	0·20	0	0

a single screen. Comparison of the 400 circle with the 4000 circle data demonstrates how the smaller items are more liable to sampling error than the larger ones. The two random screens A and B gave essentially similar results.

3. *Measurement of actual areas by point analysis*

Point analysis may be performed separately from "effective area" measurement. However the two operations may be more conveniently combined. This can be achieved by placing a point at the centre of each

circle on the screen. The data from the two sources can then be simultaneously collected. Determination of the numbers of points to be
applied involves similar problems to those discussed above.

In practice it is possible to use circles containing several points.
Using 7·5 mm circles, 7 points is about the optimum number, since any
larger number obscures too much tissue. The points are most conveniently arranged in some standard pattern over the circle. A regular
hexagon gives reasonable coverage (77·8%) of the circle contents if the
points of the hexagon lie on a circle with two-thirds the radius of the
outer one (see Fig. 12). Hexagonal close packing is thus achieved. The

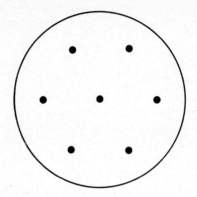

Fig. 12. Arrangement of points within a circle to give best coverage for seven points.

orientation of the hexagon with respect to the main screen may be
either random or systematic. The differences are negligible.

Data collection from these three sources can be facilitated by adopt-
ing a standard format allowing space for point data on all single items
and circle data on all possible items obtainable with that cell type. The
three types of data collection described above have to be combined in
various ways. In practice this may mean that point and circle data
need to be collected together (this will become clear from the subsequent account). Thus it may become necessary to perform some parts
of the analysis twice, unless the portions of the data collection to be
made in concert are known beforehand.

4. *Correlation of grain, circle and point data*

a. *Consideration of the complete grain distribution.* The frequency
distribution of circles over the various ultrastructural features is an
estimate of the frequencies of silver grains expected over those features
if the grains were scattered randomly. Thus a suitable statistical

comparison between circle and grain frequency distributions will reveal if the grain distribution is random. Such information is especially useful when studying the binding of drugs and hormones. Clearly, in these cases, a random distribution throughout the cell is unlikely to be of great biological significance. Table VIII shows a comparison

TABLE VIII

Analysis of the Grain Distribution on EM Autoradiographs of Kidney Cells from a Rat injected with H^3-Aldosterone

	Ribosomes	Mitochondria	Nuclei	Plasma membrane other items	Plasma protein	Other items
% Silver grains	4·8	7·1	4·3	48·6	6·0	29·2
% Circles	19·1	11·1	8·3	28·0	0·9	32·6

Comparison of silver grain distribution with circle distribution:
$\chi^2 = 29·3$ $P = <0·001$, i.e. grain distribution is highly non-random.

between circle and grain distribution over rat kidney convoluted tubule cells from an animal injected 40 minutes previously with H^3-aldosterone. In order to apply χ^2 to this sample, several small items have been pooled. The χ^2 value indicates that the grain distribution is significantly different from a random one ($P = <0·001$). (These results are more fully documented in Williams and Baba, 1967.)

In almost all cases the label is non-random. In these instances those components of the χ^2 value which are highest indicate the features which are especially rich or poor in label. These items can then be studied in detail as required. The items rich in label may of course be single, junctional or compound in nature.

b. *Consideration of individual items*. (i) Calculation of specific activities. The number of silver grains per unit area of a feature can be used as a measure of radioactivity per unit volume. For the more extended features (e.g. endoplasmic reticulum, nucleus) the actual area determined from point analysis may be used. In these cases a true specific activity could be calculated, and if necessary the absolute amount of isotope in the structure found (Bachmann and Salpeter, 1967).

However, this approach does not allow the study of junctional regions, and indeed poses again the problem of silver grains that lie over these regions. This problem can be overcome if grain counts are

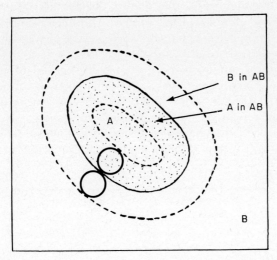

FIG. 13. Diagrammatic representation of the junctional region (AB) at the edge of an object A (stippled) surrounded by a more extensive region B. Note the relative proportions of A and B in AB. Note also the relative areas of A in AB and A not in AB.

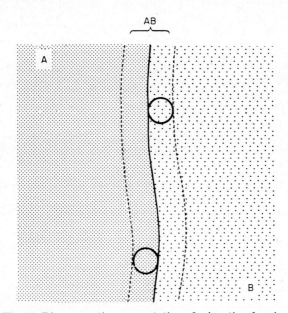

Fig. 14. Diagrammatic representation of a junctional region.

referred to effective areas. The *relative* specific activities of different features are then obtained. The inability to obtain absolute quantitation is of little consequence, since this is seldom of biological significance. In most experiments it reflects mainly the isotope dose, specific activity (C/mM), route of administration, etc. However, use of effective area rather than actual area involves using some portions of the tissue area twice (e.g. Fig. 13, Fig. 14) A in AB is used in A and in AB. A better estimate of the relative specific activities of A and AB when using effective areas is obtained if A in AB is ignored when studying A. This is only important if A in AB is a significant proportion of A. If this is

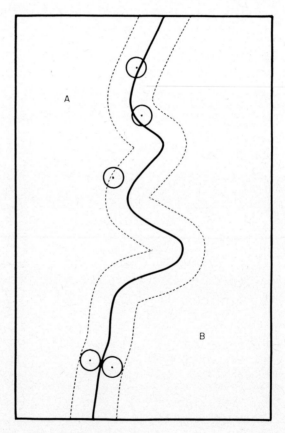

Fig. 15. The method of analysing the relative contents of A and B in a junctional region AB (between the dotted lines). Note that some circles have their centre on A but overlap B, while others have their centres on B but overlap A. When sufficient circles are applied randomly the relative proportions of these two categories give the relative contents of A and B in AB.

so, the effective area of A can be corrected by subtracting the A portion of circles in AB (see next paragraph).

(ii) Analysis of junctional regions. The relative area contributions of A and B to a junctional region AB can be conveniently determined by combined point and circle analysis. Thus, if during a circle analysis "n" circles fall on AB, a portion (a) will have their centres on A but overlap B, and the remainder (b) will have centres on B but overlap A. Thus (a)/n = the proportion of A in AB, and conversely (b)/n = the proportion of B in AB (see Fig. 15).

Sufficient circles must of course be applied to obtain estimates with suitably narrow confidence limits. If the specific activity of A and B are known, then the "expected" number of silver grains from these two sources can be predicted, and compared to that actually found.

i.e.
$$G_{AB} = \frac{G_{AA}}{A_{AA}} \times A_{AB} + \frac{G_{BB}}{A_{BB}} \times A_{BA}$$

where

G_{AB} = grains on AB
G_{AA} = grains on A
G_{BB} = grains on B
A_{AA} = effective area of A
A_{BB} = effective area of B
A_{AB} = circles with centre on A but overlapping B
A_{BA} = circles with centre on B but overlapping A.

Similarly, a triple item could be analysed:

$$G_{ABC} = \frac{G_{AA}}{A_{AA}} \times A_{ABC} + \frac{G_{BB}}{A_{BB}} \times A_{BCA} + \frac{G_{CC}}{A_{CC}} \times A_{CBA}$$

(iii) Analysis of compound regions. It is possible using the circle and point method to determine the effects of the small "included item" on the grain count of the more extended one. Thus, if we consider a compound region AC (see Fig. 16), if the specific activity of C is known then the effect on the grain count of C can be observed, *provided it is assumed* that C in AC is similar to C alone. This is probably a reasonable type of assumption, since at the present time we have very little information on the relative activities of similar organelles in different parts of the same cell type.

For example, striated muscle from rats injected intraaortically with H^3-Cortisol shows radioactivity perhaps associated with the sarcotubular system or the Z band (see Fig. 17). The sarcotubular system is too narrow to form a distinct single item, and in circle analysis always occurs as a compound item. Grain and circle data for

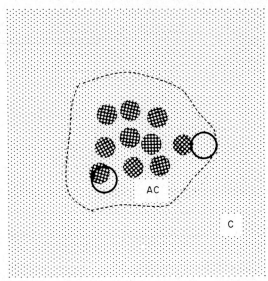

Fɪɢ. 16. Diagrammatic representation of a compound item (AC) composed of granules (A) smaller than the circle size (dense stipple) surrounded by a large area C (light stipple).

a sample of this material, autoradiographed using Ilford L4 emulsion, is shown in Table IX. Note that the compound item "sarcotubular system/myofibrils" has a grain count much higher than would be expected if the grain count was random—$\chi^2 = 78.47$. Point analysis

TABLE IX

Combined Circle and Point Analysis of EM Autoradiographs
Prepared from the Striated Muscle of a Rat Injected with H^3-Cortisol

	Myofibrils	Sarcotubular system/ myofibrils	Nuclei and other items
% Silver grains	19·2	78·7	2·1
% Circles	67·3	23·7	9·0
Relative number of silver grains per circle	1·0	12·5	0·8

Composition of Sarcotubular system/Myofibrils measured by point analysis:
Sarcotubular system 29%
Myofibrils 71%
This suggests that the specific activity of the Sarcotubular system is about 40× that of the myofibrils

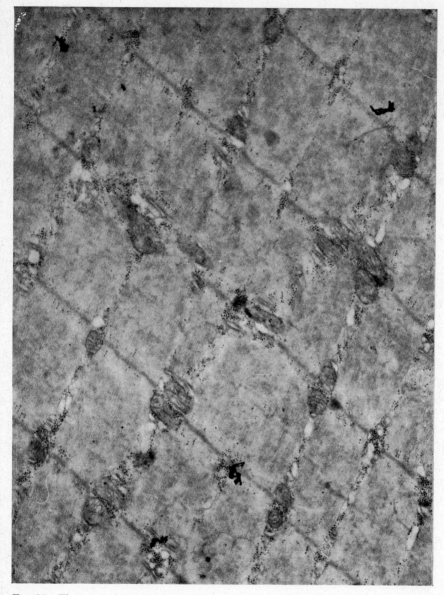

FIG. 17. Electron microscopic autoradiograph of a section of striated muscle from a rat injected with H³-cortisol 30 minutes previously. ×19,000

indicated that sarcotubules only take up 29% of the compound item. If the known specific activity of the myofibrils is taken into account, it appears that the sarcotubular system has a specific activity about 40× that of the myofibrils. This calculation assumes that the specific activity of the myofibrils alone is the same as in the immediate vicinity of the sarcotubules. The alternative explanation would be that the myofibrils are preferentially labelled in those parts immediately adjacent to the sarcotubular system. As mentioned above, striated muscle autoradiographs are open to analysis by plotting grain frequencies along various axes. Application of this method to H³-cortisol-labelled rat striated muscle, gives results completely in

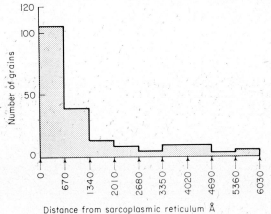

Fig. 18.

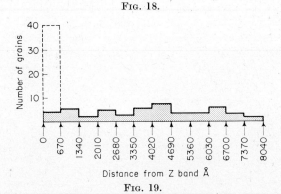

Fig. 19.

FIGS. 18 and 19. Histograms showing the frequency distributions of the distances of silver grains from (a) sarcoplasmic reticulum and (b) the Z line in EM autoradiographs of striated muscle from a rat injected intraperitoneally with H³-cortisol 30 minutes previously. In 18 the fall-off in grain frequency with increasing distance is clear. In 19 the open block represents silver grains which as well as being adjacent to the Z line are also close to the sarcotubular system.

accordance with those obtained with the point and circle technique (see Figs 18 and 19). Note that the grain frequency is high only in the close vicinity of the sarcoplasmic reticulum. There is no correlation with the muscle banding. The only occasions when silver grains occur over the Z-line are when it intersects the sarcotubular system.

Thus, in a sense, an ultrastructural feature which is smaller than the circle size might be identified as a radioactive "source", even though it is below the "resolution" of the autoradiographic method.

(iv) Evaluation of cross-fire effects. The feasibility of a comparison between the specific activities of two organelle types depends on the magnitudes of cross-fire effects. Thus, relatively extensive features such as areas of ergastoplasm, nuclei or myofibrils give rise to silver grains that in the main overlie the organelle from which they are derived. On the other hand, smaller organelles (e.g. lysosomes) give rise to silver grains many of which may lie outside the organelle profile. Hence specific activity measurements on small organelles are likely to be inaccurate. Small organelles may also gain substantial numbers of grains from the surrounding material. The practicability of comparisons between organelles can only be determined by estimating the magnitude of the cross-fire effects involved. The point and circle method outlined above can be used for this purpose. Consider an organelle type A surrounded by a region B (Fig. 13). If A in AB is a substantial proportion of A, then large errors are likely to arise. The relative magnitudes of "A in AB" and "A not in AB" can be measured. There are several types of case:

a. Comparison of different samples of the same small organelle type, e.g. mitochondria. If the surrounding material is similar in both cases and relatively lightly labelled, the two sets may be compared. However, small size and shape differences could have a large effect.

b. Comparison of different types of small organelle. This may be possible but can be rendered difficult if the shape or size differs and if the surrounding material and its specific activity vary.

c. Comparison of an extended source with a small source, e.g. ergastoplasm with mitochondria. This is not possible unless steps are taken to correct the grain count of mitochondria for cross-fire losses and gains. This can be attempted by confining counting to a central plug in the middle of each organelle. It may be impossible if the mitochondria are small as in many leucocytes, or elongated as in many kidney tubule cells.

d. Comparison of two extended sources. This clearly presents relatively few problems.

When considering small organelles, a factor that merits attention is the shape of the frequency curve obtained by casting random circles on to the object. If the organelle is of sufficient diameter at its narrowest point, a plateau occurs in the distribution. If the plateau is large enough, then the area it represents can be used to obtain grain counts for specific activity measurements. In the case of small organelles, the curve does not reach a plateau and hence the grain count will not be a true reflection of specific activity. The minimum diameter necessary to achieve a plateau is three times the circle size. In the L4-500A section system, this corresponds to a diameter of $(3 \times 0.25\,\mu = 0.75\,\mu)$. A square or circular region of ten times the circle diameter $(10 \times 0.25\,\mu = 2.5\,\mu)$ has 36% of its area also included in junctional regions. In this case overall loss of grains would therefore be 18%. Although this applies to many organelles, it must be borne in mind that regions which make up a high proportion of the effective area of the cell may nevertheless occur as many small pieces. This situation gives rise to much higher losses.

Curves of this kind assume uniform labelling; this is not by any means always true. However, the approach is a useful one. Calculations of probability curves for even simply shaped surfaces is difficult (see Kendall and Moran, 1963) but useful information can be found by actual experiment.

(v) The effect of varying the circle size. When measuring effective areas by applying "random circles", the relative proportions of single and compound or junctional items is a practical measure of the resolution in any particular ultrastructural system. A decrease in the circle diameter (equivalent to using a smaller grained emulsion or a thinner section) should give a decrease in the percentage falling on compound or junctional regions.

Thus the increase in discrimination* expected when changing from one system to another can be examined. Ilford L4 emulsion used on 500 A sections and Kodak NTE emulsion used on 350 A sections were compared, using circle sizes calculated from the data of Bachmann and Salpeter (1965). Such a comparison was made by applying 1000 circles of each size to the same micrographs of (i) rat kidney convoluted tubule cell, (ii) rat liver cell and (iii) rat striated muscle.

The results are shown in Tables X, XI and XII. The percentage of the cell area which changes from compound or junctional to single state is small—about 5–6% (see Table XIII). The effect on larger items such

---

* The term discrimination used here refers to the ability to distinguish two organelle types as radioactive sources. It takes account of the nature of the specimens and must not be confused with the physical definition of resolution as used above by Bachmann and Salpeter (1965).

as nuclei is, as expected, negligible. However, small improvements are made in the discrimination of small particulate items such as glycogen rosettes and smooth membrane vesicles in liver. The effect on the discrimination of liver mitochondria is small. In comparison, the smaller muscle mitochondrial profiles are made more prominent.

The overall percentage of circles changing from junctional or compound to single is only a crude measurement of the improvement obtained. A more significant improvement may occur in the discrimination of some small organelles. If these features are of particular interest then the change to a smaller grained emulsion is worthwhile. The

TABLE X

Comparison of Effective Area Measurements Obtained Using Circle Sizes Equivalent to Ilford L4 Emulsion on 500A Sections, and Kodak NTE on 350A Sections. Kidney Cell Profile

	Ilford L4	Kodak NTE
Nucleus	15·18	14·95
Ribosomes/plasma membrane	1·79	1·78
Dense bodies/ribosomes	8·04	6·44
Phagosomes	3·37	3·96
Phagosomes/ribosomes	4·46	3·76
Nucleus/ribosomes	2·18	2·28
Mitochondria	15·08	16·93
Ribosomes	22·71	24·05
Mitochondria/ribosomes	16·17	14·26
Mitochondria/ribosomes/plasma membrane	1·88	1·49
Small vesicles/ribosomes	2·28	2·37
Mitochondria/ribosomes/nucleus	0·30	0·10
Dense bodies	5·86	7·23
Dense bodies/mitochondria/ribosomes	0·50	0·40

Percentage changing from "compound" or "junctional" to single = 4·92.

improvement obtained can also be estimated from the probability density curves obtained by superimposing circles on outlines of typical features (see above). The greater cost and increased difficulty of handling of finer grained emulsions has also to be borne in mind.

Consideration of Table XIII illustrates that the discrimination of the method (as judged by the percentage of "single" circles) is affected less by the circle size than by the nature of the specimen itself, since the proportion of single versus compound or junctional items varies a great deal with the cell type. This variation is greater than that caused by varying the circle size over one cell type. Some organelles, e.g.

TABLE XI

Comparison of Effective Area Measurements Obtained Using Circle Sizes
Equivalent to Ilford L4 Emulsion on 500A Sections, and
Kodak NTE on 350A Sections. Liver Cell Profile

	Ilford L4	Kodak NTE
Er./Sm. Er.	0·47	0·41
Er./Ribosomes	15·47	16·56
Glycogen/Sm. Er.	20·08	17·04
Mitochondria	6·51	6·92
Dense bodies/Sm. Er./Glycogen	2·58	1·83
Dense bodies/Er./Ribosomes	0·47	0·54
Glycogen	15·60	18·33
Dense bodies	1·09	1·32
Myelin figures	0·61	0·68
Mitochondria/Er./Ribosomes	6·24	5·70
Sm. Er.	8·68	10·18
Mitochondria/Sm. Er./Glycogen	2·58	1·77
Sm. Er./Plasma membrane	0·41	0·14
Amorphous cytoplasm	1·49	1·63
Nucleus/Sm. Er./Glycogen	1·36	1·15
Plasma membrane/Sm. Er./Glycogen	0·68	0·68
Nucleus	12·42	12·49
Myelin figures/Glycogen	0·54	0·41
Mitochondria/Sm. Er.	0·20	0·20
Amorphous cytoplasm/Glycogen	1·56	1·22
Mitochondria/Glycogen	0·68	0·41
Golgi	0·27	0·27

Percentage changing from "compound" or "junctional" to single = 5·26.

TABLE XII

Comparison of Effective Area Measurements Obtained Using Circle Sizes
Equivalent to Ilford L4 Emulsion on 500A Sections, and
Kodak NTE on 350A Sections. Striated Muscle

	Ilford L4	Kodak NTE
Mito/Tub	1.37	0·21
Mito/Tub/Myofibrils		
Tub/Myofibrils	6·73	5·76
Mito/Myofibrils	11·66	8·70
Mito	0·63	1·57
Myofibrils	67·33	72·22
Z band/Myofibrils	6·51	5·55
Z band/Myofibrils/Mito	0·32	0·21
T-system/Myofibrils	1·68	1·46
Nucleus	2·42	2·52
Other	1·35	1·80

Percentage changing from "compound" or "junctional" to single = 5·93.
Mito: Mitochondria.   Tub: Sarcotubules.

TABLE XIII

Summary of the Effect of Circle Size on the Percentages of Circles Falling
on Single and Junctional or Compound Features

Cell type	Ilford L4 on 500A section (circle diameter = 2500A)		Kodak NTE on 350A section (circle diameter = 1600A)		
	% Single	% Compound or junctional	% Single	% Compound or junctional	Total No. of items
Kidney proximal convoluted tubule	62·2	37·8	67·1	32·9	18
Striated muscle	71·7	28·3	78·1	21·9	11
Liver	46·7	53·3	51·9	49·1	22

mitochondria, are much more easily discriminated in the kidney cell than in the other two, due to the different size and shape that the organelle takes in the different cell types (see also Figs 20 and 21).

The conformation of the specimen, therefore, is of great importance in determining the discrimination that is possible. The circle size (based on specimen thickness and grain size) has somewhat less influence.

D. *Recording Results in Micrograph Form*

It is always difficult when reporting electron microscopic investigations to present sufficient information in the form of micrographs. A relatively small number of micrographs must necessarily be selected to represent what the author believes to be typical findings. Recording electron microscopic autoradiography is much more difficult, since each micrograph normally records few silver grains and hence has a very low informational content. This situation differs sharply from a record of an optical microscopic autoradiograph, which may depict hundreds or thousands of silver grains. Thus an electron microscopic autoradiograph recorded in micrograph form is never an adequate substitute for an objective analysis involving some hundreds of grains, but serves largely to demonstrate the experimenter's technical competence.

E. *Absolute Quantitation*

In the previous section relative quantitation was described and discussed. Absolute quantitation, however, is not generally of importance since the amount of label in a specimen generally reflects such factors as the isotope dose, route of injection, pool size of the precursor and its metabolites etc. and is therefore not of especial interest.

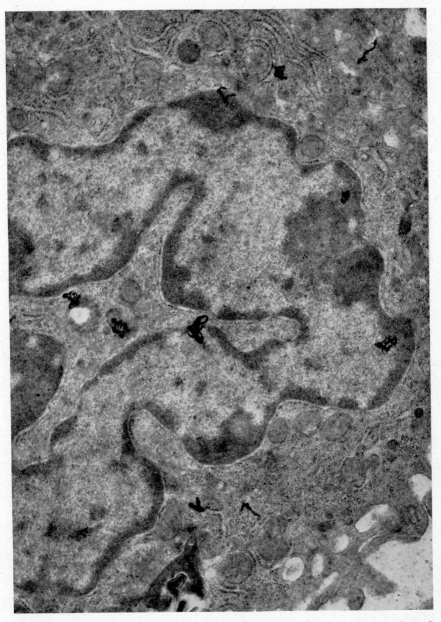

Fig. 20. Electron microscopic autoradiograph of a section of a mouse peritoneal macrophage labelled with H³ leucine. Note the relative sizes of the silver grains and the organelles such as mitochondria. ×25,000. Compare with Fig. 21.

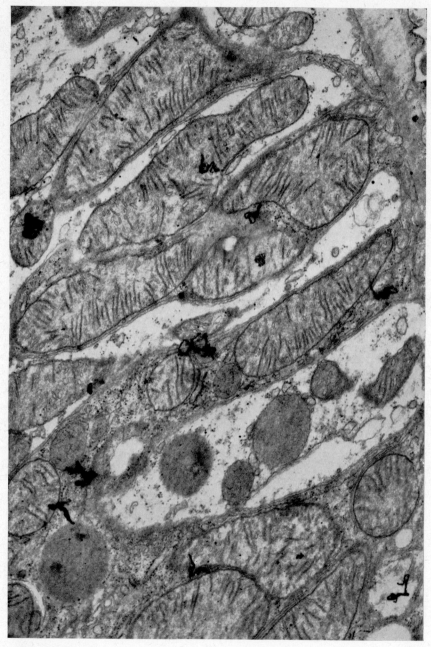

FIG. 21. Electron microscopic autoradiograph of a section of rat kidney proximal convoluted tubule from an animal injected with H^3 aldosterone 40 minutes previously. ×25,000. Note the relative sizes of silver grains and mitochondria and compare with Fig. 20.

However, if sufficient information is available and the experiment warrants it, EM autoradiographs are amenable to absolute quantitation. If sections are used the first requirement is that the section is of reasonably constant and of known mean thickness (see Section II, B). The second requirement is that the structure studied shall be of known area (measured by point analysis, Section III) and hence of known volume. Thirdly, it must represent a known fraction of the total volume of the object (determinable from serial sections). If the object to be studied is particulate and mounted whole, none of these requirements apply.

In order to quantitate the response to these objects in the emulsion, the efficiency of the autoradiographic process must be known, i.e. the number of grains developed in the emulsion after a given number of disintegrations in the specimen.

The efficiency of autoradiographic processes varies considerably with the isotope, emulsion used, exposure conditions, form of development (Bachmann and Salpeter, 1967; Kopriwa, 1967; Caro and Schnös, 1965; Wisse and Tates, 1968) and extent of chemographic effects

TABLE XIV

Overall Autoradiographic Efficiency to Various Isotopes in Monogranular Emulsion Layers

Emulsion	Isotope	Development	Efficiency overall	Authors
Ilford L4	H³	D19B 1 min 20°C	20%	Caro and Schnös (1965)
Ilford L4	P³²	D19B 1 min 20°C	2·5%	Caro and Schnös (1965)
Ilford L4	H³	Microdol-X 3 min 24°C	10%	Bachmann and Salpeter (1967)
Ilford L4	S³⁵	Microdol-X 3 min 24°C	5%	Bachmann and Salpeter (1967)
Kodak NTE	H³	Dektol 2 min 24°C	5%	Bachmann and Salpeter (1967)
Kodak NTE	S³⁵	Dektol 2 min 24°C	1·4%	Bachmann and Salpeter (1967)
Kodak NTE	H³	Gold latensification– ascorbic acid–Elon 8 min 24°C	12%	Bachmann and Salpeter (1967)
Ilford L4	H³	Microdol-X 5 min 20°C	12%	Wisse and Tates (1968)
Ilford L4	H³	Gold latensification– ascorbic acid–Elon 7·5 min 20°C	50%	Wisse and Tates (1968)

(Rogers, 1967). Results obtained by various authors suggest efficiencies of 1–50% (see Table XIV). When calibrating a particular system, careful attention must be paid to producing efficiency data under conditions precisely mimicking those of the specimen studied.

One case is on record where absolute measurements were made, to calculate the number of acetyl choline-esterase molecules in the mammalian motor endplate (Salpeter, 1967). The EM autoradiographic system gave reasonable correlation with optical microscope β-track autoradiography and liquid scintillation counting (Rogers *et al.*, 1966).

IV. DISCUSSION

An account has been given of an objective procedure for assessing EM autoradiographs. Many of the problems that have to be considered must be dealt with before or during autoradiograph production. For example, microtome performance and section thickness variation, preparation of monogranular layers of emulsion and the preservation of the isotopic material during fixation and embedding, are all problems to be considered before the autoradiographs are prepared. Many of these problems are at least partly solved and in most cases they are not severe enough to preclude the use of the technique. In this discussion it is assumed that these problems have been satisfactorily resolved. Likewise, the problems of tissue selection must be overcome by prior experiment using both morphological examination at the optical and EM levels, and autoradiography at the optical level. Again it is assumed that these aspects of the experiments are completed. Discussion is concentrated upon the analysis techniques.

Within the cell, decisions have to be made on what features are to be considered as single items in this particular system. For example, ergastoplasm would normally be considered as a single item, although it contains cisternae, unit membranes, ribosomes and amorphous cytoplasm. In some fortunate circumstances it is possible to use cisternae as separate items. Whether any particular feature is taken to be single or compound must be decided by the experimenter. The circle size appropriate to the particular system will influence his decisions, although existing biological and biochemical knowledge will also be taken into account. The technique has the advantage over the optical equivalent in that even when tritium is used the preparation is always "infinitely thin". Hence any feature appearing in the micrograph is capable of making an image if radioactive. However, it is possible for some structures in the section to go undetected. This is especially true of membranes cut very obliquely. Membrane profiles are

thus systematically underestimated in point and line analysis methods
(Loud, 1962). This error must also occur in the circle analysis method.

The technique can be criticized on the grounds that the circles do
not represent 100% probability of circumscribing the source of the
disintegration. The method described in this paper is based on circles
of 50% (or conceivably up to 70%) probability, based on the data of
Bachmann and Salpeter (1965). The data of Caro and Schnös (1965)
and Granboulan (1965) give similar estimates as far as they can be
compared. Although the use of circles with probability up to 70%
might perhaps be achieved when even smaller grained emulsions
become available, 100% probability circles are not possible. Clearly
therefore, the use of circles of limited confidence level is of necessity
a part of the EM autoradiograph approach and has to be accepted by
the investigator. However, it is necessary to ask in what way the
results and conclusions are likely to be influenced by the use of a circle
in lieu of the complete probability distribution, which is a bivariate
surface. Such a distribution, even if it could be represented only up to
90% probability would necessitate the use of a set of concentric circles.
The outermost circle would be larger than most organelles. The re-
placement of such a set of circles by a single one obviously makes the
results appear more clear-cut than they really are. Dome-shaped
probability curves are made into curves with flat plateaux. The precise
nature of the falsities so produced cannot be determined until a suitable
analysis can be devised which takes into account the complete
probability curves and superimposes them on to the morphology of the
tissue. A perusal of the available literature on geometric probability
(e.g. Robbins, 1944; Garwood, 1947; Morgenthaler, 1961) reveals the
truly formidable nature of this task. However, provided the cases
where there are extensive cross-fire effects are avoided, no gross
artifacts should be produced. In many cases where adjacent items
differ little in specific activity, gains and losses will largely cancel out.
The use of EM autoradiography in association with other quantitative
methods is important in providing a measure of control. The statistics
of the relationship between the developed silver grain and the original
silver bromide crystal have not so far been fully worked out. It is
possible that the probability distribution is not circular; it could, for
instance, be elliptical. However such data when available could be
worked into a technique such as that described here, with little
difficulty.

An undoubted drawback of the method is the labour of data
collection. This is unfortunately a feature of all quantitative histochemical procedures, especially those at the EM level,

The advantages of the analysis technique described here are several. Firstly, it enforces a consistent and objective approach, which is much needed in EM autoradiography. Secondly, the method allows analysis of grains which lie astride the edges of two items, thereby eliminating a source of bias and providing a source of information on limiting membranes. Thirdly, it allows information to be obtained about some items which are smaller than the "circle size". Fourthly, it gives a "rule of thumb" measure of "resolution" in the practical terms of the particular biological specimen being investigated. The importance of the specimen is therefore emphasized. This technique is as yet imperfect. However, the analytical approach together with recent measurements of absolute autoradiographic efficiency (Salpeter, 1967; Bachmann and Salpeter, 1967) indicate the direction that must be taken if a move towards a quantitative approach in EM histochemistry is to be made.

ACKNOWLEDGEMENTS

This review includes material which has not been previously published elsewhere. The author is indebted to the Science Research Council and the Medical Research Council for financial support during the course of this work, and to the Smith, Kline and French Foundation for grants for technical assistance, and to the Nuffield Foundation for the provision of facilities; also to Professor R. Barer and Dr. D. J. Goldstein for helpful discussion, and to Mrs. E. Woodcock, Mr. M. Turton and Mr. K. Robinson for technical assistance.

REFERENCES

Amsterdam, A. and Schramm, M. (1966). *J. Cell Biol.* **29**, 119–207.

Andrews, M. W. (1965). *J. R. microsc. Soc.* **84**, 439–448.

Appleton, T. C. (1965). *J. R. microsc. Soc.* **83**, 277–281.

Ashworth, C. T., Leonard, J. S., Eigenbrodt, E. H. and Wrightsman, F. J. (1966). *J. Cell. Biol.* **31**, 301–318.

Bachmann, L. and Salpeter, M. M. (1965). *Lab. Invest.* **14**, 1041–1053.

Bachmann, L. and Salpeter, M. M. (1967). *J. Cell Biol.* **33**, 299–305.

Bachmann, L. and Sitte, P. (1960). *Proc. 4th Int. Cong. Electron Microscopy, Berlin.* Vol. 2, p. 75. Springer-Verlag, Berlin.

Bailey, N. T. J. (1959). "Statistical Methods in Biology." London University Press, England.

Baker, J. R. (1946). *Q. Jl microsc. Sci.* **87**, 441–470.

Barland, P., Smith, C. and Hamerman, D. (1968). *J. Cell Biol.* **37**, 13–26.

Bennett, H. S. and Luft, J. H. (1959). *J. biophys. biochem. Cytol.* **6**, 113–114.

Bernhard, W. (1965). *Année biol.* **4**, 5–19.

Bernhard, W. and Nancy, M. T. (1964). *J. Microscopie*, **3**, 579–588.

Bowes, J. H. and Cater, C. W. (1965). *J. R. microsc. Soc.* **85**, 193–200.

Bradbury, S. and Meek, G. A. (1960). *Q. Jl microsc. Sci.* **101**, 241–250.

Buschmann, R. J. and Taylor, A. B. (1968). *J. Cell Biol.* **38**, 252–255.

Carlier, H., Clément, G. and Noirot-Timothée, C. (1967). *C.r. hebd. Séanc. Acad. Sci. Paris.* **265**, 235–238.

Caro, L. G. (1962). *J. Cell Biol.* **15**, 189–199.
Caro, L. G. and Palade, G. E. (1964). *J. Cell. Biol.* **20**, 473–495.
Caro, L. G. and Schnös, M. (1965). *Science*, **149**, 60–62.
Caro, L. G. and van Tubergen, R. P. (1962). *J. Cell Biol.* **15**, 173–188.
Casley-Smith, J. R. and Day, A. J. (1966). *Q. Jl. exp. Physiol.* **51**, 1–10.
Chalkley, H. W., Cornfield, J. and Park, H. A. (1949). *Science*, **110**, 295–297.
Coimbra, A. and Leblond, C. P. (1966). *J. Cell Biol.* **30**, 151–175.
Cope, G. H. (1968). *J. R. microsc. Soc.* **88**, 235–257.
Cope, G. H. and Williams, M. A. (1968). *J. R. microsc. Soc.* **88**, 259–277.
Cope, G. H. and Williams, M. A. *J. Microscopy*, **90** (in press).
Cope, G. H. and Williams, M. A. (1969b). *J. Microscopy*, **90** (in press).
Cosslett, A. (1960). *J. R. microsc. Soc.* **79**, 263–271.
Cosslett, A. (1967). *J. R. microsc. Soc.* **86**, 315–316.
Dallam, R. D. (1957). *J. Histochem. Cytochem.* **5**, 178–181.
Dermer, G. B. (1968). *J. Ultrastruct. Res.* **22**, 312–325.
Doniach, I. and Pelc, S. R. (1950). *Br. J. Radiol.* **23**, 184–192.
Droz, B. and Warshawsky, H. (1963). *J. Histochem. Cytochem.* **11**, 426–435.
Elbers, P. F., Ververgaert, P. H. J. T. and Demel, R. (1965). *J. Cell. Biol.* **24**, 23–30.
Engfeldt, B. and Hjertquist, S. O. (1967). *Acta path. microbiol. scand.* **71**, 219–232.
Erankö, O. (1955). "Quantitative Methods in Histology and Microscopic Histo-chemistry." Karger, New York, U.S.A.
Fedorko, M. E. and Hirsch, J. G. (1966). *J. Cell Biol.* **29**, 307–316.
Fewer, D., Threadgold, J. G. and Sheldon, H. (1964). *J. Ultrastruct. Res.* **11**, 166–172.
Flitney, F. W. (1966). *J. R. microsc. Soc.* **85**, 353–364.
Garwood, F. (1947). *Biometrika*, **34**, 1–17.
Granboulan, P. (1965). *In* "The use of radioautography in investigating protein synthesis." (C. P. Leblond and K. Warren, eds.). Academic Press, London, England.
Hake, T. (1965). *Lab. Invest.* **14**, 1208–1212.
Hennig, A. (1967). *In* E. R. Weibel and H. Elias "Quantitative methods in morphology," pp. 99–129. Springer-Verlag, Berlin.
Herz, R. H. (1959). *Lab. Invest*, **8**, 71–81.
Hirsch, H. M., Zelickson, A. S. and Hartmann, J. P. (1965). *Z. Zellforsch. mikrosk. Anat.* **65**, 409–419.
Huxley, H. E. and Zubay, G. (1961). *J. biophys. biochem. Cytol.* **11**, 271–296.
Idelman, S. (1965). *Histochemie*, **5**, 18–23.
Jersild, R. A. (1966). *J. Cell Biol.* **31**, 413–427.
Józsa, L. and Szederkenyi, G. (1967). *Acta histochem.* **26**, 255–260.
Kendall, M. G. and Moran, P. A. P. (1963). "Geometrical Probability." Charles Griffin and Co., London, England.
Koller, T. (1964). *J. Cell Biol.* **27**, 441–445.
Koller, T. and Bernhard, W. (1964). *J. Microscopie*, **3**, 589–606.
Kopriwa, B. W. (1967). *J. Histochem. Cytochem.* **15**, 501–515.
Korn, E. D. and Weisman, R. A. (1966). *Biochim. biophys. Acta*, **116**, 309–316.
Lamerton, L. F. and Harriss, E. B. (1954). *J. photogr. Sci.* **2**, 135–144.
Leduc, E. H. and Holt, S. J. (1965). *J. Cell Biol.* **26**, 137–155.
Leduc, E. H., Marinozzi, V. and Bernhard, W. (1963). *J. R. microsc. Soc.* **81**, 119–130.

Loud, A. V. (1962). *J. Cell Biol.* **15**, 481–487.

Luft, J. H. (1956). *J. biophys. biochem. Cytol.* **2**, 799–802.

Luft, J. H. and Wood, J. G. (1963). *J. Cell Biol.* **19**, 46A.

Maser, M. D., O'Brien, T. P. and McCully, M. E. (1967). *J. Microscopie*, **6**, 305–312.

Maunsbach, A. B. (1966). *J. Ultrastruct. Res.* **15**, 197–241.

Meek, G. A. and Moses, M. J. (1963). *J. R. microsc. Soc.* **81**, 187–197.

Merriam, R. W. (1958). *J. Histochem. Cytochem.* **6**, 43–51.

Millonig, G. and Marinozzi, V. (1968). *In* "Advances in Optical and Electron Microscopy," Vol. 2, pp. 251–341. (R. Barer and V. E. Cosslett, eds.). Academic Press, London, England.

Morgan, T. E. and Huber, G. L. (1967). *J. Cell. Biol.* **32**, 757–760.

Morgenthaler, G. W. (1961). *Biometrika*, **48**, 313–324.

Moses, M. J. (1956). *J. Histochem. Cytochem.* **4**, 418–441.

Neutra, M. and Leblond, C. P. (1966a). *J. Cell Biol.* **30**, 119–136.

Neutra, M. and Leblond, C. P. (1966b). *J. Cell Biol.* **30**, 137–150.

Northcote, D. H. and Pickett-Heaps, J. D. (1966). *Biochem. J.* **98**, 159–167

Peachey, L. D. (1958). *J. biophys. biochem. Cytol.* **4**, 233–242.

Pease, D. C. (1966). *J. Ultrastruct. Res.* **14**, 356–378.

Peters, T. and Ashley, C. A. (1967). *J. Cell Biol.* **33**, 53–60.

Peterson, M. and Leblond, C. P. (1964). *J. Cell Biol.* **21**, 143–148.

Quiocho, F. A. and Richards, F. M. (1966). *Biochemistry*, **5**, 4062–5076.

Ray, R. C. and Stevens, G. W. W. (1953). *Br. J. Radiol.* **26**, 362–367.

Revel, J. P. (1964). *J. Histochem. Cytochem.* **12**, 104–114.

Robbins, H. E. (1944). *Ann. math. Statist.* **15**, 70–74.

Rogers, A. W. (1967). "Techniques of Autoradiography." Elsevier, Amsterdam.

Rogers, A. W., Darzynkiewicz, Z., Barnard, E. A. and Salpeter, M. M. (1966). *Nature, Lond.* **210**, 1003–1006.

Rösch, S. (1959–60). *Z. wiss. Mikrosk.* **64**, 236–246.

Ross, R. and Benditt, E. P. (1965). *J. Cell Biol.* **27**, 83–106.

Ryter, A. and Kellenberger, E. (1958). *Z. Naturf. B.* **13**, 597–605.

Sadoh, T. and Christensen, G. N. (1967). *Wood Sci. and Technol.* **1**, 26–44.

Salpeter, M. M. (1967). *J. Cell Biol.* **32**, 379–389.

Salpeter, M. M. and Bachmann, L. (1964). *J. Cell Biol.* **22**, 469–477.

Saunders, D. R., Wilson, J. and Rubin, C. E. (1968). *J. Cell Biol.* **37**, 183–187.

Schneider, G. and Maurer, W. (1963). *Acta histochem.* **15**, 171–181.

Schneider, G. and Schneider, G. (1964). *Proc. 2nd Int. Cong. Histochem. Cytochem. Frankfurt/Main*, p. 169.

Simard, R. (1967). *J. Cell Biol.* **35**, 716–722.

Sirlin, J. L. and Loening, U. E. (1968). *Biochem. J.* **109**, 375–387.

Stein, O. and Stein, Y. (1967). *J. Cell Biol.* **33**, 319–339.

Stein, O. and Stein, Y. (1968). *J. Cell Biol.* **36**, 63–77.

Stirling, C. E. (1967). *J. Cell Biol.* **35**, 605–618.

Stumpf, W. E. and Roth, L. J. (1964). *Stain Technol.* **39**, 219–223.

Stumpf, W. E. and Roth, L. J. (1966). *J. Histochem. Cytochem.* **14**, 274–287.

Swift, H. and Rasch, E. (1958). *Sci. Instr. News*, **3**, 1.

Taxi, J. and Droz, B. (1966). *C.r. hebd. Séanc. Acad. Sci. Paris*, **263**, 1326–1329.

Tolansky, S. (1948). "Multiple Beam Interferometry." Oxford University Press, London, England.

Tranzer, J. P. (1965). *J. Microscopie*, **4**, 319–336.

Watson, J. H. L. (1956). *Lab. Invest.* **5,** 451–458.

Watson, M. L. (1958). *J. biophys. biochem. Cytol.* **4,** 727–730.

Williams, M. A. and Baba, W. I. (1967). *J. Endocr.* **39,** 543–554.

Williams, M. A. and Carr, I. (1968). *Expl. Cell Res.* **51,** 196–210.

Williams, M. A. and Meek, G. A. (1966). *J. R. microsc. Soc.* **85,** 337–352.

Williams, R. C. and Kallman, F. (1955). *J. biophys. biochem. Cytol.* **1,** 301–314.

Wisse, E. and Tates, A. D. (1968). *Proc. 4th Regional Conf. Electron Microsc. Rome,* Vol. II, 465–466. Tipografia Poliglotta, Vaticena, Rome.

Wolfe, D. E., Potter, L. T., Richardson, K. C. and Axelrod, J. (1962). *Science,* **138,** 440–442.

Wood, J. G. and Luft, J. H. (1965). *J. Ultrastruct. Res.* **12,** 22–45.

Author Index

Numbers in italics are those pages on which the references are listed at the end of chapters

Subject Index

A

Angular measurement, 81, 82
Area, measurement of, 67–69
Ash minerals, identification of, 135, 145, 152
  in bacteria, 126–131, 139
  in mitochondria, 118–123, 135
  in tissues, 150–152
  in viruses, 123–126, 152
Autoradiography,
  absolute quantitation in, 263
  background and chemography, 239, 240
  cross-fire effects, 259–263
  effect of emulsion in, 260–263
  efficiency, 266–267
  electron microscopical, 219
  embedding for, 219–228
  grain distribution in, 243–245
  junctional regions in, 243–245, 255
  of drugs and hormones, 226
  photographic technique, 238, 239
  retention of macromolecules in, 220, 221
  retention of lipids in, 221–228
  silver grains in, 243–245
  statistical analysis in, 241, 243–263
  ultramicrotomy in, 228–238

B

Bacterial spores, mineral content, 126–131, 139

C

Catalase, structure of, 196–200
Crank-Link, 21

D

Delesse principle, 69
Depth of focus, 27

Diameter,

  Feret's, 40, 46
  Martin's, 40
Domain structure (magnetic), 183–190

E

Electron diffraction, of ash minerals, 135–138, 145
  selected area, 138, 161, 173
  small angle techniques, 155–218
    biological uses, 196–203
    camera length, 156, 173–175
    coherence, 175
    fine structure, 190–192
    four lens method, 164–166
    limiting resolution, 157, 168–173, 177
    photography, 168
    selected area method, 161–163, 173
    test specimens for, 168–175
    three lens methods, 157–161
    ultra high resolution, 166–168
    very long camera method, 163–164
Electron microscope specimen grids, 104
Electron probe microanalysis, 146, 152
Electron scattering, small angle theory, 206–214
Electrostatic charging of specimens, 193–196
Embedding media, 107, 143, 150
Evaporated films, structure of, 178–183

F

Ferritin, structure of, 200
Fixation, 106, 141, 150
Fourier potential of crystal, 190
Fourier transform, 169, 172, 215

Cumulative Index of Authors

Cumulative Index of Titles